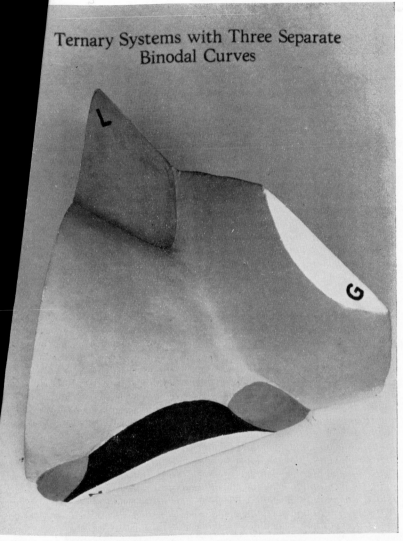

Ternary Systems with Three Separate
Binodal Curves

Oblique photograph of triangular prism model of system with three separate
curves.   See Figures 74–76.

Al

**INTERSCIENCE LIBRARY
OF CHEMICAL ENGINEERIN**

Editors:

HERBERT M. SCHOEN
Quantum Incorporated
Wallingford, Connecticut

JOHN J. McKETTA, JR.
Department of Chemical Engineering
The University of Texas
Austin, Texas

ADDITIONAL VOLUMES IN PREPARATION

LIQUID-
LIQUID
EQUILIBRIUMS

by

ALFRED W. FRANCIS

Mobil Chemical Company
Research and Technical Laboratories
Edison Township, New Jersey

1963
INTERSCIENCE PUBLISHERS
a division of JOHN WILEY & SONS
New York • London

Copyright © 1963 by John Wiley & Sons, Inc.

All rights reserved

Library of Congress Catalog Card Number 63-13596

Printed in the United States of America by Mack Printing Co., Easton, Pa.

INTRODUCTION

The editors and publisher have long felt that there is a need for a chemical engineering library directed primarily toward chemical engineers, but also intended for use by other engineers and scientists in some way involved in the broad field of the "engineering of chemistry."

The volumes to be included in the series will all be of a moderately advanced level and will not be designed as texts, although they are expected to find some outlets in graduate and senior courses.

The series will not be limited to volumes which are considered chemical engineering subjects as such, but will also include the support subjects frequently a part of the chemical engineer's areas of endeavor. These will range from the theoretical topics, general business, unit operations, and specific processing areas. In addition, titles will be chosen so as to present specialized sub-areas to those not specifically engaged in them. The library will expand as the need for additional topics is created.

The editors hope that the readers will let them have their criticisms, comments, and suggestions so that improvements can be made in future volumes.

HERBERT M. SCHOEN
JOHN J. McKETTA, JR.

PREFACE

The separation of substances by solvent extraction is a major field among chemical engineering processes. It has as its basis the mutual solubilities of two or more liquid phases, usually involving three components; the solvent and two substances to be separated.

In many cases the solubility relations are relatively simple, and the operation is primarily an engineering one. In others, especially when it is desired to modify solubility by a fourth component or diluent, even water, the relations may become more complex. Other complications may arise through presence or solid phases, mutual chemical reaction of components, coincidences in certain physical properties for the two phases, etc. Some strictly ternary systems have "freak" graphs which may aid or hinder normal operation.

Physical chemical textbooks, with a limited space for these features, have been superficial, sometimes postulating unknown or even impossible diagrams. American physical chemists and chemical engineers lately have been far less active in this field than those of Russia. This volume attempts to review these relations from a theoretical, but certainly *experimental* viewpoint, and largely in nonmathematical and nonengineering terms.

As a basis for discussion, and to facilitate further study, a comprehensive compilation of systems showing two or more liquid phases in equilibrium has been included, together with a bibliography.

Besides those who assisted recently in the preparation of this book (listed on pages 122 and 123), others who stimulated the author with discussion in past years were Dr. Farrington Daniels, his thesis instructor at Worcester Polytechnic Institute in 1917 (and many discussions more recently); Dr. Atherton Seidell (deceased), compiler of *Solubility Tables;* Prof. N. O. Smith of Fordham University, Prof. J. C. Smith of Cornell, Prof. W. B. Kay of Ohio State University, Prof. Joel H. Hildebrand of California, and Dr. George C. Johnson of Mobil Oil Company in Paulsboro, New Jersey.

Alfred W. Francis

Metuchen, New Jersey
April 21, 1963

CONTENTS

ix

1 | INTRODUCTION

Phase Equilibriums

Physical equilibriums between two phases may involve two solids, two liquids, solid–liquid, vapor–solid, or vapor–liquid. Under usual conditions, all vapors are miscible, although there may be exceptions (344B; 571, p. 230; 698; 698A). Vapor–solid, or sublimation, is of relatively slight importance and might be considered a special case of vapor–liquid.

Vapor–liquid equilibriums are of intense interest to chemical engineers because they are the very foundation of all forms of distillation: simple, vacuum, pressure, azeotropic, extractive, steam, molecular, and doubtless others. The expression "phase equilibria" (*Chemical Abstracts* prefers "equilibriums") is used very generally in engineering publications as synonymous with "vapor–liquid equilibriums." Pressure is, of course, a controlling factor in these studies, as well as temperature.

Solid–solid equilibriums form a branch of metallurgy, or of inorganic research, and may involve very complex phase diagrams. Although they follow many of the same principles as in liquid–liquid equilibriums, they will not be discussed in this book (except incidentally). Researches in those fields are extensive but very time consuming because of slow equilibrium, high-temperature control, opaque reagents, difficulties in sampling and analysis, etc. A concise physical-chemical treatment of phase relations in metallurgy, which has been helpful to the present author in his own field, is that of Marsh (417).

Solid–liquid equilibriums were the basis of much of the early inorganic researches and resulted in further development of analyt-

1

ical chemistry and of apparatus, such as thermostats and auxiliary equipment. This was needed because such measurements of solubility are usually relatively slow; hours and sometimes days are required for a reasonable approach to equilibrium. The field now includes almost as many organic substances as inorganic ones. The broad field of adsorption is not touched in this book. It is considered a solid–liquid equilibrium, even though the liquid component is present in both phases.

Extensive development of research on liquid–liquid equilibriums is more recent. Compared with vapor–liquid relations, pressure over moderate ranges has very little effect, although Timmermans and co-workers (275, p. 397; 682) showed substantial changes in liquid miscibility over wide ranges of pressure. Even temperature has a diminished importance, so that for practical precision thermostats can sometimes be eliminated, especially if the temperature is far below the critical solution temperature.

Compared with solid solubility determinations, those of liquids have a tremendous advantage in providing almost instantaneous equilibrium after agitation, unless one of the components has a high viscosity. Moreover, compositions can be determined largely or entirely by synthetic means, such as titration. Alternatively, observations of refractive index or density on one or both liquid phases are often adequate for complete analysis.

Aside from theoretical considerations, research on liquid–liquid equilibriums had to wait for development of selective solvent extraction before it became of much importance. Chemists for generations had extracted organic compounds from water with ether, chloroform, carbon tetrachloride, or hydrocarbons; but in these examples selectivity was almost complete. All that was necessary was to have a solvent immiscible with water. When the extract is an organic base or a phenol, the solvent may be an acid or an alkali, respectively, requiring a chemical reaction; but the technique is approximately the same.

In the separation of mixtures of hydrocarbons, especially lubricating oils, extraction by a solvent is far from completely selective and is not even uniform for various solvents. However, the process is very simple in principle; and apparently development was largely an engineering one. Choosing a solvent often depended more upon its cost or availability, boiling point, stability, density, toxicity, viscosity, freezing point, interfacial surface tension, water solubility, suitable solvent power at a convenient temperature, or even refractive index, than upon its selectivity. It still does, but comprehensive scouting researches (151, 160, 161, 510) showed that selectivity, which is still important, is made up of several factors and can be affected by methods of application.

Fundamentally, solvent extraction involves the treatment of a mixture of two or more substances with a solvent not miscible with the mixture but having a greater solvent power for one component of the mixture than for the others. The two liquid phases are segregated, and the solvent is removed from each, usually by distillation. The components are thus partially separated. The operation can be repeated in many steps (not necessarily with intermediate removal of solvent) or combined with other processes to complete the separation to any desired degree. The whole art of solvent extraction depends on liquid–liquid equilibrium.

The idea that liquid–liquid relations are relatively simple has diminished the challenge to research men. The present author was assured by an organic chemistry colleague that not more than four or five men in the country were interested in liquid–liquid equilibriums. The length of the present bibliography may be a refutation of this statement. But it must be admitted that in recent years American physical chemists have been much less active in liquid-phase studies than have those of Russia and other Eastern countries.

Many of these foreign papers have come out with novel aspects, interesting both practically and theoretically. Abstracts of these papers, even though in English, are often difficult to follow without the original graphs. Many abstracts were made by Russian abstractors, and their expressions in this technical field are ambiguous.

The notion that all is known about liquid–liquid relations is refuted by theoretical incongruities in phase diagrams in papers and textbooks by reputable chemical engineers and by physical chemists. Two of the most prolific Russian workers in this field have disagreed violently on a theoretical point (367, 368B, 769). The present author also has had to revise his opinions about certain phase relations as a result of his own experiments and those of others. It is hoped that in uncertain cases experiment will be decisive.

For example, it should not be asserted, as it has been, that a certain type of diagram is "typical" although no example of that type is mentioned or even known. Such statements are discouraging to further research. If an example of the type mentioned is later discovered, the investigator finds it awkward to dispose of the apparent precedent. Moreover, without a valid example, such a loose prediction may indicate impossible relations and be very misleading. To avoid such a risk, the graphs in this book are actual systems drawn to approximate scale with components labelled, except when impossible or postulated graphs are shown for illustration (and so marked).

On the other hand, if a certain relation is valid in several cases without exception and is reasonable, it might be accepted tentatively until a clear exception can be found. This might stimulate research. Several such generalities are presented in this book.

The pattern of solid solubility studies was followed with liquid solubility studies perhaps a little too slavishly in some respects. One is that temperatures at which crystals first appear on cooling have been listed as critical solution temperatures in some compilations (384, 603), as though it was of little or no importance whether the new phase was liquid or crystals. It has been shown (178, Fig. 5, taken from the work of Hoerr *et al.* (264A)) that the two temperatures are not necessarily the same. Another difference from solid solubility studies is that there is little risk of subcooling equilibrium, although Davis (122), Flaschner (155), and Oriani (485) show slight subcooling in certain cases.

Still another difference is that molar compositions are often significant in crystallization of molar compounds. Some consider a maximum in a freezing curve the only valid evidence of such a compound. By contrast, in liquid–liquid relations it is usually of no advantage to plot solubilities on a molar basis, since separation of liquid phases rarely follows molar composition, even when there is reason to suspect the presence of molar compounds in solution. Weight percentage is preferable for convenience and uniformity.

Only a few systems involving solid polymers are cited in this book. This is justified on the grounds that they are not liquids, although in phase relations they show some of the characteristics of liquids, in

contrast to more highly crystalline solids. Some of their liquid characteristics are critical solution temperatures, enormous temperature coefficients of solubility in certain ranges, and very slight subcooling.
Some ternary graphs shown in textbooks, e.g., Flory (156, p. 552),
and numerous original papers in polymer chemistry are "impossible" in the sense that tie lines run into side lines, etc. Such incongruities are due to the very abnormal properties of the polymers.
That is, the tie lines do not really run into the side line but only to
a film of very difficultly soluble polymer.

Antonoff and co-workers (17, 18) considered that the assumption
of practically instantaneous equilibrium was not justified. They
indicated delays of six to 20 days for perfect equilibrium between
simple liquid pairs. However, they gave no information on length
of agitation, reagitation after sampling, nor precautions to eliminate
droplets of the other phase from samples. Since one of the pairs
involved, phenol and water, settles out so slowly that in a ternary
system of three liquid phases (180, p. 1029) the third phase was not
even noticed by the original investigators, there must be real risk
that separation of phases was imperfect in Antonoff's experiments.

The applications to solvent extraction have required the interest
of chemical engineers not only in the engineering designs but also in
phase studies. Occasionally, some fundamental aspects of these
phase relations are overlooked. Attention will be called to some of
these points, since modern physical chemistry textbooks are superficial in the field of phase studies.

Complaint has been made that this book overemphasizes the
freak graphs sometimes found in phase relations. The intent was to
use such graphs to diminish the confusion in normal graphs resulting
from oversimplification.

The present author does not concede that there are not still novel
types of phase relations among liquids to be discovered and perhaps
used. The more promising directions are among liquefied gases;
with reagents having possibilities of mutual interaction, either
reversible or irreversible; and in combinations with distillation,
extractive distillation, extractive evaporation, adduct formation,
adsorption, etc. Examples of all of these are already known and
practiced.

Phase Rule

Gibbs' phase rule is the "bible" of phase equilibrium and is discussed in most physical chemistry textbooks. It can be stated as

$$P + F = C + X$$

where P is the number of phases, F is the number of degrees of freedom, C is the number of components, and X is the number of physical factors, usually two (temperature and pressure) independent of concentration, affecting equilibrium.

The phase rule is not challenged; but in studies of liquid–liquid equilibrium it has not been found as useful as hoped because of difficulty in establishing unequivocally the number of components (especially in a system with a hydrocarbon mixture in which the components may run to thousands). Changes in the number of components are balanced by corresponding changes in F, which include variations in the components' respective concentrations; but the hydrocarbon mixture cannot be arbitrarily reduced to a nominal *one* because its fractionation may be the aim of the process studied. A further complication is the possibility (in other cases) of mutual interaction of the components.

When opalescence is involved, the number of phases may be uncertain because of the possible presence of either a solid or a liquid dispersed phase. Even X may be slightly indefinite, since in colloidal systems equilibrium may be scarcely affected by variations in pressure or temperature but may be affected by surface tension. Nevertheless, the principles of the phase rule are applied throughout this book.

2 | BINARY SYSTEMS

Binodal Curves

Only one dimension is required to show composition in a binary system since the percentages total 100%. Accordingly, the vertical coordinate in a complete graph is used commonly to show the temperature (see Fig. 1). The two side lines indicate the two pure components.

As the curve shows, mutual solubilities of the two liquids usually increase slowly at low temperatures and then more rapidly until (with the correct ratio of components) at the critical solution temperature (CST), or apex of the curve (also called plait or consolute point), there is miscibility in all proportions. If the composition (not necessarily 50%) is not correct for this phenomenon, the deficient layer dissolves in the other one. More of the deficient component can be added. At the consolute point the interface between the two liquid phases fades out near the middle of the system with a cloudy opalescence. The interface resembles the meniscus of a pure liquid at its critical temperature. However, pressure is not required unless the temperature is above the boiling point of the system, which may be slightly below that of either component (see Figs. 2, 3).

The curve is called a "binodal curve." Any horizontal line across the curve is a tie line, indicating equilibrium between the compositions on the two sides of the curve at the same temperature. At any point on a given tie line the compositions of the two phases are uniform, though the relative volumes of the phases vary with the position of the point.

7

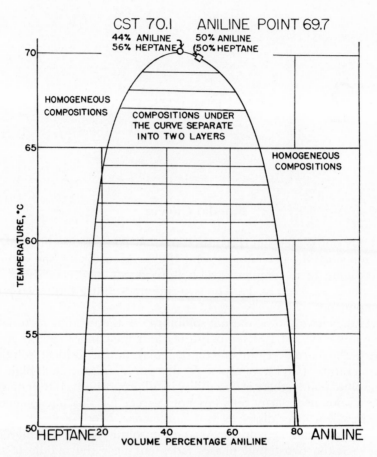

Fig. 1. Binary system *n*-heptane–aniline illustrating CST and aniline point

The curve is also a phase boundary curve, indicating that compositions under the curve separate into two layers while those outside the curve are homogeneous. However, these two curves are coincident only for a strictly binary system.

The binodal curve resembles a parabola, except that the two legs approach parallelism at lower temperatures. Usually the curve is slightly unsymmetrical. Vogel (734) indicates requirements for a symmetrical curve. The "parabolas" are analogous in principle to curves showing the densities of liquid and vapor phases of a pure

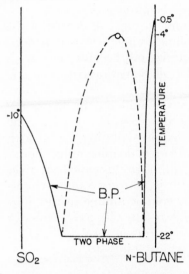

Fig. 2. Boiling point at atmospheric pressure, system sulfur dioxide–*n*-butane.

Fig. 3. Vapor pressure at 25°C, system ammonia–propane.

substance as a function of temperature up to the critical temperature. Equations for those curves were developed (159A, 166). A modification of equation 2 in those papers

$$(X - X_c)^h = G(t_c - t)$$

can be calculated for the upper portion of the binodal curves. X and X_c are percentages of one of the components, and t and t_c are the temperatures, the subscript indicating the consolute point. G and h are constants, h being more nearly 3 than 2 as it would be for a parabola, i.e., it is almost a cubic. Rice (548), Rowden and Rice (570), and Zimm (783) studied these relations with high precision for the system aniline–cyclohexane with a CST of about 29.6°C, conveniently close to room temperature. Zimm (784) made similar studies on CCl_4–C_7F_{14} (CST 28.23°C).

CST and Aniline Points

Figure 1 illustrates the difference between the CST and the aniline point. The latter is an arbitrary test and is defined as the mixing temperature of equal volumes of pure aniline and oil or other hydrocarbon mixture. It is usually within one degree of the CST. In the petroleum industry aniline points are used widely, almost as much as gravity, to characterize oils because they are a good measure of aromatic content of the oil. Sometimes the aromatic content determines an oil's quality.

High aromatic content may depress the aniline point below the freezing point of aniline, $-6.2\,°C$. In such cases a "mixed aniline point" is often used (402, 618). This requires diluting the oil with an equal volume of n-heptane or with an oil of definite aniline point, usually $60\,°C$, before making the test. Although this expedient gives good practical results in many cases, it is not very sound theoretically. A slight departure from 50% by volume aniline in the dilution or in the final test may give erratic results (40, 547). A better practice is to use a different solvent, such as furfural (547, 588), although this solvent has the fault of instability to oxygen and requires frequent redistillation.

For highly aromatic hydrocarbon mixtures, ethylene diformate was suggested (161) as a test solvent because of its much higher CST with aromatics. However, it has the disadvantage of ready hydrolysis to glycol and formic acid, both of which raise the CST greatly. A more satisfactory solvent for testing is nitromethane (462). For highly paraffinic oils with excessively high aniline points, N-methylaniline has been recommended (217) for characterization by CST.

CST with other solvents is used for analysis for other substances. It is a very sensitive test for the percentage of water in alcohols, especially methanol, using carbon disulfide or hydrocarbons, which are highly antagonistic to water. Similar results have been obtained with acetic acid and aromatic hydrocarbons, etc. (309).

The CST of o-nitrotoluene is a linear function of composition for mixtures of isomeric hydrocarbons, and so furnishes a convenient analysis for butane–isobutane (167, 183). Other solvents whose CST's with hydrocarbons were exploited for analysis or characterization are aniline (40, 99, 412, 462), benzyl alcohol (28, 412, 462), ethyl phthalate (443), ethyl sulfate (462), furfural (588), nitrobenzene (412, 443), nitromethane (462), and sulfur dioxide (395, 610, 611).

Partly because of their use in analysis, but more especially because of their significance in selecting solvents for extraction of hydrocarbon mixtures, an extensive experimental study (160, 161) of hydrocarbons CST's was made. The difference between the CST's of a solvent with two hydrocarbons is a good measure of the selectivity of that solvent for the two hydrocarbons. The study above was followed by compilations and further observations (178, 179). Any CST gives a fair measure of the miscibility of a pair of liquids. In fact, Brusset and Bono claim to estimate the whole binodal curve from the CST (79). The book *Critical Solution Temperatures* lists over 6000 CST's (178).

Lower Critical Solution Temperatures

It seems anomalous that two liquids should separate into layers at one temperature but mix in all proportions at a *lower* temperature. Yet at least 154 examples of lower critical solution temperature (LCST) are known (mostly listed in 178, Table III). LCST's are of three classes. Some of them involve a light hydrocarbon (ethane, propane, isobutane), carbon dioxide, ethyl ether, etc. not far below the critical temperature of the light component. Evidently, near their critical temperatures these substances acquire some of the characteristics of gases and have lower miscibilities with heavier liquids. The latter even include hydrocarbons, especially poly-olefins or polycyclic hydrocarbons, or, in the case of ethane, any high-molecular hydrocarbons. This type of system usually has also an "upper critical end point" (204), or critical temperature of the upper layer, which is slightly higher than the critical temperature of the pure lighter component. It is possible, though the evidence is not conclusive, that high pressures of the order of 1000 atm would eliminate the gaslike quality of these light substances and make them miscible with higher hydrocarbons and other substances.

Another type of LCST applies to liquid sulfur and aromatic hydrocarbons (benzene, toluene, *p*-xylene, triphenylmethane) (635). The LCST is higher than the CST, as in Figure 4. This anomaly is probably due to different molecular structures of sulfur in the two temperature ranges. Very high pressure may eliminate some of these LCST's.

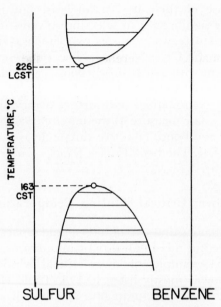

Fig. 4. Sulfur–benzene system with CST and an LCST above the CST.

A similar variation in molecular structure probably accounts for phase relations in a unary system (645) of phosphorus pentoxide at high temperature. Two liquid phases and two solid phases are present; only one of each is stable.

A third common type of LCST involves water or glycerol and a glycol ether or an organic base, such as an alkylpyridine. Presumably, certain bonds are broken by raising the temperature, permitting separation of the liquids. Dolgolenko (129) believed they were due to hydrates. Zhuravlev (768) investigated "Irrationalities in viscosity and density in certain binary aqueous systems," including tri-ethylamine. He concluded, "Chemical interaction of components always occurs in stratifying binary systems with a lower consolute temperature. Physical isotherms of the triethylamine–water system confirm this."

This is a very sweeping generalization to draw from a single example. It *may* be true for 59 systems, mostly aqueous, of the third class mentioned above. But it certainly does not hold for 95 other systems with LCST's in the first two groups.

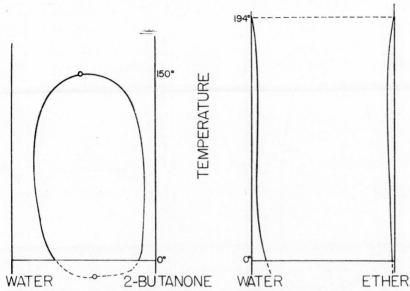

Fig. 5. Water–2-butanone system with a pseudoisland, a CST, and a metastable LCST.

Fig. 6. Water–ethyl ether system with neither CST nor LCST observable.

This third type often has also a CST, so that a binary island curve may result (321). One or both of these points may be missing. Thus, 2-butanone (methyl ethyl ketone) has a metastable LCST estimated at -6 to $-20\,°C$ (see Fig. 5) either by extending the curvatures of the solubility curves below $0\,°C$ or by lowering the freezing point of water by the presence of 1.5% ethyl alcohol (603, p. 243). The CST of water–ethyl ether is missing (see Fig. 6) because the critical vapor temperature, $194\,°C$, of ether intervenes to cause a diminution of solubility instead of an increase.

Coincidences in Properties

Since the compositions at the extremities of a tie line (any horizontal line) of a binary binodal curve are in equilibrium, they always have the same melting points (see Fig. 7), boiling points (see Fig. 2), and vapor pressures (see Fig. 3). The pressure for the two-phase system is nearly the sum of the separate vapor pressures. Figure 2 is an isobar, a graph at uniform pressure (atmospheric).

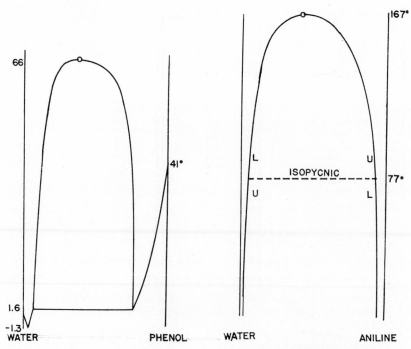

Fig. 7. Water–phenol system.   Fig. 8. Water–aniline system illustrating a binary isopycnic. (Courtesy of *Ind. Eng. Chem.*)

The phase boundary curve is shown with a dashed line because pressures along it are above atmospheric pressure.

Most of the other physical properties differ for the two liquid phases. But some interesting phenomena appear when they are equal also.

ISOPYCNICS

When the densities of the two phases are equal, the phases do not stratify into separate layers but remain as a mosaic of separate drops or cells varying in appearance with color, interfacial surface tension, viscosity, and time (see Fig. 8). Sometimes one phase separates into a labile shapeless mass ("schmoo"). The tie lines of such systems have been called "isopycnics" (163, 178, 180). At least ten binary isopycnics are known (163), five of them due to

Mondain-Monval and Quiquarez (450), who, however, did not use the expression. At high pressure near the critical temperature of one of the components, an isopycnic of a gas and a liquid may occur. Examples are ammonia–nitrogen (571, p. 229) and water–xenon (159A, p. 42). Isopycnics in ternary systems are much more common and are discussed in Chapter 4.

ISO-OPTICS

When the refractive indices of the two phases are equal for some wave length in the visible spectrum, the emulsion resulting from vigorous agitation of the system usually shows structural colors (163, 172, 179) when viewed under certain conditions (see Fig. 9). The tie lines of these systems have been called iso-optics. The

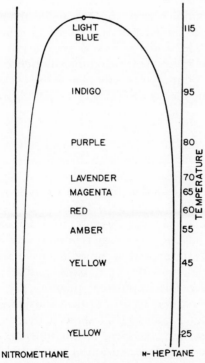

Fig. 9. Nitromethane–*n*-heptane system illustrating binary iso-optics. (Courtesy of *Ind. Eng. Chem.*)

color is complementary to that for which the wave length is equal, so that the opalescent spectrum includes yellow, amber, brick red, magenta, lilac, purple, indigo, and light blue in that order, usually with descending temperature, although it can be reversed.

The color appears in transmitted light where there is a light barrier, such as a partition between window panes. The light at such a point comes only by *reflection* (not refraction) from surfaces of droplets, but has lost the light of the wave length mentioned, since for that light the emulsion is optically homogeneous. The color usually varies with the temperature because of unequal temperature coefficients of refractive index for the two phases.

The phenomenon was used recently to observe refractive indices of 37 liquefied gases above their boiling points (171). The indices were matched against known indices of water, salt solutions, or other liquids substantially immiscible with the samples. When the indices of the samples were too low to be matched by that of a nonvolatile liquid, the former were raised by dilution with benzene or carbon disulfide, and the indices were estimated by extrapolation. Refractive indices of two other liquefied gases have been observed (197) still more recently. These are cyclopropane (1.3331) at 18°C, and neopentane (1.3321) at 28°C. Ternary iso-optics, which are more common than binary ones, are discussed in Chapter 4.

It is surprising that Mondain-Monval and Quiquarez in four publications (450–453) overlooked the iso-optics although they were searching for opalescence (colorless) near the plait points in about 50 systems. They concluded that for that type of opalescence the two refractive indices must *differ* by at least 0.0004—just the opposte of the structural colors, which require close proximity of the two indices but have no necessary relation to the consolute point.

Sikinner (629) presented a binodal curve with 2,2-thiodipropionitrile and toluene with two maxima and a concavity between. Since such a curve is impossible theoretically (see Fig. 10), he ascribed its observation to an "optical illusion." It was probably another iso-optic; Francis (197) showed that near its plait point that two-phase system is as clear as a homogeneous one.

A coincidence in surface tension of two liquid phases in equilibrium presumably means approach to zero for interfacial tension and therefore mixing at the plait point. However, in certain ternary

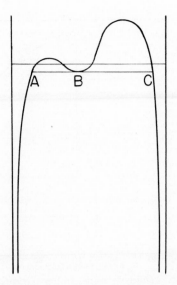

Fig. 10. Binary system with two critical solution points (hypothetical).

systems "the surface tension . . . for the interliquid phase surfaces increases anomalously up to the point of miscibility" (234, 504). These authors may have overlooked the earlier paper of Morgan and Evans (458) which discusses this phenomenon.

Distinction Between Binodal Curves and Melting Curves

There is only a superficial resemblance between the melting curve of a crystalline compound of two components and a binodal curve of liquid–liquid equilibrium in a binary system with temperature as an ordinate.

In the former the composition at the crest of the curve (melting point) is a simple mole ratio of the components. There is no critical opalescence at that point, and the horizontal tie lines do not extend entirely across the curve. They reach from either side of the curve to a vertical line, which leads to the crest of the curve. They indicate equilibrium of the excess liquid solution, not with the liquid on the other side of the curve, but with the crystalline complex in the middle, which is physically present as a separate phase

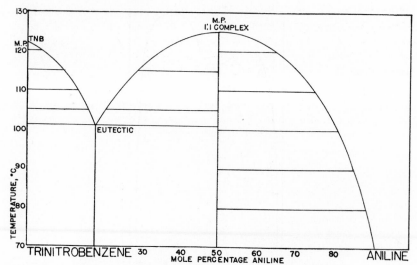

Fig. 11. Trinitrobenzene–aniline freezing curve.

(275A) (see Fig. 11). A solid–liquid incongruent melting curve has no parallel among binodal curves, nor does a eutectic.

Another distinction between the two types of curves is that the solid–liquid curves run into the side line at the melting point of the solid. A liquid–liquid binodal curve of pure liquids never touches the side lines.

Ricci (546, pp. 179, 217) suggested that a binary system might have two separate binodal curves, not vertically above each other as in the sulfur systems (see Fig. 4) but laterally, i.e., at a single temperature. In other words he indicated that there could be binary systems with two liquid-miscibility gaps. He cited as an example the methyl iodide-pyridine system observed by Aten (27). Ricci admitted (pp. 150, 179) the invalidity of this example; but he extended the idea to postulating ternary systems with four liquid phases (p. 217). He saw no fundamental difference between binary systems with two liquid-miscibility gaps and systems with two or more solid phases appearing at different compositions at the same temperature (546, p. 208). The latter are commonplace.

Francis (201, p. 449) objected to multiple liquid-miscibility gaps in a binary system on theoretical grounds. Such a hypothesis would require a tie line, such as *ABC* in Figure 10, showing three binary compositions as three phases in equilibrium (201, p. 450). This would be analogous to having three fluid phases near the critical point of a pure substance. Francis did not consider Aten's example valid. In that system methyl iodide and pyridine are miscible in all proportions at room temperature and below (197, 756); but at room temperature they react within a few seconds with high evolution of heat (almost explosive) and form a crystalline solid, m.p. 116 °C, which is undissociated (27) (see Fig. 12). Since the reaction

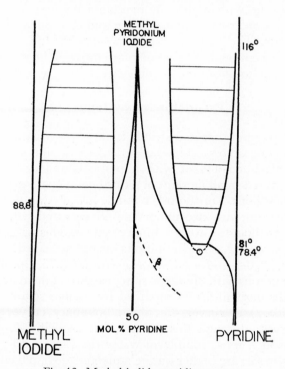

Fig. 12. Methyl iodide–pyridine system.

is irreversible, there is no more reason to consider methyl iodide as a component in the area to the right of the center line than to consider iodine as a component. The components in the binary system involved in the inverted curve of Figure 12 are pyridine and methyl pyridonium iodide. Similarly, the components on the left side are methyl iodide and methyl pyridonium iodide. The figure shows two independent binary systems that have a common component. A more complete discussion of the effects of irreversible reactions between components on phase relations is given for ternary systems in Chapter 7.

Many papers have presented studies of abnormalities in viscosity, surface tension, dielectric constant, etc. at or near plait points (9, 344A, 435B, 524, 557A, 605–609, 649, 784, 786, 787). Favorite systems for these studies are water with triethylamine or phenol and cyclohexane with aniline or methanol because the CST's of the systems are near room temperature and convenient for the use of thermostats. The first mentioned system has a LCST, which might show exceptional relations. No attempt will be made here to discuss the conclusions of these studies.

Pseudobinary Systems

It has been noted that in a strictly binary system any horizontal (isothermal) line across a binodal curve is a tie line and that the binodal curve is coincident with a phase boundary curve. The presence of even a small amount of a third component negates both of these conclusions. On the other hand, it is often a convenience to show a system with two major components and with a minor component as though it were a binary system. This practice is not objectionable so long as the limitations are not neglected.

For example, *International Critical Tables III* (275, pp. 409, 416) shows three graphs with "binary" systems. Two of them are plots of phenol–water miscibilies as modified by various solutes (salts or tartaric acid). The curves are phase boundary curves and not binodal curves, although this point is not explicit. Many of the solutes are much more soluble in water than in phenol; and the percentages of salt are higher on the aqueous side of the curve than on the phenol side. A composition under the curve separates into layers; but rarely does either of these layers have a composition corresponding to any point on the curve. It is not practical to draw the actual binodal curve that would show these pairs of compositions because the compositions vary with the relative volumes of the two layers. In other words, the binodal curve is fuzzy.

Timmermans (683) showed that with still higher concentrations of salts and of organic solutes the water–phenol phase boundary

3 | TERNARY SYSTEMS

Methods of Plotting

In many respects isotherms of ternary systems with two liquid phases are analogous to binary systems, the concentration of the third component replacing temperature as a homogenizing agent. Many of the principles already discussed are applicable with suitable adjustments.

Instead of a rectangular graph (see however 535), an equilateral triangle (41, 594, 595) is usually used both to emphasize the equivalence (in some respects) of the three components and to avoid confusion, since the percentages of two components are decreased by the presence of the third one. A plastic stencil, Figure 17 (180, p. 832), is convenient for drawing ternary systems. The triangle is 73 mm on a side. Five typical binodal curves are marked by numbers. Curves not fitting exactly can be drawn in portions, as with a French curve.

It does not require a "trick" method to show compositions of three components on a plane diagram in a triangular graph, as some unfamilar with them have supposed. The restriction that these compositions total 100% reduces the dimensions by one. Each side of the triangle is a binary system. In Figure 18 the letters A, B, and C indicate pure components. The composition at point c is a binary mixture of 40% A and 60% B; that at point b is 55% A and 45% C; and that at point a is 65% B and 35% C. A point P within the triangle indicates a ternary mixture of 30% A, 50% B, and 20% C; each is measured by the perpendicular distance to the opposite side, in relation to the altitude of the triangle. The sum of the three perpendiculars always equals the altitude.

25

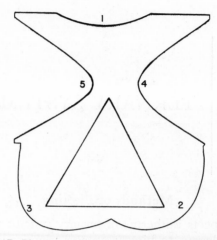

Fig. 17. Plastic stencil for drawing ternary systems.

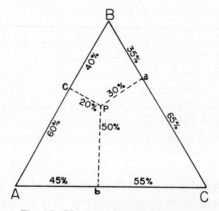

Fig. 18. Plotting of ternary systems.

In explaining the method of plotting, some textbooks have indicated that compositions are measured along lines parallel with the side lines and are in proportion to the length of side lines. There is no difference in results by the two methods. The method of perpendiculars seems clearer to the present author and therefore preferable.

In all of the ternary graphs shown in this book, and in most of the discussion, percentages are on a weight basis. This is true also in the majority of publications. For certain systems involving solid molar compounds between the components, a molar basis of plotting may be desirable to emphasize this aspect (see Fig. 11). However, it is unnecessary, especially for systems showing only liquid phases.

The plotting of ternary systems with volume percentages is not recommended except as a rough expedient. Volume percentage is an equivocal measure. Even in a homogeneous mixture like water and ethyl alcohol, or benzene and heptane, volume changes are considerable. In the former example, "50% alcohol" is defined as a mixture containing 500 ml pure alcohol per liter of mixture, not as a mixture of 500 ml each of alcohol and water. The two mixtures differ by over 1% because of substantial contraction. In the second example, benzene and heptane, there is an expansion of about 1%, and presumably volume percentage is based on total separate volume, not mixed volume. Figure 1 was plotted as volume percentage merely because of the empirical definition of the aniline point.

Types of Curves

To a binary system which separates into two layers, the base line of the triangle, a third component is added gradually. The third component distributes itself between the two layers. If it is miscible with each of the other two components, the mutual miscibility of the layers usually increases until the layers are completely miscible. The interface usually disappears at either the top or bottom of the system; that is, one phase dissolves in the other. But with the proper ratio of original components, this mixing occurs at the plait, or consolute, point near the middle of the system, as it does on heating a binary system under similar conditions.

The graph is usually of the simple bite type, as in Figures 19 through 24. The curve is shallow, as in Figure 19 (180, p. 976), when the original mutual miscibility is fairly high. The curve may be almost symmetrical, approximately the arc of a circle, with the plait point near the apex of the curve. The tie lines (not shown) are nearly parallel with the base line.

A narrow deep curve, as in Figure 20, (180, p. 824), is possible but unusual. It requires a temperature between the CST's of the solvent with each of the other two components, which must be

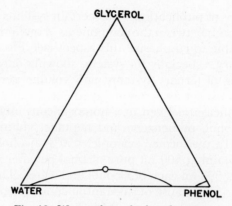

Fig. 19. Water–glycerol–phenol system.

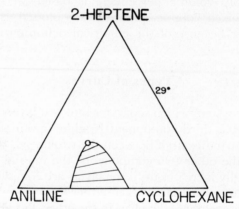

Fig. 20. System with a deep, narrow curve (oblique axis).

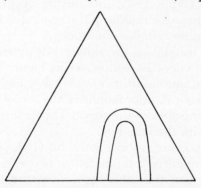

Fig. 21. System with deep, narrow curve (vertical axis is erroneous).

close together, such as 28 and 29.5°. The "axis" of such a curve is nearly parallel with one side line, not like Figure 21 (433), shown also in some textbooks.

When the original miscibility is lower, more homogenizing component is required. The curve is higher, resembling a parabola, but usually unsymmetrical. The plait point is on one side, and the tie lines are steeper, as in Figure 22 (180, p. 964). Or the curve can be very high, as in Figure 23 (180, p. 842), and resemble a hyperbola with the side lines acting as asymptotes. The plait point almost

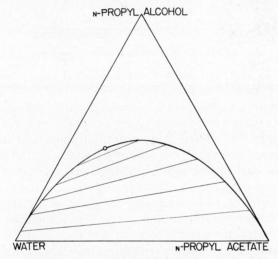

Fig. 22. Water–*n*-propyl alcohol–*n*-propyl acetate system.

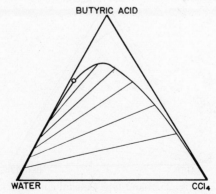

Fig. 23. Water–*n*-butyric acid–carbon tetrachloride system.

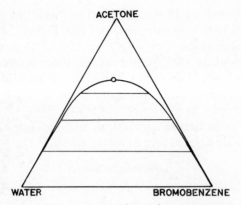

Fig. 24. Water–acetone–bromobenzene system.

touches one side. A symmetrical curve with the plait point near the apex, as in Figure 24, is rare (180, p. 951).

When the third component is not miscible with one of the others, the binodal area is a band across two sides of the triangle, as in Figure 25 (180, p. 996). There is no real plait point, and the tie lines near the edge of the graph are almost parallel with the sides of the triangle. The dashed line shows an imaginary portion of the curve external to the triangle. The dashed line contains the plait point.

The two sides of a binodal band are parts of the same binodal curve, not "two separate binodal curves," as sometimes expressed (597). A binodal curve is the locus of *both* ends of the tie lines. In this book and in the author's papers (169, 173, 174) "separate

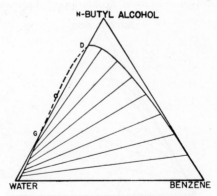

Fig. 25. Band-type binodal curve.

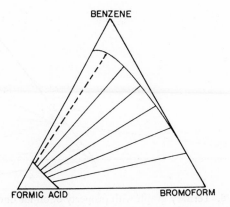

Fig. 26. Band-type curve with substantial binary solubility.

binodal curves" involve isolated heterogeneous areas of compositions separating into two liquid phases.

Figure 26, a band with substantial miscibility at both ends, is
unusual (180, p. 1069). Figure 27 is a system with two organic
substances almost equally miscible with water (180, p. 986).
Figures similar to Figures 19, 22, 23, and 25 might apply to the
same system at different temperatures (decreasing in the order
named).

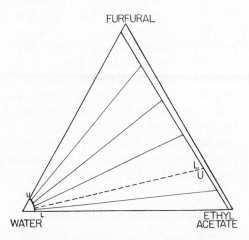

Fig. 27. Band-type curve with isopycnic.

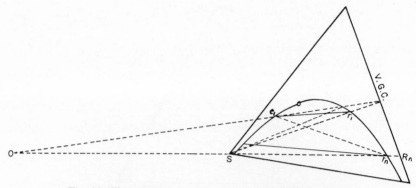

Fig. 28. Ternary graph with property of oil for one side.

For the solvent extraction of an oil, a triangular graph is some-times drawn (see Fig. 28) with a solvent at one corner and the opposite side denoting not a mixture of two pure components but a physical property of an oil, such as aniline point (273A), iodine number (694, p. 35), viscosity index, specific gravity (679), or viscosity gravity constant (VGC) (69; 219, pp. 180–82; 273A; 614, p. 420; 679). This is legitimate with limitations; and the graphs can be used in much the same way as a ternary system. The solvent con-tent of a composition within the triangle is proportional to the perpendicular distance of its point to the opposite side. As is stated in *Chemistry of Petroleum Hydrocarbons* (200, pp. 206–207), "The oil composition is such that removal of solvent would give an oil of the VGC (or property named) resulting from following a straight line through the point from the solvent corner to the opposite side. The binodal curve in such a diagram must be indefinite. The extremities of any tie line would vary in solvent content with the position of the point on the tie line, that is, of the relative volumes of the layers. In fact, it may be doubted that the tie lines in such systems are quite straight . . .The determination of the operating point, O, must be largely empirical. The construction would re-quire extreme precision of points e_1 and r_n, etc., which does not exist."

Orientation of Tie Lines

Unlike those in a binary system, the tie lines in a ternary system usually are not horizontal or parallel with the base line. Udovenko and Fatkulina (704) indicated that this restriction is necessary for a really parabolic shape of curve. The orientation of tie lines is of great interest to chemical engineers because it determines the selectivity of a solvent. The selectivity is

$$\frac{a(100 - b)}{b(100 - a)}$$

where a and b are the percentages of one component in the solvent-free extract and in the solvent-free raffinate, respectively. Numerous investigations have presented correlations for these slopes (1A, 22, 29, 31, 70, 73, 79, 90, 92, 121, 131, 243, 257, 272, 275, 280, 281, 490, 501, 503, 614, 693, 704). Some of the correlations are discussed by Alders (1A). All require experimental observation of a few typical tie lines. Backman (31) showed that if A and B are the two nonconsolute components,

$$x = a(x/y) + b$$

where x is the weight percentage of A in the A-rich layer, y is the weight percentage of B in the B-rich layer, and a and b are constants. A plot of x against x/y gives a straight line with considerable precision in several systems tested.

Figure 29 illustrates another method, that presented in *International Critical Tables III* (275, pp. 398–400) by A. S. Coolidge. In Figure 29 the method is applied to a solutropic system (discussed below). A straight construction line, AJ, is drawn parallel to one side of the triangle from one end of one tie line, AB. Another straight line, BJ, is drawn parallel to another side of the triangle through the other end of the same tie line. The intersection of these two construction lines, J, is a point on the conjugate curve $RQPJKLMN$, which runs from a point near the apex of the triangle through the plait point, P, across the base line to another point, N, far below. Each tie line thus determines a point on the conjugate curve. By reversing the procedure the composition on the binodal curve can be located that is in equilibrium with any particular point on the binodal curve.

By drawing the construction lines in different directions, parallel to other sides of the triangle, Sherwood and Pigford (614) and Briggs and Cummings (73) obtained shorter conjugate curves and saved considerable space because the lower, inverted triangle was omitted.

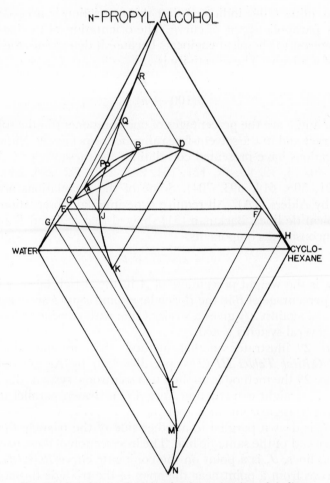

Fig. 29. Graphic method for the determination of tie lines.

Still other conjugate curves have been drawn in a similar manner, though perhaps their use would be less accurate because of greater curvature of the conjugate lines. All of the conjugate curves pass through the plait point. Systems with two pairs of nonconsolute components, Figures 25, 26, and 27, have no plait point and are not adapted to this method of correlation.

Hand (243) showed that if the composition of one of the non-consolute components is multiplied by an empirical constant, e.g.,

2.1, and those of all of the components readjusted to total 100%, the binodal curve often becomes symmetrical with the plait point at the apex and all of the tie lines horizontal. This makes an attractive picture; but the trouble of reconverting to actual percentages makes it not as convenient as it appears. The method is still very popular among foreign investigators in this field. The method, also, is not adapted to correlating double nonconsolute systems, such as shown in Figures 25, 26, and 27, or solutropic systems (discussed below). In one system, water-ether-acetic acid (especially according to ref. 95), the Hand constant is 1.0, and all of the tie lines are almost horizontal.

Avenarius and Tarasenkov (29) postulated that all tie lines of a system converge toward a point on the extended base line, as in Figure 30. This would be very simple and convenient if it were

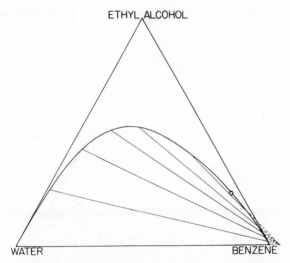

Fig. 30. Tie lines pointing toward a common point.

more generally valid. For a double nonconsolute system (see Fig. 25) it would mean that all tie lines are isologous and unselective. Yet, many solvent extraction processes operate successfully with such systems. In Figures 26 and 27 all of the tie lines are practically isologous, that is pointing directly toward the solvent corner. Isologous means equal ratio, since the ratio of quantities of two of the components remains constant under such conditions.

In a band-type graph (see Fig. 25) a portion, *DG*, of the side line *AB* is a tie line which points directly toward the solvent corner, *A*, and is therefore isologous and unselective. Those tie lines close to it and also those close to the base line have very slight selectivity; but intermediate tie lines have useful selectivity.

In systems of both types the tie lines usually slope toward the solvent corner, and so diminish selectivity. But for the bite type even the top tie line, the infinitesimal one straddling the plait point, which is identical with the tangent to the binodal curve at the plait point, is not steep enough, when prolonged, to intersect the base line within the triangle. If it were, there would be the anomaly of a raffinate richer in the consolute component than the extract. Some systems of glycerol with higher alcohols (141) were thought to be of this type (see Fig. 31); and the present author once

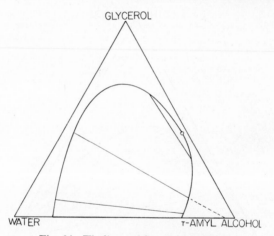

Fig. 31. Tie lines with excessive slope.

considered the system diethylene glycol–thiophene–benzene to show the phenomenon (see Fig. 32). A more careful examination proved the original results to be caused by a trace of water in the diethylene glycol (177). His studies of the glycerol systems likewise showed no excessive slope of the tie lines. A trace of hydrocarbon in the alcohol could have caused the original observation.

In a system with two separate binodal curves (see Fig. 60) the tie lines of the two curves when extended (dashed lines) probably

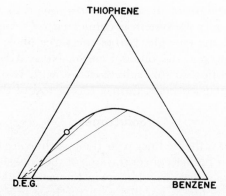

Fig. 32. Tie lines with excessive slope (erroneous).

should cross so as not to intersect their own base lines within the triangle.

To be consistent with the generality just proposed, the straight line from the solvent corner tangent to the binodal curve, *ADF* in Figure 33, must contact the curve below the plait point. This provides a partial check on the position of the plait point, which must be between the two points *D* and *E* (177; 201, p. 447). The plait point is usually near one of the tangent points and is commonly on a portion of the curve which is relatively straight (197, 491), contrary to what might be expected.

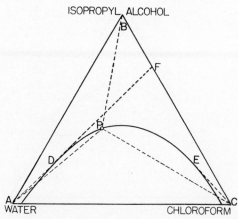

Fig. 33. Diagram illustrating rule for position of plait point.

A further corollary of these generalizations is as follows: if any plait point in a ternary system is connected by straight lines to all three corners of the triangle, two of the three lines, *PA* and *PC* in Figure 33, must cross the binodal curve. No real system seems to be a clear exception to this rule. Systems with two or three plait points, to be discussed later, form a severe test of this corollary.

Solutropes

In some systems the tie lines near the base line are inclined in one direction, and at higher concentrations of the consolute component they slope in the other direction, as in Figure 34 (643), and Figure 35 (493). One tie line is parallel with the base line and is called a "solutrope" (636); and the system is called a "solutropic system" by analogy with azeotropic systems, which are unselective in distillation. The nomenclature is unfortunate, since a solutrope is not unselective in extraction (643), as implied by the analogy. An unselective tie line would be one directed toward the solvent corner of the graph (an isologous line). J. C. Smith (643) called such a tie line an azeotropic tie line. However, the term "solutrope" has gained wide acceptance.

Solutropes are not rare. More than 70 solutropes are illustrated (180), and several more are listed in the tables of this book. Many

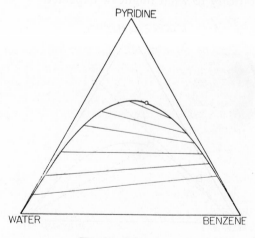

Fig. 34. Solutrope.

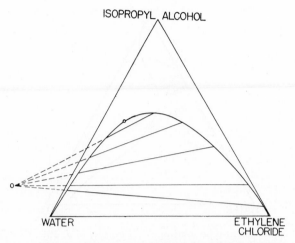

ISOPROPYL ALCOHOL

WATER

ETHYLENE
CHLORIDE

Fig. 35. Solutrope. Correlation of tie lines.

are listed by J. C. Smith and co-workers (643). There are even double solutropes (54; 180, p. 960; 348; 349), that is, the slope of the tie lines is reversed twice. Smith and co-workers (643) and Vriens and Medcalf (739) showed that many solutropic systems lose this feature when plotted on a molar basis. This phenomenon is hardly significant, however, since it depends on the relatively low molecular weight of water (as they indicated). Some other nonsolutropic aqueous systems would become solutropic on a molar basis, e.g., water–trichloroacetic acid–ethyl bromide (180, p. 876).

For solutropic systems most of the methods of correlation of tie lines mentioned would fail badly, though Ishida (277, 280), Izmailov (299), and Palatnik (493) presented methods applicable to them (see Fig. 35) (299). The methods with conjugate curves are satisfactory, as shown in Figure 29. Rotinyants (569) seems to dispute the possibility of solutropes.

Solutropes are found usually only in bite-type binodal curves because it is anomalous for a component to be more soluble in another component with which it is not completely miscible than with one with which it *is* miscible. This phenomenon occurs, however, in certain aqueous systems of hydrogen halides, namely, with hydrogen bromide and *n*-heptane (200, p. 202) and with hydrogen chloride and *n*-hexyl alcohol, as in Figure 36 (175, Fig. 5). (The colors mentioned on the tie lines are iso-optics.)

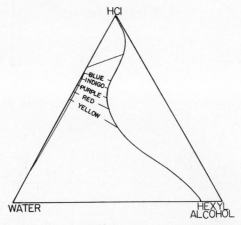

Fig. 36. Band-type solutrope.   (Courtesy of *J. Phys. Chem.*)

Principles of Extraction

Partial separation of mixtures of pairs of hydrocarbons by extraction with appropriate solvents is illustrated in Figures 37 and 38. The systems shown are benzyl alcohol–cyclohexane–*n*-heptane (136A) with only one nonconsolute pair (bite-type) and diethylene

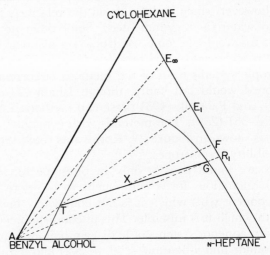

Fig. 37. Principles of extraction for a ternary system with a bite-type binodal curve.

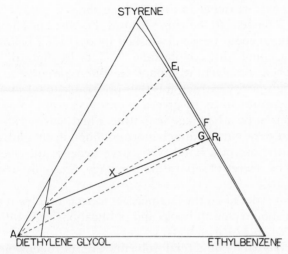

Fig. 38. Principles of extraction for a system with a band-type binodal curve.

glycol–styrene–ethylbenzene, a double nonconsolute system (band-type) (66).

To the feed mixture of hydrocarbons, F, is added solvent, A, giving the gross composition, X, in two layers. After agitation to establish equilibrium and after settling, the layers have the compositions T and G, the extremities of the tie line through X. The layers can be segregated and the solvent separated from each by washing with water or by distillation. The composition of the extract is shown by prolonging a straight line, AT, to the side line, giving E_1; the composition of the raffinate is shown by extending AG to R_1.

Separation of the components can be improved by additional stages of extraction. Instead of removing solvent from T and G after segregation, more solvent can be added to G and more feed to T and the operation repeated; a new extract layer and a new raffinate layer result. The extract layer of the raffinate is mixed with the raffinate layer of the extract, etc., and the process is continued as long as necessary. Counter-current flow with suitable agitation and settling can be made to provide these operations automatically, giving eventually almost pure raffinate—n-heptane and ethylbenzene, respectively, in the two systems shown in Figures 37 and 38.

Similarly, the system of Figure 38 can be made to give an extract of almost pure styrene. A bite-type system, as in Figure 37, will fail to give an extract richer in cyclohexane than E_∞, the composition shown by a tangent to the curve from A. Further enrichment by extraction alone could be accomplished by operating below the CST of benzyl alcohol with cyclohexane, 2 °C, or by slight dilution with an appropriate cosolvent to expand the bite-type curve to a band.

For a high-purity extract, it is thus preferable to select the solvent and temperature so as to give a band-type graph. On the other hand, this is of no advantage in getting a high-purity raffinate. The use of a bite-type curve is much more common in engineering operation than the use of a band-type curve because the selectivity, as measured by degree of separation per stage, is usually better for the bite type.

For greater detail on the engineering aspects of solvent extraction the reader should consult books and publications (1A, 140, 200, 201, 204A, 219, 491, 520, 614, 694).

The principal commercial solvents are nitrobenzene, phenol, Chlorex, furfural, and sulfur dioxide. These are chosen mainly for cost, though each has certain shortcomings. Nitrobenzene has the highest solvent power, having such a low curve with most oils that it is applicable only to high-boiling or relatively paraffinic oils. Nitrobenzene usually requires refrigeration. Phenol is used primarily with propane as a cosolvent. Chlorex and furfural have certain instabilities—the former to water and heat and the latter to air. Furfural and sulfur dioxide have such low solvent power for lube oils that they are used mainly for light oils and Diesel or jet fuels. On the other hand, sulfur dioxide is miscible with most gasoline hydrocarbons and so can be used to concentrate benzene and toluene only by using a "wash oil," a highly paraffinic oil to hold back low paraffins, or by diluting the sulfur dioxide with solvents such as ethylene glycol or formamide (196), much lower in solvent power.

4 | EXPERIMENTAL

Determination of Two-Phase Areas

Alders (1A, pp. 35–47) describes three methods of deriving the
binodal curve: the construction method, the analysis method, and
the titration method. The first depends on observing the relative
volume and two separate physical properties, usually density
and refractive index, for each of two layers after settling of a
heterogeneous liquid system. A linear relation is assumed between
these properties of the pure components and those of the mixtures.
The validity of the method depends on this relation. But since deviations from linearity are so common, and sometimes so considerable and unpredictable, especially for heterogeneous systems,
the present author does not recommend this method. If density
and refractive index are parallel, as occurs in certain mixtures,
another property is required.

The analysis method requires the complete analysis of each liquid
phase, such as titration of a component like acetic acid. At least
two analyses are required for each point. This method is excellent
except that only rarely are as many as two of the components
analyzed easily. Methods of analysis involving washing out a
component with water, distilling out the most volatile component,
or distilling two components from a nonvolatile one are awkward
to apply to the small samples usually available. Methods of analysis
described later in this section are generally applicable and therefore preferable.

The present author prefers the titration method. A study by this
method is expedited by preliminary titrations on a small scale.
With care these may be adequate in accuracy for large portions

of the diagrams, especially when there is a shortage of one of the components. The more critical sections of the graphs can be repeated on as large a scale as desired.

A definite volume, e.g., 5 ml, of one of the nonconsolute components, e.g., the solvent, is titrated with the other nonconsolute component. Cloud point, turbidity, or the appearance of a trace of a new liquid phase is used as the end point. A 10-ml, glass-stoppered, graduated tube is convenient because it permits vigorous shaking, rapid adjustment of temperature in a suitable bath, and accurate readings of separate volumes of the layers when required. When samples of the lower layer are important for analysis, the reaction vessel may be for convenience a 25-ml buret with a ground-glass stopper.

Next, a definite volume of the consolute component is added, and another titration is made with the same nonconsolute component. (See the dashed lines in Fig. 39.) These titrations usually are

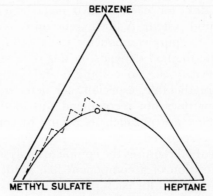

Fig. 39. Experimental observation of binodal curve.

continued until the tube is full. Sometimes they give the binodal curve up to the plait point or to the apex. Ternary compositions are calculated from the three volumes and the respective densities.

The process is repeated, starting with a definite volume of the other nonconsolute component. Since too much of the titrating liquid may be added sometimes and back titration with the consolute component may be required, it is well to let a turbid mixture settle so as to observe the volume of the new layer. Because settling is often slow, it saves time to study both sides of the curve simultaneously by using two glass-stoppered tubes and two burets for the consolute component; or, the consolute component can be added in discrete amounts from a graduated pipet.

If the two sides of the curve have not been joined by these two operations, a third one and fourth one can be made starting with smaller amounts of the original components. The plait point can be observed directly by this process. The composition is adjusted until the interface between the layers is near the middle in volume and the addition of 0.1 ml or less of the consolute component makes the whole volume clear. A pearly appearance or a yellowish haze, which do not settle and which are cleared with a trace of consolute component, are characteristic of the plait point. After passing the plait point along the binodal curve (see Fig. 39), the new liquid phase resulting from turbidity in titration is normally at the bottom if it was previously at the top, and vice versa. A similar reversal occurs on crossing an isopycnic (discussed below).

The titration method just described is incomplete; it does not give the tie lines. These can be found if a direct analysis for one of the three components is available and is applied to each of the layers. In principle the most general analysis is the observation of the refractive index of each layer and the combination of these with observations of refractive index made upon known compositions along the binodal curve. This analysis is reliable provided the system is strictly ternary, i.e., none of the three components is a mixture. Unfortunately, it is sometimes applied while disregarding this limitation. Density observations on the two phases are less convenient and require larger samples; but they are often more reliable and may be more accurate. A titration of one of the components, preferably the consolute one, is an even more accurate method if the component is an acid, a base, or some other substance that gives a rapid chemical reaction.

A simple method which gives fairly accurate tie lines in a system with a high binodal curve (low binary solubilities), as in Figure 23 or 24, is as follows. Equal volumes, e.g., 3 ml each, of two non-consolute components are charged to a 10-ml, glass-stoppered, graduated tube, shaken vigorously, and settled. The positions of the interface and upper meniscus are noted. An additional shaking and settling usually check these positions within 0.01 ml. A definite volume, 0.5 ml, of the third component is added, and observation is made of the rise in position of the interface and meniscus, showing the distribution of the solute. Percentages of components are adjusted for their densities.

This procedure is continued until (a) the tube is full, (b) the system is homogeneous, or (c) the change in position is irregular (excessive rise, or falls). After (a) the experiment is repeated with smaller volumes of the first two components. After (b) it is repeated starting with larger volumes. After (c), which is usually due to an unsymmetrical curve, the experiment is repeated starting with a different ratio of volumes. This is adjusted until the isologous line leading toward the upper corner of the triangle passes through the plait point, confirming its position. Another cause of (c) is the presence of a solutrope, which is thus readily detected.

Isopycnics and Iso-optics

Only the lower tie lines observed by the above distribution method have much accuracy. In some systems, however, high accuracy of certain tie lines, regardless of position, is possible by purely synthetic means. One method is available when the two liquid phases in equilibrium have the same density and remain as a stable emulsion of large globules. These ternary isopycnics are much more common than binary isopycnics (see Chap. 2) because relative density of the layers is changed more rapidly by the addition of a third component than by temperature changes in a binary system. About 150 examples of ternary isopycnics are known (163). They are shown as dashed tie lines in Figures 26, 27, 40, 41, and others. They are just as common in band-type graphs as in bite-type graphs. They may occur also in island curves (see Chap. 6) and in binodal areas of three-phase graphs (see Chap. 5). One system was made up of three layers of the same density, 1.15 g/cm^3 (163, 180, p. 1070). It required five components. Another system, shown in Figure 40 (163), has two isopycnics, so that in following around the binodal curve the relative densities of the phases are reversed five times—at the plait point and at each end of each isopycnic. U and L indicate upper and lower layers in three of the figures mentioned.

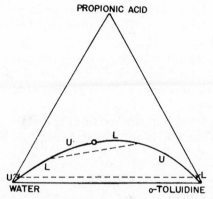

Fig. 40. Double isopycnic (U = upper layer, L = lower layer).   (Courtesy of *Ind. Eng. Chem.*)

The isopycnic tie line is located by adjusting the composition to give a small isopycnic solvent-lean layer and then finding another composition to give a small solvent-rich layer. These compositions are on the same tie line, as is also an isopycnic point near the middle of the binodal area. If these three points are not on the same straight

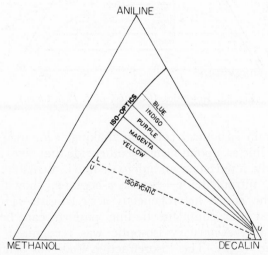

Fig. 41. Isopycnic and set of iso-optics (U = upper layer, L = lower layer). (Courtesy of *Ind. Eng. Chem.*)

line, there must be a fourth component or impurity in one of the three nominal components. This is discussed below under impurities (see Chap. 8).

With change in temperature an isopycnic usually shifts upward and disappears at the plait point (like other tie lines); or it shifts downward and disappears at the base line at the temperature of the binary isopycnic.

Iso-optics also furnish means for finding certain tie lines. A point within but near one side of the binodal area (see Figs. 41, 42) that

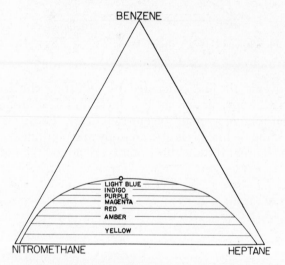

Fig. 42. Iso-optics. (Courtesy of *J. Phys. Chem.*)

gives a certain structural color on shaking, e.g., magenta, is on the same tie line as a point near the other side that gives a matching hue. Similarly, a purple or an indigo tie line is available. In at least one system, nitromethane–benzene–*n*-heptane, shown in Figure 42 (172), the entire heterogeneous area consists of colored tie lines so that the complete tie-line pattern can be observed colorimetrically. A ternary iso-optic was recognized by Gladel and LaBlaud (228). The "isorefractive lines" of Schuberth and Leibnitz (597) are curves of uniform index entirely in the homogeneous area and are different from iso-optics.

The use of a binodal curve to analyze homogeneous compositions (outside the curve) has been suggested (491, 625). Such a mixture is titrated with one of the nonconsolute components until the composition reaches the binodal curve, as indicated by turbidity. The percentage of some component, such as acetic acid, either in the original composition of the sample or in that reached on the binodal curve, is observed by titration. Or the composition of the saturated phase is determined by its refractive index or other physical property.

Any ternary composition in a known system can be determined (179, p. 249; 200, p. 203) by observing the amounts of two of the components required to adjust the composition to that of the plait point, which at any temperature is unique for the system (unless there are two plait points).

Another method for locating tie lines (after the binodal curve is determined) requires adjusting the slope of a tentative tie line until the ratio of its segments, formed by the point showing gross composition of the system, is inversely equal to the weight ratio of the layers. This method is unreliable when any one of the three components is impure.

Systems under Pressure

When one or more of the components to be studied is a liquefied gas, i.e., boils below room temperature, the glass-stoppered tube is inadequate. Instead, thick-walled, sealed, Pyrex glass tubes can be used. The less volatile components are introduced first, with successive weighings to centigrams or milligrams. To avoid the risk of spilling, a cork or wire cradle can be used to hold the tube in a slightly inclined position on the balance pan. Then the tube is cooled in a cold bath of acetone and dry ice. The liquefied gas from a lecture bottle is passed in through a capillary glass funnel and is condensed in the tube. The stem of the tube is sealed while the tube is in the bath, saving the tip. After warming to room temperature, the tube and tip are weighed to determine the weight of liquefied gas condensed.

It was once the practice to cool an acetone bath directly with lumps of or crushed dry ice. But since such a bath saturated with carbon dioxide occasionally bubbles over, possibly while sealing the neck of the tube, with risk of fire, it is preferable to cool the bath indirectly with lumps of dry ice in a large test tube containing a *little* acetone. The large test tube is immersed in an acetone bath in a quart wide-mouth Dewar flask. Such a bath is nearly as cold, and never "burps."

If one of the components is water or a salt solution, but no soluble organic component is present, there is risk of bursting the glass tube when freezing the water (not dangerous). The volume of water should be kept small; and it should be frozen from the bottom up by gradual immersion in the cold bath, or with a swirling motion. This technique succeeds with water and with most salt solutions; but it fails with certain components, such as alums, possibly because of subcooling.

For maximum strength the tube is preferably about 12 mm o.d. and 7 mm i.d., about 200 mm long with a round bottom, and drawn down at the top and sealed to a stem about 4 mm in diameter (see Fig. 43). Such a tube, properly made, is safe for at least 40 atm.

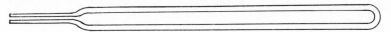

Fig. 43. Glass pressure tube.

Adequate safeguards should always be used. Safeguards suggested are as follows. Use safety goggles at all times. At marginal times (near maximum pressure) use also a plastic face shield. The sealed glass tube may be given a preliminary heating inside a steel tube at about 10°C higher temperature than that to be observed. The tube may be heated in a bath of water or glycol in a large, thick-walled test tube within cork rings which can be moved to observe any portion of the tube. The rings insulate the bath, improving adjustment of temperature, and also act as a baffle if an explosion occurs.

The relative quantities of reagents to be introduced are estimated. Pertinent observations are: whether or not the system is homogeneous; if the system is heterogeneous, the volumes of small upper or lower layers, the presence of isopycnics or iso-optics, and the presence of a plait point or a solid phase. After observations at several desired temperatures, the tube is cooled again in the cold bath, the end of the stem is broken off, and more of the appropriate reagent is added. The tube is sealed, warmed to room temperature, weighed with all three tips, and new observations are made. This procedure continues until either the tube is full, the stem is too short to be sealed again, or all needed information is obtained. Six or eight sealings can often be made with one initial filling. Pressure in these sealed glass tubes can be measured easily with a mercury manometer (203A). However, in the presence of two liquid phases the total pressure can be estimated from the vapor pressures of the components with fair precision; therefore, the use of this gage rarely justifies the additional glass blowing, the weakening of the tube, and its more awkward handling. Details of the method are here omitted, although it was used to observe the pressures of Figure 3.

Sealed glass tubes are not recommended for studies with liquid carbon dioxide, ethane, ethylene, hydrogen chloride, or nitrous oxide, which have vapor pressures of 60 to 70 atm at room temperature. These liquids have been observed in a visual autoclave (165, 171, 173, 175, 186–188, 192, 193, 196, 197). Nonvolatile reagents were pipetted in through a glass funnel. Weights of liquefied gas were estimated from their incremental volumes and their apparent densities (173). Nitrous oxide was used only with water or with carbon tetrachloride because of ignorance of its possible reactions with organic compounds under high pressure. However, Kuenen (275, p. 356) ignored any such risk.

Observations for most ternary graphs were made at atmospheric pressure. Some, when a liquefied gas was a component, were made under pressure. In either case each tie line is an isobar. The total pressure and all three partial pressures are the same at each end and all along each tie line (but not the same on different tie lines) even though the percentage of a liquefied gas may be over 90% at one end of a tie line and 5% or less at the other. This relation is exemplified by steam distillation or other two-phase distillation. Azeotropic distillation is similar, even though the boiling liquid may be homogeneous.

5 | MULTIPLE PHASE BOUNDARY CURVES

Solid–Liquid and Liquid–Liquid Equilibriums

Curves showing equilibrium of a liquid in a ternary system with a crystalline solid are not usually considered as binodal curves, though they have some of the same characteristics. If the solid is one of the three pure components, its equilibrium is usually a simple curve cutting off one corner of the triangle graph, Figure 44 (180, p. 1014), Figure 47 (168; 180, p. 943), and Figure 48 (190). Tie lines radiate to this curve from the corner but are not very significant.

The solid may also be a complex of two components so that its composition is represented by a point on one side line. Again, tie lines radiate from that point to the curve, which has a superficial resemblance to a binodal curve except for the orientation of the tie lines and the lack of a plait point, as in Figure 45 (180, p. 857). Ricci (546, p. 208) in discussing miscibility gaps stated, "For clarity and familiarity, we speak of the *MG* in the liquid state, but the relations, of course, hold equally for the solid state." The present author disagrees with this viewpoint (see Chap. 2). There are wide differences in miscibility relations between liquid and crystalline substances. These are due to the fixed compositions of the latter, normally a pure substance, and the variable compositions, within limits, of the former.

The systems of Figures 46, 47, and 48 (168, 186, 190) are anomalous in having a *liquid* complex, *C*, of nonmolar composition of propylene and silver nitrate, which is a nonsolvent for propane, i.e., it is perfectly selective for propylene–propane mixtures. On the other hand, the anhydrous silver nitrate does not

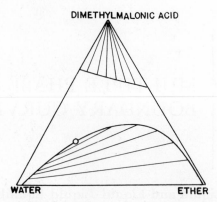

Fig. 44. Binodal curve and an equilibrium of a liquid with a solid component.

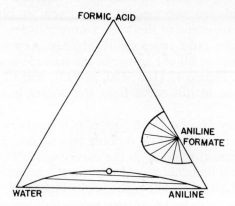

Fig. 45. Binodal curve and an equilibrium of a liquid with a solid complex of two components.

form a complex with less than 75% propylene in a hydrocarbon mixture. 1-Butene has similar relations; but most other olefins fail to react with anhydrous silver nitrate. *Solutions* of silver nitrate in water, as in Figure 47 (123, 190, 202), and in acetonitrile, as in Figure 48 (190, 205), absorb ethylene, styrene, and other olefins.

Systems with additional solid phases, some ternary, may be of great complexity but will not be discussed in this book. They are important in metallurgy and in geology.

If a system has both types of equilibrium, liquid–solid and liquid–liquid, the graph may be constructed by drawing each curve

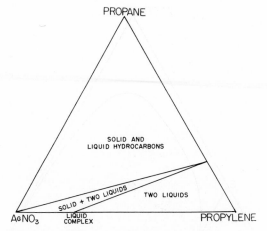

Fig. 46. Liquid complex of silver nitrate with an olefin in the presence of a paraffin. (Courtesy of *J. Am. Chem. Soc*)

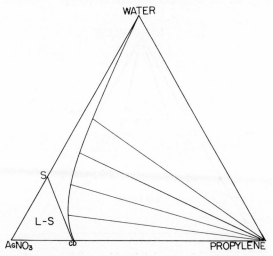

Fig 47. Silver nitrate–water–propylene system. (Courtesy of *J. Am. Chem. Soc.*)

tentatively as though the other were absent. See Figures 44, 45, and 47–54 (168; 180, pp. 857, 942, 943, 1011, 1014; 186; 191). If the curves intersect, the liquid compositions at the two points of intersection are both in equilibrium with the solid, and therefore

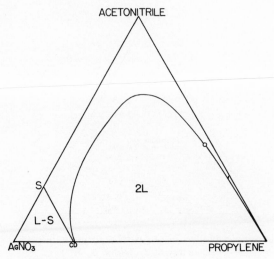

Fig. 48. Silver nitrate–acetonitrile–propylene system.

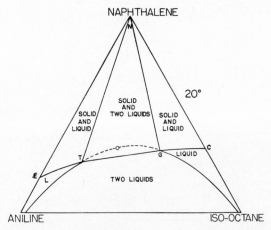

Fig. 49. Ternary system whose solid–liquid equilibrium submerges the plait
point of a binodal curve.

with each other, so that the straight line connecting them is a tie
line. See line *TG* in Figures 49, 50, 51, and 53 (180, pp. 860, 918,
957, 1103). The points of intersection are not eutectics, as they
are sometimes called because of resemblance to intersections

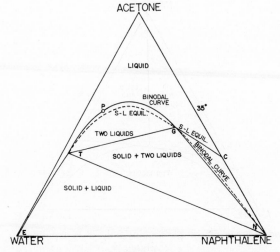

Fig. 50. Binodal curve submerged below a liquid–solid boundary except for a loop near its plait point.

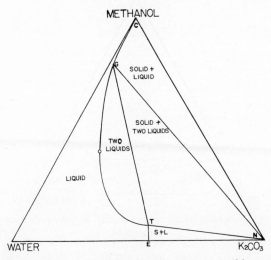

Fig. 51. System illustrating salting out of a water-miscible component.

of two curves of solid–liquid equilibrium. Sometimes the first point of contact (on cooling the system) of two such curves is the plait point of the binodal curve, erroneously called a peritectic. See point K in Figure 52 (180, p. 1103).

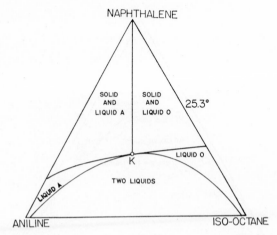

Fig. 52. Binodal curve whose plait point only is in equilibrium with a solid phase.

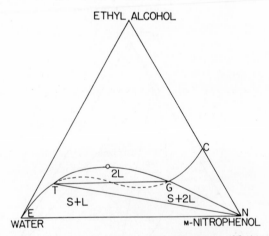

Fig. 53. System with a binodal curve and a solid–liquid equilibrium curve nearly coincident.

It is also possible for the liquid–solid curve to make an initial contact with the binodal curve at the tie line which is a portion of the base line. The solid is thus in equilibrium with *both* ends of that tie line and, therefore, usually with another almost pure component. This relation is illustrated by the dehydration of alcohols and other

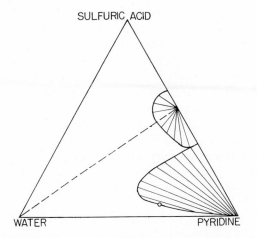

Fig. 54. System with a liquid in equilibrium with a solid and with another liquid, both phase boundaries being on the same side of the triangle.

organic liquids with potassium hydroxide, potassium carbonate, calcium chloride, etc. (see Figs. 51, 54). It is not possible for the initial contact of a solid–liquid phase boundary to be an intermediate point on the binodal curve. These relations are analogous to the disappearance (or initial appearance) of isopycnics at the top or bottom of a binodal curve.

If the solid is the consolute component, as in Figure 49, the plait point may be eliminated or at least submerged to a metastable area (dashed line). If the solid is one of the nonconsolute components, the bulk of the binodal curve becomes metastable, as in Figures 50 and 53 (180, pp. 918, 957), and the remainder of it may become a small loop with a real plait point, P. The dashed S curve in Figure 53 is analogous to the Van der Waals curve.

In either case there is an internal triangular area, NTG, as in Figures 49, 50, 51, 53, representing by its corners three phases— a solid and two liquid phases. There are also two areas, NTE and NGC, roughly triangular but with one curved side each, showing equilibrium of the solid with one liquid. The upper part of Figure 50 and the left side of Figure 51 show homogeneous composition; but in Figure 49 there are two homogeneous areas, one on each side of the binodal curve.

Similar relations would result from the intersection of a binodal curve with a curve for equilibrium with a solid complex; but such systems are presented more logically with separate graphs. A system is possible, though certainly rare, with both types of curve out of the same side of the triangle, as in Figure 54. If two components have enough affinity to form a solid complex, they are not likely to separate into two liquid layers. In the example shown (180, p. 1011) the immiscible liquids are doubtless pyridine and pyridine sulfate. The graph should perhaps have been divided into two separate triangular graphs, as shown by the dashed line. The system of water–sulfuric acid–and nicotine is even more complex (see Fig. 55) (159).

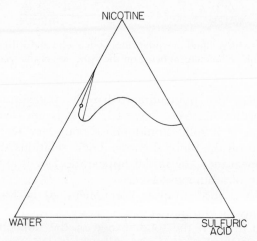

Fig. 55. Binodal curve involving a salt in solution.

The existence of a solid ternary complex without the presence of solid binary complexes would be interesting. The present author is not aware of such an example. It would be an island curve of a different type from that to be discussed shortly.

Multiple Liquid–Liquid Equilibriums

Equilibriums of three components as functions of temperature can be shown by an equilateral triangular prism with temperature as the vertical dimension. Most systems giving two liquid layers are represented by a ridge (or tunnel) passing obliquely through the prism and cutting one or two of its vertical faces but never cutting a vertical edge (see Fig. 56) (1A, p. 31; 694, pp. 14, 15). Isotherms, or horizontal planes, cut this ridge giving deeper and deeper binodal curves with descending temperatures (see Figs. 19, 22, 23, 25). The system selected shows CST's with aniline relatively near together, 95.7 and 72.4°C (178, p. 189). A curve near the crest of the ridge, a plait line, is formed by the plait points of the curves.

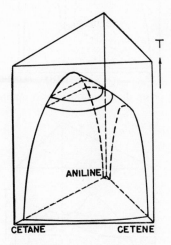

Fig. 56. Triangular prism diagram showing formation of binodal curves of increasing depth.

The ridge is not necessarily straight. If it is slightly convex upward and also nearly horizontal, an isotherm may cut off the hump thus formed and give an island curve, as in Figure 57 (discussed below, Chap. 6). If the ridge is concave upward and also nearly horizontal, an isotherm may cut off two separate binodal curves as in Figure 58. The classical example of this is the system of Schreinemakers (595), water–ethyl alcohol–succinonitrile, cited in most physical chemistry textbooks but often so distorted as to be misleading in some aspects. A graph drawn to scale is shown in Figure 59. The merger of the curves, which is of considerable interest, cannot be observed on this system because of the crystal-

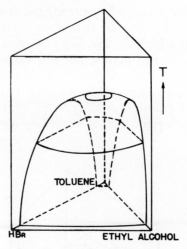

Fig. 57. Triangular prism diagram showing formation of island curves.

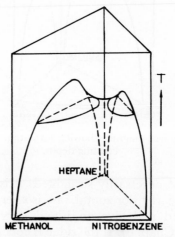

Fig. 58. Triangular prism diagram showing formation of two separate binodal curves.

lization of two of the components, succinonitrile and water. The short vertical line at the right of Figure 59 is the equilibrium with succinonitrile crystals.

In the prism diagram of another system, methanol–nitrobenzene–iso-octane, a lower isotherm shows these two curves expanding

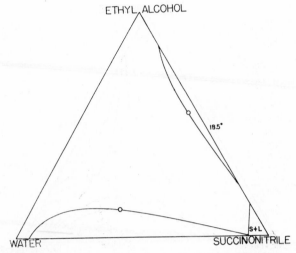

ETHYL ALCOHOL

18.5°

S+L

WATER   SUCCINONITRILE

Fig. 59. Classical example of two separate binodal curves.

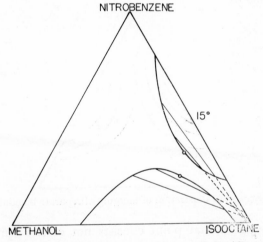

NITROBENZENE

15°

METHANOL   ISOOCTANE

Fig. 60. Two separate binodal curves with extended tie lines that cross.

toward each other until they touch, with both plait points at the lowest point on the ridge (see Figs. 60, 61) (169). This point is the "col," or saddle point. The col is both the low point on the ridge and the high point of a pass (analogy to topography).

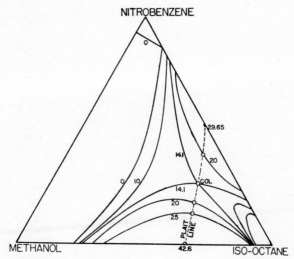

Fig. 61. Merging of two separate binodal curves.   (Courtesy of *J. Am. Chem. Soc.*)

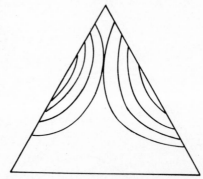

Fig. 62. Erroneous illustration of merging of separate binodal curves.

The isotherm at that point consists not of two curves with a common tangent, as shown in some schematic graphs such as Figure 62 (433; 546, p. 214; 694, p. 17), but of two more nearly straight curves intersecting at a finite angle, as in Figure 61 (169, 351, 364, 371, 632, 765). They might be considered the common asymptotes of two pairs of curves analogous to a hyperbola. The pair of curves below the col isotherm consists of two sides of the

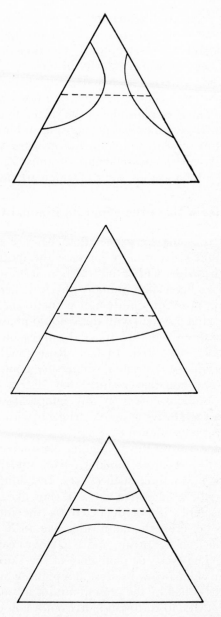

Figs. 63–65. Graphs illustrating "law of inverted similitude."

resulting concave binodal band; and the pair above that temperature shows the two binodal curves. The pairs appear in opposite
quadrants formed by the "asymptotes" mentioned.

Krupatkin (356) noted a regularity in ternary systems with two
immiscible pairs. Graphs of such systems may show either a band
or two separate binodal curves. A line, presumably the horizontal
projection of the crest or plait line of the ridge, divides any binodal
curves into roughly symmetrical portions, as in Figures 63, 64, and
65. He called this regularity the "law of inverted similitude," and
he illustrated it with many schematic graphs. Zhuravlev (761A)
showed several similar graphs, some of which are rather speculative.

Systems with Three Separate Binodal Curves

These systems would be expected to be rare because a third
component would not normally increase the mutual solubility of
two components with neither of which it is miscible. However,
such systems have been cited in many physical chemistry textbooks
as an intriguing possibility, although without an actual example.
It was assumed that a system with three liquid phases would necessarily give the three separate binodal curves on warming until
the binodal areas separated. In fact, Rose (567B) showed four
supposed isotherms for the system water–succinonitrile–ethyl ether.
His graphs were imaginary, since that system does not have
three separate binodal curves at any temperature. Moreover, a
three-phase area is always a simple triangle with straight sides—
never highly curved as shown by Rose.

A single ridge across the triangular prism could produce an
isotherm with two separate binodal curves under the conditions
mentioned, but never three such curves. In addition to the main
ridge there may be a side ridge like a **T** (not like a **Y** because the
main ridge probably is not deflected by the intersection). The
side ridge does not cross the main ridge like an **X** because there is
no remaining face to the prism, and two ridges cannot come from
the same face. The crest, or plait line, of the side ridge therefore
strikes the main ridge below its crest at a point, which for want of a
better name was called by the present author a "subcol" (shown in
Figs. 66, 72–74, 81) to distinguish it from a col, discussed above.
(See Figs. 61, 67, 69, 72, 73, 75 (174)). K stands for a subcol which

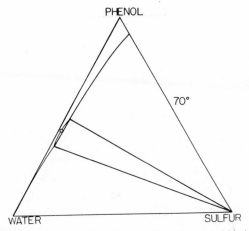

Fig. 66. Binodal band interrupted by the eruption of a new side ridge from within the main ridge (band).

has an angular intersection of surfaces. At this point the tie line through the main ridge splits (with decreasing temperature) into two tie lines across that ridge and together with a third tie line across the side ridge forms a triangle of three liquid layers in equilibrium.

A three-phase area in a system of three components, two of which are still miscible (see Fig. 66), was considered an anomaly by Vreeland and Dunlap (738), although graphs of that type had been shown earlier (179, p. 253; 180, pp. 1015, 1029, 1035; 200, p. 208). Actually, it seems to be the normal mechanism, since all of about 13 systems with three liquid layers published before 1953 had been formed in that way.

The extension of the anomaly mentioned to three-liquid phase systems with two pairs of miscible components also had been published (see Fig. 81) (180, p. 1029; 200, p. 208). The further extension to cases with three pairs of miscible components (island triangles) was suggested (201, p. 450, Fig. 15) although no experimental example had been reported. It is difficult to draw such a figure in obedience to the generality about position of plait points discussed in the last two paragraphs of this chapter; and this difficulty makes such a graph improbable.

Five examples of systems with three separate binodal curves at atmospheric pressure are now known (174, 197). They result from

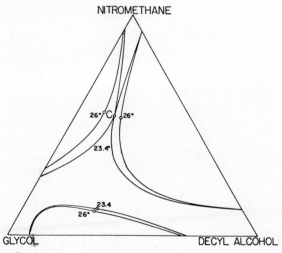

Fig. 67. Two isotherms of the system ethylene glycol–nitromethane–*n*-decyl alcohol that show three separate binodal curves.   (Courtesy of *J. Phys. Chem.*)

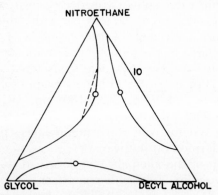

Fig. 68. Isotherm at 10°C of system ethylene glycol–nitroethane–*n*-decyl alcohol that shows three separate binodal curves. An isopycnic (dashed line) is shown. (Courtesy of *J. Phys. Chem.*)

a combination of two of the mechanisms described. That is, the main ridge is concave and gives two binodal curves; and a side ridge results in the third curve. These systems all involve as components ethylene glycol, nitromethane or nitroethane, and a higher alcohol.

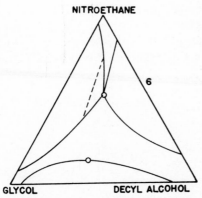

Fig. 69. Isotherm at 6°C, the col temperature, of system ethylene glycol–nitroethane–*n*-decyl alcohol. The dashed line is an isopycnic. (Courtesy of *J. Phys. Chem.*)

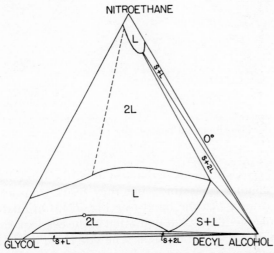

Fig. 70. Isotherm at 0°C of system ethylene glycol–nitroethane–*n*-decyl alcohol. An isopycnic (dashed line) is shown. (Courtesy of *J. Phys. Chem.*)

As the systems are cooled, the mechanism of meeting of the curves is approximately that suggested schematically by Wetmore and LeRoy (748). In the two decyl alcohol systems, two of the curves meet at both plait points, forming a band (see Figs. 67–70). On further cooling, the third curve approaches a concave portion of this band with its plait point (see Fig. 70). Contact would probably result in three liquid layers, but for the crystallization of the alcohol. The system with 2-ethylhexanol was studied only qualitatively (197). It has three shallow curves at 25 °C, two of which merge above 0 °C.

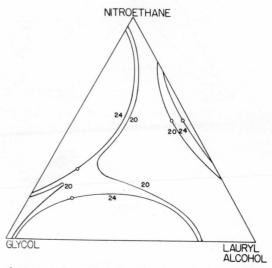

Fig. 71. Isotherms at 24 and 20°C of system ethylene glycol–nitroethane–lauryl alcohol. Three separate binodal curves are present at 24°C. (Courtesy of *J. Phys. Chem.*)

In the lauryl alcohol–nitroethane system, the three liquid phases formed on cooling are stable; but they result from eruption of a new curve from *within* the band (see Fig. 72). On further cooling, this curve meets with its plait point that of the original binodal curve from the third side of the triangle. The side ridge thus has a second col, as shown in the elevation, Figure 73 (across Fig. 72 at the dash-dot line). However, the second col does not result in a fourth binodal curve at any temperature because two of the binodal curves are merged below 21 °C; and above 16.5 °C the fourth curve is submerged.

If the crest or plait line of the side ridge slopes downward in temperature on intersecting the main ridge, the intersection takes place at the plait point of the side ridge but not at that of the main

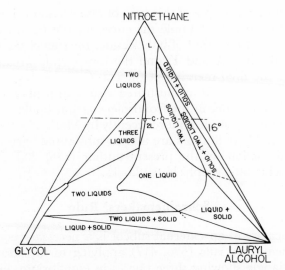

Fig. 72. Isotherm of same system at 16°C indicating a col, *C*, and a subcol. (Courtesy of *J. Phys. Chem.*)

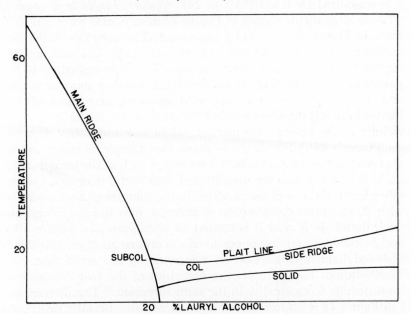

Fig. 73. Vertical elevation of the same system along the line of 54% nitroethane of Figure 72 (dash-dot line).   (Courtesy of *J. Phys. Chem.*)

ridge. Only one example of this type of intersection is known (174, Fig. 2a); and in that example the curve for the main ridge seems to be concave at the point of intersection, the subcol, K, Figure 74. Point K splits into X and Y, and the three-liquid area, XYZ appears *before* the final merging at the col, C (see Figs. 75, 76). The system of Figures 74–76 is illustrated also with a photograph of a plaster of Paris model in the frontispiece of this book.

This system was studied more recently by Markuzin and Nikanorova (415A). These authors are also in substantial agreement with previous discussion by the present author (179, 200, 201), with respect to schematic graphs in textbooks.

Schreinemakers' Rule

The concavity at an external subcol is a necessary consequence of Schreinemakers' rule (596, 417) applying to the corners of an internal triangle showing three phases in equilibrium, either solid or liquid or both. The rule is illustrated in Figures 77 and 78, and it is explained by Ricci (546, p. 244, *numbers changed to fit graphs*). "The arrangements shown in Figure 77 at a, b, and c are possible, those in Figure 78 at d and f impossible. The tangents of the two solubility curves at their intersections must both lie inside or both outside the isothermally invariant area. This is so regardless of the nature of the saturating phases involved, whether solid or liquid, and whether pure components, solid solutions, or compounds. In Figure 77 at a it may be seen that the components in the immediate vicinity of the intersection increase while at b and c they decrease each other's solubility. If the α-phase, for example, is added to and dissolved in the solution which is saturated with β, the total composition is brought into the unsaturated area and β dissolves. On the other hand, if the α-phase is added to the solution γ, also saturated with β, the total composition is brought into the heterogeneous field, liquid + β, and β is caused to precipitate. In Figure 78 d and f would be exerting opposite effects on one another, and this is thermodynamically impossible, somewhat in the sense that in a binary liquid, for example, the fugacities of the two components must deviate from ideality in the same direction." The intersection e in Figure 78 is impossible for another reason—because one phase subtends over 180°.

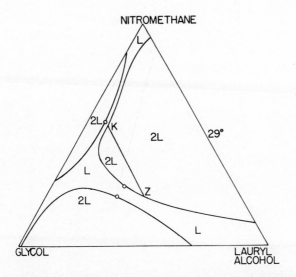

Fig. 74. Isotherm at 29°C of system ethylene glycol–nitromethane–lauryl alcohol. Three separate binodal curves are present. The merger of curves is external. (Courtesy of *J. Phys. Chem.*)

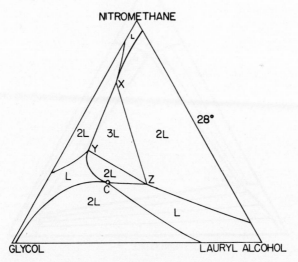

Fig. 75. Isotherm of same system at 28°C. (Courtesy of *J. Phys. Chem.*) (See frontispiece.)

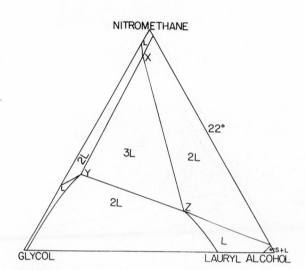

Fig. 76. Isotherm of same system at 22°C.   (Courtesy of *J. Phys. Chem.*)   (See frontispiece.)

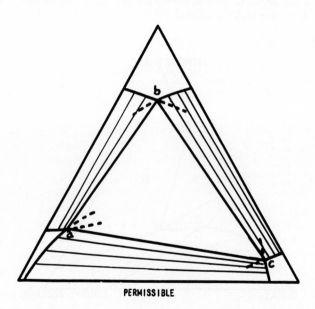

Fig. 77. Postulated ternary graph illustrating permissible intersections of phase boundaries according to Schreinemakers' principle.

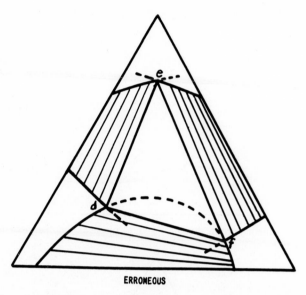

Fig. 78. Postulated ternary graph illustrating erroneous intersections of phase boundaries.

It is unfortunate that Ricci failed to observe this rule in some of his schematic graphs (546, Figs. 10–19b, 10–20c, 11–18b). The rule would be necessarily violated when two *convex* binodal curves are contacted *externally* at points other than both plait poir.ts, as postulated also in other publications (140, p. 720; 259; 260, p. 2708; 274, 694, p. 17) and in at least four other physical chemistry text-books, with graphs similar to Figure 79. All of these relied on the observations by Hill and co-workers (258, 260), which were of *internal* contact only.

The importance of "convex" and "externally" is explained by the contrast in Figure 80 and 81 (200, pp. 210–211). In the former (schematic), the prolongations of *EJ* and *DH* are necessarily within the triangle of three-phase area, *HIJ*, while those of *PJ* and *FH* (if convex) are necessarily outside the three-phase area—a clear violation of Schreinemakers' rule. In the real system, Figure 81 (180, p. 1029), the corresponding extensions are all external in consistency with the rule. This and related real systems are shown also by Francis, Mertslin and Nikurashina, and Nikurashina

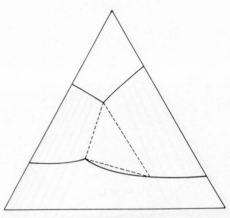

Fig. 79. Erroneous graph shown in several physical chemistry textbooks.

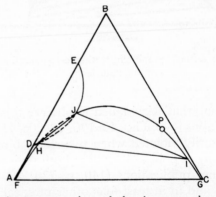

Fig. 80. Schematic (and erroneous) graph showing external contact of two convex curves.

et al. (174, 434, 479, 480). Schreinemakers' rule is violated also in other published graphs, both illustrative and experimental, showing three phases (417, 738).

Carbon Dioxide Systems

A comprehensive investigation of 464 systems of liquid carbon dioxide (165, 173) furnished examples of many systems with multiple binodal curves. Typical graphs are shown in Figures 82 and 83. The top corner in each graph represents carbon dioxide. The

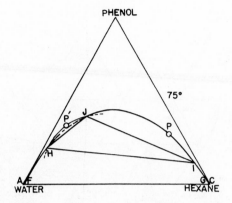

Fig. 81. Real system water–phenol–n-hexane showing eruption of a new binodal curve from within another binodal curve.

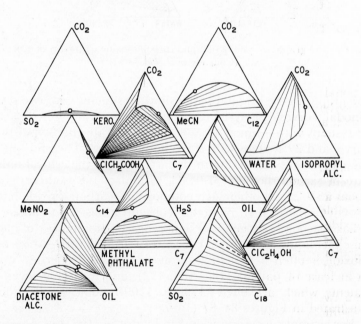

Fig. 82. Ten ternary graphs of observed systems of liquid carbon dioxide with pairs of other liquids.   Carbon dioxide is at the top corner in each graph. (Courtesy of *J. Phys. Chem.*)

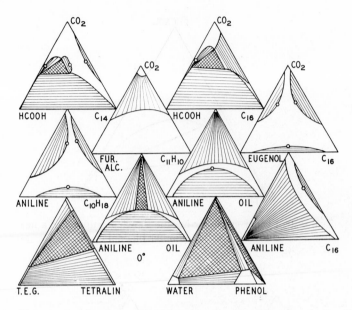

Fig. 83. Ten graphs of systems of liquid carbon dioxide with pairs of other liquids.
(Courtesy of *J. Phys. Chem.*)

268 graphs in the original paper show 76 systems with two separate binodal curves, 21 systems with three separate binodal curves, 38 systems with a binodal band and a separate (bite-type) binodal curve, and 29 systems with three liquid phases. The multiplicity of these unusual types is due to the proximity of the critical temperature of carbon dioxide, 31.04 °C, to that of the isotherm studied, about 25 °C. Like other such components, carbon dioxide has dual solvent properties. In moderate concentrations, up to about 40%, it has a strong homogenizing action on almost any pair of partially miscible liquids. At high concentrations, e.g., 70–80%, carbon dioxide is often a precipitating agent. These properties are used in at least 14 patents (186, 188, 192), and including seven other patents which are cited (173, p. 1109). Some applications are illustrated in Figures 84–87 (165).

For example, a composition S in Figure 84 (165, Fig. 5) separates into two liquid layers, E and R. The oil contained in E is more paraffinic than that in R because carbon dioxide has a selectivity

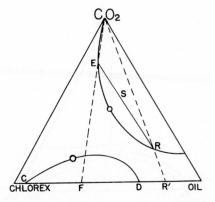

Fig. 84. Illustration of use of liquid carbon dioxide in double solvent extraction.
(Courtesy of *Ind. Eng. Chem.*)

opposite to the usual one. After the layers are segregated, carbon dioxide is released from each, giving F and R'. F separates into two layers, C and D. After Chlorex is distilled from each layer, the oil in D is recovered as the most paraffinic oil, being the raffinate (from Chlorex) of the extract (from carbon dioxide). The oil in C is near the composition of the feed and is recycled.

Similar double extractions are possible with aniline and triethylene glycol by following slightly different flow-sheet routes (deducible from Figures 85 and 86) (165, Figs. 7, 8). Figure 87 does not show a double extraction but indicates greatly increased solvent power for the oil in acetone, which would be applicable also to furfural and 20 other solvents studied.

The high pressure of liquid carbon dioxide makes precise observations of equilibrium more difficult; but complete removal of solvent from oil products is facilitated. One system studied, water–ethyl alcohol–carbon dioxide, was later examined with greater precision by Baker and Anderson (38).

Because the precipitation property of carbon dioxide is intensified on raising the temperature up to and beyond the critical temperature, the usual effect of temperature on solubility is reversed; and there are actually a few LCST's a little below room temperature. But most of the systems were studied at only one temperature, approximately 25 °C.

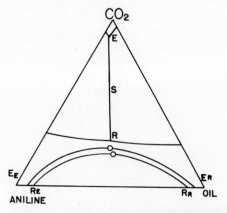

Fig. 85. Illustration of the use of liquid carbon dioxide in double solvent extraction. (Courtesy of *Ind. Eng. Chem.*)

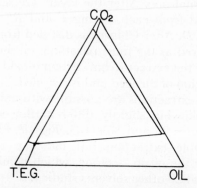

Fig. 86. Extraction of oil by liquid carbon dioxide and another solvent using three phases. (Courtesy of *Ind. Eng. Chem.*)

In spite of the abundance of unusual graphs in the carbon dioxide systems, there seem to be no island curves. Probably the reverse temperature effect militates against this phenomenon. The same lack occurs among *aqueous* systems of hydrogen halides (175) although these systems also show an abundance of graphs with two separate binodal curves. The curves result from the anomalous incomplete mixing of the hydrogen halides with water in spite of their great affinity for water. This is discussed in Chapter 7.

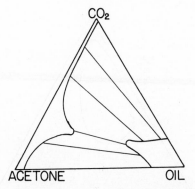

Fig. 87. Enhancement of solvent power of a solvent by use of liquid carbon dioxide. (Courtesy of *Ind. Eng. Chem.*)

Although solvent power decreases rapidly with approach to the critical temperature of a solvent, it does not disappear entirely at that point. Unlimited solubility of naphthalene in ethylene at temperatures up to 90 °C and pressures up to 270 atm was reported by Diepen and Scheffer (127A). Todd and Elgin (690A) found similar high solubilities of 17 other liquids in ethylene above its critical temperature, 9.6 °C. In six solvents—acetonitrile, capronitrile, cetane, *o*-dichlorobenzene, and hexyl and *n*-propyl alcohols—two liquid layers were observed in this temperature range. Kriechevski and Tsiklis (344B) showed that ammonia–nitrogen mixtures at high pressures have two liquid phases above the critical temperature of ammonia.

Holder and Maass (265) made similar observations on the solubility of hexachloroethane in ethane above its critical temperature, 32°C. A plot of solubility, S, in wt-% against density, D, in g/ml, of the ethane phase by the present author (201, pp. 448, 449) showed almost a straight line, $S = 130 (D - 0.133)$, with scarcely a jog at the critical density, 0.23 g/ml.

A limitation on the position of the plait point was indicated in Chapter 3. Apparently it still holds with multiple binodal curves having two or three plait points. Three types of real systems with three real plait points each are shown in Figures 67, 68, 71, 74, 83 (first graph), 88, and 89 (173–176). A simple way of expressing this generality is that from any plait point only one corner of the ternary graph is "visible," assuming that the plait point's own

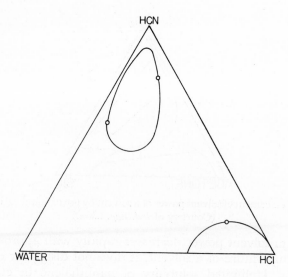

Fig. 88. Ternary system with an island curve and a separate binodal curve (water–hydrogen cyanide–hydrogen chloride).   (Courtesy of *J. Phys. Chem.*)

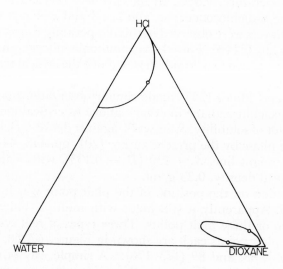

Fig. 89. A system using dioxane instead of hydrogen cyanide.   (Courtesy of *J. Phys. Chem.*)

binary curve, but not the others, is opaque. This limitation seems very arbitrary, but it is logically derivable from the principles mentioned above. A practical result of this postulate is that an opalescent composition near any plait point is cleared by an additional trace of only one component.

The reverse of this generality also seems to hold: namely, from any corner of the graph a straight line can be drawn to only one plait point without crossing the binodal curve containing that point. There is, thus, a correspondence in plait points and components—one point for each component. In the large majority of systems, however, some of the plait points are imaginary, i.e., outside the triangle completely or submerged below another binodal curve or a solid–liquid equilibrium. It is suggested that more than three plait points are theoretically impossible in a ternary system and, therefore, that two separate islands could not be expected. Systems with one island and a separate bite-type binodal curve are known (see Figs. 88, 89) (175, Fig. 2; 176, Graph 2; 358; 519). But no system is known with a separate band-type curve, perhaps because such a curve conceivably has two imaginary plait points.

6 | ISLAND CURVES

A "closed curve," or more expressively an "island curve," is a binodal curve around an area of composition in a phase diagram that separates into two liquid phases; but the curve is entirely surrounded by areas of homogeneous composition. It is not, as some have defined it, an example of "ternary layering without binary layering" (357) or of "complete miscibility in each of the three binary systems but not in the ternary system" (200, p. 211) or of any equivalent expression. Examples are known of systems with a separate binodal curve (binary layering) and yet with an obvious island (see Figs. 88, 89).

An island curve has two plait points, the limiting infinitesimal tie lines on each side of the island. When an island curve expands because the temperature of the system is lowered (or raised), it either touches one side line, forming an ordinary bite-type binodal curve, as in Figure 90 (764) and Figure 91 (180, p. 952), or it touches two sides, forming a band-type binodal curve. Both types of contacts occur at plait points.

Island curves result commonly from the simultaneous presence of weak acid and base that form reversibly a soluble salt which has a lower miscibility than either the free acid or free base. An example is methylaniline–acetic acid–n-heptane (200, p. 211; 201, p. 445). The island curve looks as though it were formed by the overlapping of two binodal curves with the acid and base each acting as the consolute component for the other (see Fig. 92). The imaginary portions of the two curves are shown with dashed lines. However, there are no angular intersections or breaks in the curve. The axis of the island (dash-dot line) is not in the direction of the point on the side lines, S corresponding to methylaniline acetate, as might be

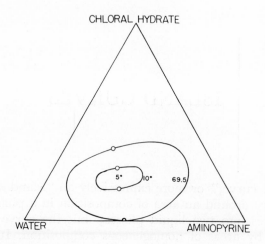

Fig. 90. Ternary system with an LCST at 5°C and an island curve tangent to the side line at 69.5°C, the LCST of the binary system water–aminopyrine.

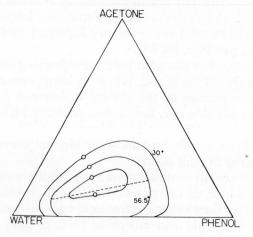

Fig. 91. Classical example of an island curve.   Note the isopycnic in the 56.5°C curve.

expected. Apparently about three moles of acetic acid to one of methylaniline are required to produce the maximum concentration of methylaniline acetate in solution and to cause separation of a liquid layer.

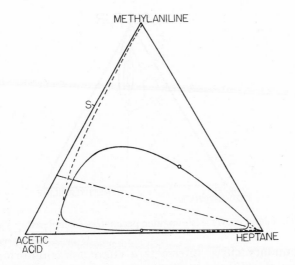

Fig. 92. Island curve resulting from the formation of a soluble salt, methylaniline acetate.

Similar islands are shown in the literature (mostly Russian) (180, pp. 826, 881, 952, 991, 1012–1013, 1028, 1066–1067, 1076, 1099; 350; 355; 357; 358; 709; 761–764; 770–772). Krupatkin (357) considered that island curves resulted from reversible combinations of two components, which also would have rather flat freezing curves ("incipient phase separation"). However, in few published examples of island curves is the mole ratio of these two components along the axis of the curve quite that expected. Zhuravlev (771, 772) was much concerned over this point, and he stated that "no evidence was found for chemical compound formation" in the examples studied by him. Since the reactions are reversible and do not introduce a fourth component in a thermodynamic sense, provided the reaction is rapidly reversible, the discrepancy with molar ratios seems unimportant. The systems may still be considered ternary (see Chap. 7).

A fault in some of the published graphs of these island curves and adjacent isotherms is the showing of angular intersections of curves by Zhuravlev and others (180, pp. 1066–7; 761; 764). Some of the islands shown are lens shaped (see Fig. 93.) Unless the

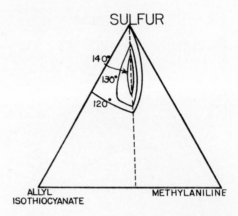

Fig. 93. Island curves with angular perimeters (considered erroneous).

phase boundary curve intersects a curve for equilibrium with a solid phase, there is no justification for such an angular intersection.

In some of these systems, especially those involving sulfur as a component, the triangles shown are divided by isologous dashed lines from the sulfur corner to the equimolar composition of allyl isothiocyanate and o-toluidine or methylaniline, as in Figure 93 (763; 180, pp. 1066–1067). If these lines indicate that the reactions are irreversible, the systems would be shown better by two separate equilateral triangles. However, the absence of such a division in the dimethylaniline system (763) with similar reagents suggests that the reaction is reversible in all three cases but perhaps not instantaneous.

In the last chapter the improbability of two separate binodal island curves in a ternary system was indicated because the system would have four plait points. Zhuravlev and Volkov (777) present an apparent exception with the system aniline–acetic acid–iso-octane. They observed two separate ternary critical points, or islands—one at 81.2 and one at 85.5°C ("twin peaks")—with a col between at 80.5°C (see Fig. 94). A possible explanation is the reaction of aniline with acetic acid to give a fourth component, aniline acetate. The reversibility of this reaction may not be sufficiently rapid to provide a thermodynamically ternary system (discussed in Chap. 7). This would be analogous to the hysteresis, or delay in reaching equilibrium, which definitely exists in the aqueous acetic anhydride systems.

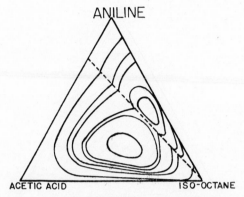

Fig. 94. Twin island curves due perhaps to interaction of aniline and acetic acid.

Even when there is no irreversible reaction of hydrogen halides with the alcohols, and with acetic and propionic acids, acetone, and other solvents, there must be a reversible complex formation in solution, since there was an abundance of island curves formed in ternary systems with hydrocarbons (175). The smaller islands are shaped like apple seeds with the rounded point close to the hydrocarbon corner. The size of the island varies regularly with the numbers of carbon atoms in the alcohol or acid and in the hydrocarbon. Larger islands, like that with propionic acid–heptane–hydrogen bromide, as in Figure 95, are roughly triangular with rounded corners. This form of island was observed also in other systems not involving hydrogen halides, namely: water–phosphoric acid–phenol (350); sulfuric acid–methanol–propylene (195); acetic acid–o-toluidine–heptane (see Fig. 96) (175) (footnote 20).

The classical example of island curves is that of water–acetone–phenol, shown in Figure 91 (180, p. 952), between 66 and 92 °C; in this example there is no evidence of complex formation of acetone and phenol (175). Although this may be the only published system of this type, it could hardly be considered unique. Probably pairs of components with a LCST (178, Table III) could be grouped with a homogenizing solvent to give such an island curve below the LCST mentioned.

At higher (or lower) temperatures such a system would have "undercut curves," (Fig. 90, 91) indicating slight decrease in mutual solubility of the nonconsolute components on adding small

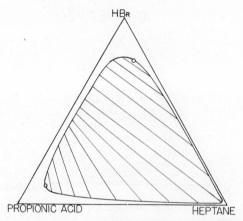

Fig. 95. "Triangular island curve" of propionic acid–hydrogen bromide–*n*-heptane.   (Courtesy of *J. Phys. Chem.*)

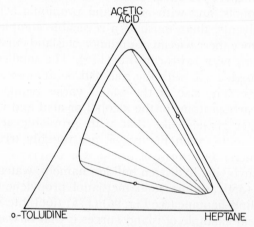

Fig. 96. "Triangular island curve" of *o*-toluidine–acetic acid–*n*-heptane.

concentrations of the consolute component. This phenomenon is fairly common, occurring with aqueous systems of ether, 2-butanone, and other solvents.

Similarly, Angelescu (10; 180, p. 898) used the expression "closed curve" in the same sense as island curve, except that it applied neither to a ternary isotherm nor to a binary system with temperature but to a ternary system with temperature and a constant concentration of one component, acetic acid. The other components were water and *o*- or *m*-toluidine (275, p. 417).

7 | EFFECTS OF REACTION BETWEEN COMPONENTS

Phase diagrams are sometimes modified substantially by reactions between components. Time may become a factor—normally excluded in equilibrium studies. If the reaction is almost instantaneous and irreversible, as in the methyl iodide–pyridine system discussed in Chapter 2, the components of the system may be merely reidentified as two or more separate systems with the newly formed components. If the reaction is controllably slow, even though irreversible, interesting physical apparent equilibriums can be observed by rapid observations. High speed photography (745A) may help.

Acetic anhydride and water, which are physically almost immiscible, undergo a slow though irreversible reaction. Hydration of acetic anhydride is by no means instantaneous, as sometimes assumed, and may require hours. If a third component is carbon disulfide or a hydrocarbon, the reaction is further retarded by the low miscibility of the latter with water. The third component also may be incompletely miscible with acetic anhydride.

In such a system, if hydration is minimized by rapid observation, the graph becomes a common type with three liquid phases, as in Figure 97 (180, p. 847). If time is allowed and agitation continued for complete reaction (no simultaneous presence of acetic anhydride and water), the system degenerates into two independent ternary systems: water–acetic acid–carbon disulfide, and acetic anhydride–acetic acid–carbon disulfide. The two systems are indicated in Figure 98 by the dashed line from CS_2 to AcOH, which is 85% acetic anhydride on the original triangle. In the presentation of this system Mochalov (448) evidently had an intermediate condition of partial hydration, shown in a graph by intersecting binodal curves with sharp cusps (see Fig. 99). Such curves make a

91

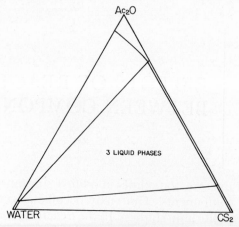

Fig. 97. System water–acetic anhydride–carbon disulfide postulating no hydration of anhydride.

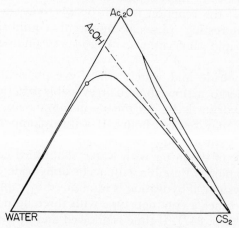

Fig. 98. System water–acetic anhydride–carbon disulfide postulating complete chemical and physical equilibrium.

very unusual diagram but are of little significance because the extent of hydration is not indicated. Mertslin (180, p. 979) showed the same type of graph but used "benzine" instead of carbon disulfide as the third component. The problem of acetic anhydride as a component has been studied by several researchers (127, 335, 342,

414, 511, 695, 696). The first of these studies with acetic anhydride and water at the boiling point, seems to ignore the hydration reaction. No corresponding observations on the similar reagent, acetyl chloride, are found—probably because of too rapid reactions.

In his study of nonaqueous ternary hydrogen halide systems Francis (175) encountered similar relations. Lower primary and secondary alcohols, including alkoxyethanols, react irreversibly but slowly with anhydrous hydrogen chloride or bromide to form alkyl halides. By operating at 0 °C these reactions were controlled so as to give reproducible physical ternary equilibriums with hydrocarbons. Although the shapes of the resulting binodal curves

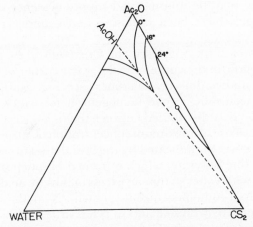

Fig. 99. System water–acetic anhydride–carbon disulfide as published by Mochalov (448), which must indicate partial hydration.

(islands) clearly indicate some complex of the hydrogen halide and the alcohol, the complex is not the result of the irreversible reactions mentioned. Sample titrations showed the presence of all of the acid introduced. Furthermore, the shapes of the islands are closely paralleled in corresponding graphs of acetic and propionic acids and acetone, in which hydrohalogenation is very improbable. On the other hand, the greater reactivity of benzyl alcohol and also of acetonitrile prevented satisfactory observations of physical equilibriums with those reagents. Peiker and Coffin (500A) stated, "A chemical reaction prohibited the investigation of solid–liquid equilibria in the halogen–H–HCN systems." It did not interfere with Francis' observations (see Fig. 88) (176).

Usanovich and Bekturov (707) noted variations in physical properties of a homogeneous system, pyridine-chloroacetic acid, with time. Doubtless a phase boundary with a third component also would be affected.

"Reversibly Ternary Systems"

If a reaction between components is readily reversible, the system can be considered "reversibly ternary" even though there may be four types of molecules in some compositions. The shape of the binodal curve may be unusual and supply evidence of such reactions. Examples have been discussed above under island curves (see Chap. 6).

A type observed by Angelescu and Cristodulo (180, pp. 988–989) contains a hollow in the curve near the water corner of systems with butyric acid and aniline or toluidines (see Fig. 100). Apparently butyric acid would be a good homogenizer for water and aniline, being almost evenly distributed between them, if it were not for a reaction with the base. A maximum concentration of 30 or 35% butyric acid (dashed curve) is indicated by the initial direction of the curve. However, aniline butyrate, which is formed in much of the system, is immiscible with water so that an excess of butyric acid, above 50% total, is required to homogenize the system. Near the water corner this salt is largely hydrolyzed, and so it has little effect. The straight dashed line is an isopycnic. Corresponding systems of dimethyl and diethylaniline (14), and the systems water–phenol–methylstyrene (613) and water–nitric acid–butyl ether (723) show similar graphs. Ust-Kachkintsev (709) has presented several systems showing interaction of components.

Another reversibly ternary system is water–sulfuric acid–ether, as observed by Tian (180, pp. 1003–1004; 681) (see Fig. 101). Diagrams of this system also contain a concave portion or saddle. Because four other investigations (180, pp. 1003–1004; 603, pp. 274–275) of the system had failed to show a concavity, the existence of such a curve was confirmed experimentally by the present author. The concavity obviously results from the formation of esters. Possibly ethylsulfuric acid, being miscible with

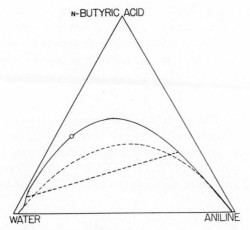

Fig. 100. Binodal curve with a hollow near the water corner probably due to reversible hydrolysis of an organic salt.

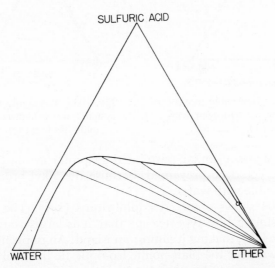

Fig. 101. Ternary system water–sulfuric acid–ethyl ether with a broad concavity probably due to the reversible formation of an ester.

water, increases miscibility in the middle of the diagram; but ethyl sulfate, which is not miscible with water, raises the curve near the right side. The shape of the curve may be an approximate measure

of the degree of hydrolysis. The plait point is near the ether corner. If the plait point were on the concave portion of the curve, it
would be necessary to assume an irreversible reaction.

Still another example of reversibly ternary systems is shown in
Figures 102, 103, and 104. The reaction between the components,

$$tert\text{-BuOH} + \text{HBr} \rightleftharpoons \text{H}_2\text{O} + tert\text{-BuBr}$$

is not a simple addition as in the other examples; the reaction is rapid
when the concentration of hydrogen bromide is above 38%. Figure
102 is the graph postulated if the hydrobromination could be prevented as in Figure 105 (175, Fig. 1) for *n*-butyl alcohol (modified
because of the complete miscibility of water and *tert*-butyl alcohol).

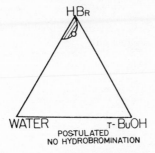

HBR

WATER   T- BuOH
POSTULATED
NO HYDROBROMINATION

Fig. 102. "Reversibly ternary
system" water–hydrogen bromide–*tert*-butyl alcohol.

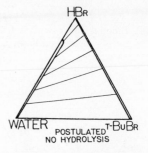

HBR

WATER   T-BuBR
POSTULATED
NO HYDROLYSIS

Fig. 103. "Reversibly ternary
system" water–hydrogen bromide–*tert*-butyl bromide.

Figure 103 shows a similar postulated graph for *tert*-butyl bromide
if hydrolysis could be prevented, because the alkyl bromide is almost immiscible with water.

Figure 104 shows observed equilibriums (197). The curve resembles a simple bite type except that it is largely cut off at its
base (on the left), making it almost an island. An isopycnic (dashed
line) is shown near the plait point. Iso-optic tie lines (blue shown)
also were observed. Other tie lines are estimated.

Compositions near the lower part of the graph are homogeneous
because of the miscibility of the alcohol with water and the slow
hydrobromination by dilute acid.

High concentrations of hydrogen bromide, probably over 80%,
are in equilibrium with moderate concentrations, about 38%.

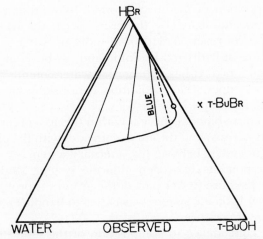

Fig. 104. "Reversibly ternary system" water–hydrogen bromide–*tert*-butyl alcohol.

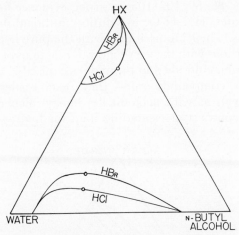

Fig. 105. Two ternary systems with two separate binodal curves. (Courtesy of *J. Phys. Chem.*)

This incongruity is due to the method of plotting, which shows total hydrogen bromide, including that which has reacted with the alcohol to form *tert*-butyl bromide. The latter also dissolves free hydrogen bromide.

The composition of *tert*-butyl bromide is represented logically, though unconventionally, by the cross *outside* the triangle on the right because its reaction with one mole of water would give a binary mixture of hydrogen bromide and *tert*-butyl alcohol by the equation mentioned. It has a "negative water content" in the same sense that SO_3 does. (Note common expressions such as "106% sulfuric acid" for oleum.)

Since the entire binodal curve is within the area of rapid reaction, there is no hysteresis; and the curve coincides with the phase boundary curve. The system behaves like a ternary system.

The corresponding hydrogen chloride system, studied only at atmospheric pressure (lower part of the graph), is probably similar. The hydrogen bromide system was easier to handle experimentally because of lower pressure.

The near coincidence in composition of the saturated solutions (in equilibrium with liquid hydrogen halides) of hydrogen chloride (66%) and of hydrogen bromide (79%) with the respective monohydrates (Figs. 88, 89, 102–105) is strong evidence for the presence of these hydrates, $HX \cdot H_2O$, in solution, although far above their melting points. Their immiscibility with the pure hydrogen halides seems incongruous with the very vigorous reactions of the latter with water. Hydrogen chloride and bromide are miscible with almost all liquid organic compounds unless they react to decompose them (forming water), as with acetonitrile, benzyl alcohol, or (slowly) with other alcohols. Corresponding data for hydrogen iodide and

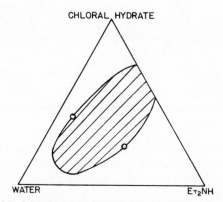

CHLORAL HYDRATE

WATER

ET₂NH

Fig. 106. Island curve apparently cut off by a side line.

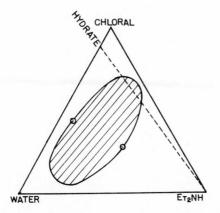

Fig. 107. Illustration explaining the incongruity shown in Figure 106.

hydrogen fluoride are not available. The system water–hydrogen bromide–sulfur dioxide (275, p. 403) shows similar molar relations.

Krupatkin (367) observed an island curve in the system water–diethylamine–chloral hydrate which seemed to contact a side line not at a plait point (see Fig. 106). The tie lines seemed to run into the side line at a sharp angle, and two plait points were present. Although he recognized the incongruity, he proposed a fantastic new theory to account for these impossible relations. Zhuravlev (769) exposed the fallacy in this theory. Presumably, chloral hydrate does not remain in solution entirely as such, but dissociates; and the chloral partly combines with the diethylamine. Both reactions are reversible, so that the system can still be shown accurately on a plane diagram. But it is clearer if the corner component is chloral, as shown by Zhuravlev (see Fig. 107). Krupatkin (368A) did not accept this explanation.

Although sulfuric acid is miscible with both ethyl ether and ethyl alcohol, some ternary systems separate (see Fig. 108) (197). The island is probably smaller with 100% sulfuric acid, but it may not disappear because of reversible formation of ethylsulfuric acid in solution. Corresponding relations with several concentrations of sulfuric acid with isopropyl alcohol and ether are shown in Figure 109 (197). The figure shows the undercutting effect of increasing concentrations of acid, even when there is not enough to form an island.

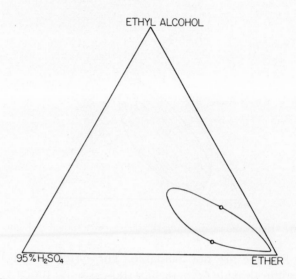

Fig. 108. System 95% sulfuric acid–ethyl alcohol–ethyl ether.

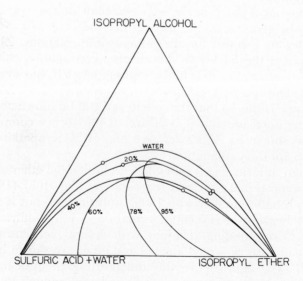

Fig. 109. Various concentrations of sulfuric acid with isopropyl alcohol and isopropyl ether.

Cuprous chloride is virtually insoluble in water, organic compounds, and hydrogen chloride. It is slightly soluble in aqueous
solutions of ammonia and other amines and amides or their salts,
and more so in hydrochloric acid; but these solutions rarely dissolve
more than 0.25 moles olefin per mole of cuprous chloride, the significant aim in numerous researches. The high solubility of cuprous
chloride, over 34%, in anhydrous mixtures of hydrogen chloride and
methanol (see Fig. 110) (193) and other hydroxyorganic compounds, combined with the high solvent power for olefins (1:1
moles in the case of methanol), is an extreme example of the effect
of interaction of components.

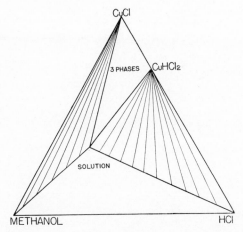

Fig. 110. Methanol–cuprous chloride–hydrogen chloride system.

In certain cases the title of this chapter might be reversed to
"Effects of Phase Relations on Reaction between Components." The
selective solution of the catalyst, aluminum chloride, in an auxiliary
reagent such as ethyl ether and that of a reaction product, ethylbenzene, was used to accelerate the ethylation of benzene substantially and to improve yields of ethylbenzene through diverting
the reagent, ethylene, to benzene rather than to the ethylbenzene
(159B, 162, 201A). Doubtless other examples could be found.

8 | "TERNARY" SYSTEMS WITH AN IMPURE COMPONENT

As in the binary systems (see Chap. 2), the presence of an impurity in one of the components of a ternary system may affect substantially the phase boundary curve. Sulfuric acid might be expected to have so strong an affinity for water that high concentrations (over 92%) would act as a single component in miscibility relations. Tian (180, p. 1065; 681) showed that this is not true (see Fig. 111).

Acid of 100% concentration shows a normal curve with ethyl ether and tetrachloroethylene. This curve is both the phase boundary and the binodal curve. The plait point is probably on the straighter part of the curve to the right because of the strong affinity of ether for the acid. The position of the isopycnic shown is estimated. Dilution of the acid to 95.6% gives only a slight hump to the right; but further dilutions to 94.6% and to 92.6% produce sharp reverse curves; for 92.6% the hump actually crosses the side line. Ether is not completely miscible with this diluted acid when the latter is present in small amounts. The humped curves are phase boundary curves and not binodal curves. No tie lines are shown (except for the 100% curve) since they would have little significance and would vary greatly in position with the relative volumes of the layers. The reaction of ether to form esters with the acid does not invalidate the curve because the reaction is rapidly reversible. This has been discussed in Chapter 7.

Another system, acetic acid–toluene–n-heptane, analogous in some respects, was presented by Othmer and Tobias (489) as a simple ternary graph of the bite type (see Fig. 112). In this example there is no 100% curve because glacial acetic acid is completely miscible with heptane as well as with toluene. Without water, the

graph would be an empty triangle. However, the complete miscibility of 97% acetic acid with toluene, indicated by Othmer's
graph, seemed improbable to Francis, who observed the system by
titration with the same reagents. The resulting phase boundary
curve is shown in Figure 113 (180, p. 1077) and is very similar to
that of Figure 111. The left sides of the two sets of curves in Figures
112 and 113 are similar; but the other parts of the diagrams are in-

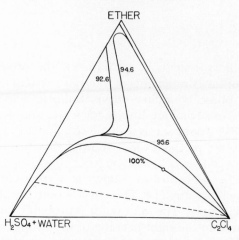

Fig. 111. System sulfuric acids (slightly diluted)–ethyl ether–tetrachloroethylene.

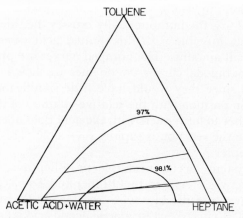

Fig. 112. System acetic acids (slightly diluted)–toluene–n-heptane (489).

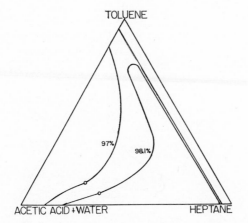

Fig. 113. System acetic acids (slightly diluted)–toluene–n-heptane.

congruous with each other. Because practically all of the water is driven into the lower layer by its immiscibility with hydrocarbons, as agreed by Othmer and Tobias, the lower layer is further diluted to a low concentration of 85%, as observed by Francis (179, p. 251). This weaker acid has a solvent power of less than 2% of hydrocarbon (even toluene) so that the composition of the lower layer is close to the left side line and is far from any curve in either graph. As in the pseudobinary systems of Figures 16 and 17, the phase boundary curve and the binodal curve are far from coincident. An additional curve showing equilibrium relations (the binodal curve) would be indefinite or fuzzy because it would vary in position with the relative volumes of the layers. It seems futile and misleading to attempt to show such a system as a ternary system instead of what it is—a quaternary system (115). Quaternary systems are discussed in Chapter 9. With adequate provision for four components (a three dimensional graph) there is no fuzziness in the binodal surface, which is coincident with the phase boundary surface. The apex of the 98.1% curve in Figure 113 is indefinite because compositions in that region show a faint haze of precipitated moisture.

At least two other published systems show graphs with similar sharp reverse curves resulting from slight dilution of the solvent with water. These are 95% ethyl alcohol–benzene–lubricating oil at 100°C, shown in Figure 114 (179, p. 250; 180, p. 1080; 201, p. 440),

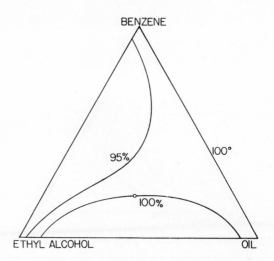

Fig. 114. Effect of slight dilution on the alcohol–benzene–lube oil system.

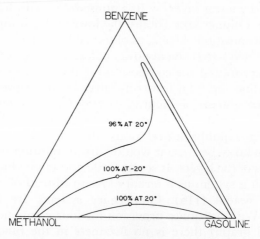

Fig. 115. Effect of slight dilution on the methanol–benzene–gasoline system.

and 96% methanol–benzene–gasoline shown in Figure 115 (180, p. 1072). Each system has an impure component—the hydrocarbon mixture; but this fact is not an appreciable factor in the curves. The last system has still another complication, which is the freezing curve of benzene.

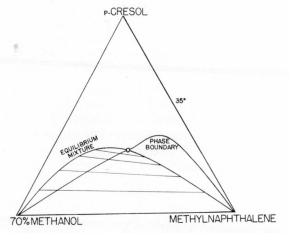

Fig. 116. Quaternary system 70% methanol–p-cresol–methylnaphthalene. The distinction between "equilibrium mixture" and phase boundary is shown.

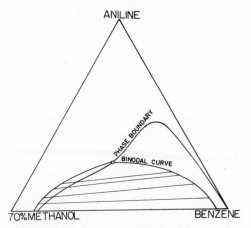

Fig. 117. Quaternary system 70% methanol–aniline–benzene. (Courtesy of *Ind. Eng. Chem.*)

Other published systems with reverse curves of the same type are shown in Figure 116 (180, pp. 1115–16; 520) and in Figure 117 (164; 201, p. 440); (see also 180 (p. 1081)). The curves are less extreme because the consolute component (top corner) is not a hydrocarbon and has an appreciable miscibility with water, the impurity in the solvent. In all of these papers the authors were well aware of the reasons for the reverse curves and the resulting complications; and they explained the latter with other appropriate graphs, two of them with quaternary graphs. In Figure 116 the "equilibrium mixture" curve and in Figure 117 the "binodal curve" (same thing) show tie lines for the compositions in which the two layers are approximately equal in volume. These curves are fuzzy and vary in position with the ratio of volumes. The phase boundary curve is not fuzzy, but it has a hump. The phase boundary results from direct titration of the reagents. The two types of curve always intersect at the plait point.

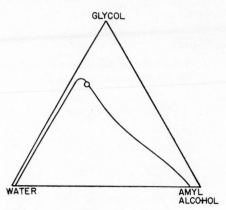

Fig. 118. Reported "ternary system" with a concavity on the plait point of a binodal curve.

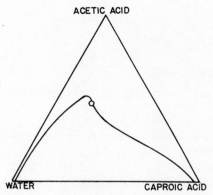

Fig. 119. "Ternary system" with a concavity on the plait point of a binodal curve.

Some published ternary systems, as in Figures 118 and 119 (379, 488), show a distinct concavity at the plait point of a phase boundary curve. A short tie line straddling this plait point would be external to the curve. A point on such a tie line would represent a homogeneous composition by definition of the phase boundary curve and a heterogeneous composition by definition of a tie line. This incongruity can be explained only by the presence of a trace of impurity in a reagent, possibly a hydrocarbon in amyl alcohol (379) or an ester in caproic acid (488), that was not removed by the method of purification (fractional distillation). The latter system with a sample of caproic acid purified by crystallization in the present author's laboratory showed no concavity.

However, concavities can occur at other points of binodal curves in strictly ternary systems, namely: near the merger of two separate binodal curves (see Figs. 61, 70–72, 74), on the shorter side in some band-type binodal curves (see Figs. 25,27); and in graphs which are modified by mutual interaction of components (see Figs. 101, 103, 104). The plait point of a binodal curve does not appear on its concavity.

Even if the impurity is so small in amount (e.g., 1% water in the solvent) or so slightly different in solubility (e.g., certain hydrocar-

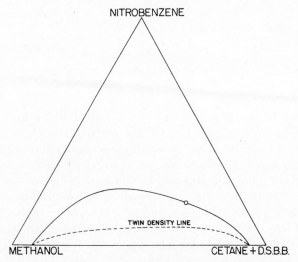

Fig. 120. Twin density line for a system with an impure component. (Courtesy of *Ind. Eng. Chem.*)

bon mixtures) that the distortion of the binodal curve is not notice-
able, there may be substantial errors introduced if a property such
as refractive index is used to determine tie lines. Any impurity, especially water, is unlikely to be partitioned in the same proportions
in both liquid phases. The use of density instead of refractive index di-
minishes this inaccuracy because a larger sample is required; but
the analysis does not become accurate.

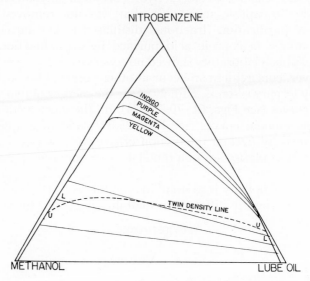

Fig. 121. Twin density line and set of twin index lines for a system with lubricating
oil (U = upper layer, L = lower layer).   (Courtesy of *Ind. Eng. Chem.*)

Tie lines, being construction lines, are straight for a strictly ternary system. An isopycnic is a tie line with special physical significance because it is the locus of points showing equal densities of the
two liquid phases. An isopycnic also is straight in a ternary system.
But if one component is impure, the locus of points of equal densities is not straight; and the equal densities are not uniform along the
line but are merely always equal to each other (Figs. 120–123)
(163). "Twin density line" is a more accurate term, though the
Greek name "didymopycnic" was suggested. It is only a coincidence
that the twin density line of Figure 120 comes at the feet of the
phase boundary line.

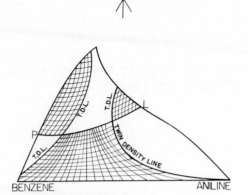

Fig. 122. Front elevation of system of Figures 117 and 123 through 125.

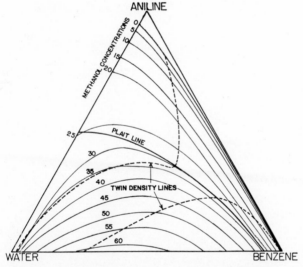

Fig. 123. Contours in triangular prism model of system of Figures 117 and 122 through 125.   (Courtesy of *Ind. Eng. Chem.*)

A similar discussion applies to iso-optics, or tie lines with equal refractive indices, and "twin index lines" (163). In this case there is a group of lines (straight or curved respectively)—one line for each wave length eliminated by equal refractive indices of the layers (see Figs. 41, 121). The curvature of these special lines is not due to the coincidences in properties; it is only revealed by them. The curvature is due to the impurity, or fourth component.

The real tie lines (straight) of Figure 121 extend slightly beyond the phase boundary curve at the right, and should stop just short of the phase boundary curve at the left. Their extremities form the binodal curve (indefinite, and not shown).

9 | QUATERNARY SYSTEMS

Since ternary systems are illustrated almost universally by graphs in the shape of equilateral triangles, it is esthetically sound to show a quaternary system by means of a regular tetrahedron. Wiegand (751) recommended a rectangular tetrahedron for this purpose. A solid figure makes an attractive exhibit, but it is awkward to present for publication, even with a photograph. A solid is difficult to construct accurately and equally difficult to use efficiently.

However, several such systems are illustrated by oblique projection of regular tetrahedrons in plane diagrams. The projections represent tabulated observations and are a favorite means for correlation of tie lines, etc. The projections are discussed by several authors (68–71, 97, 113–115, 118, 238, 272, 273, 516–518, 640, 646A). It would be difficult to do justice here to all of these discussions, even if this author were qualified to do so.

The prime interest in these systems is to facilitate study of solvent extraction, especially with two solvents. The system studied most extensively is that of water–acetic acid–acetone–chloroform (69–71, 113, 272). It was published "in the belief that a study of such a system would be helpful in the proper understanding of double solvent refining processes" (69). This desirable goal would have been approached more closely with a better choice of components. It would have been preferable if they had been those of a practical process (113, 114, 307) or if at least one pair of components had had a substantial but *incomplete* miscibility.

Unfortunately, in the system mentioned "The choice of liquids to be used was based on the ease of purification and analysis" (71). Only one pair of components, water and chloroform, were not miscible in all proportions; and the other two components were almost equally good homogenizers for these two. Acetone and acetic acid could have been paired together as a single component to give a ternary system without appreciable distortion. The quaternary combination results in a developable surface with virtually straight elements for the "frustum" of heterogeneous compositions shown in their diagrams and also in other regularities, which are not necessarily typical of most quaternary systems. Treybal (694, p. 33) also expressed doubt that the simplicity is general; but Cruikshank and co-workers (118) considered that adjustments could be made when necessary.

According to Brancker, Hunter, and Nash (69), "Equilibrium in this system may be summarized briefly as follows: The two ternary equilibrium curves acetone–chloroform–water, and acetic acid–chloroform–water define the heterogeneous region on two sides of the tetrahedron. The frustum outlined by these curves and by the sloping surface joining them defines the complete heterogeneous system.

"A plane passing through a tie line in one of the two-phase ternary systems and the opposite apex of the tetrahedron will intersect a second plane passing through a tie line of the other two-phase ternary system and its opposite apex to give a quaternary tie line, the two terminal points of which lie on the surface of the frustum."

Similar comments apply to the system water–acetaldehyde–acetone–vinyl acetate (68; 516; 180, pp. 886, 949) and to the system water–acetone–ethyl alcohol–n-butyl alcohol (646A).

Brown (78) studied two other quaternary systems (aniline–benzene or heptane–cetane–cyclohexane) which were better chosen because of the partial miscibilities of aniline with the hydrocarbons. However, the reported tie lines were based on analysis by refractive index. This method is inadequate for such systems, especially the ones containing benzene, because benzene and cyclohexane would not remain in constant ratio in the two liquid phases, as assumed (see Chap. 8). Benzene is concentrated in the aniline-rich layer and cyclohexane in the cetane-rich layer (180, p. 1118).

Fritsche and Stockton (205B) chose the system water–isobutyl alcohol–acetone–tetrachloroethane, which has a desirable partial mutual solubility of water and isobutyl alcohol. However, they observed no quaternary tie lines. Moreover, the "slices" of the model resulting from titrations with 50, 70, and 90% isobutyl alcohol may be slightly misleading. The aqueous layers would contain relatively less tetrachloroethane than isobutyl alcohol because of selective extraction. The equilibrium concentrations do not remain in the "slice."

Another quaternary system studied extensively is water–acetic acid–benzene–carbon tetrachloride (517, 518). This has two immiscible pairs, the last two components being so immiscible with water that they could have been plotted as a single component without appreciable distortion. In fact, in the two ternary systems (180, pp. 839, 890) the apexes of the binodal curves are at 66 to 68%. Again, straight elements and other simplifying relations result, which are not general for quaternary systems. Similar conclusions apply to the system water–ethyl alcohol–benzene–ethyl isovalerate and to other systems studied by Chang and Moulton (97). They stated, "These systems have the same characteristic, that two of their liquid pairs are of negligible miscibilities."

The more "practical" quaternary systems methanol–oleic acid–olive oil–carbon disulfide (113) and furfural–methyl oleate–methyl stearate–naphtha (114) studied by Crespi were free from the above limitations because methanol has considerable but incomplete miscibility with carbon disulfide and furfural with methyl oleate. The pattern of quaternary tie lines was not examined so completely as in the other systems. She presented a compilation (115) of 20 quaternary systems.

The quaternary system water–methanol–aniline–benzene was studied in great detail (164) with respect to the quaternary binodal surface but only qualitatively with respect to the pattern of tie lines, which was evidently very complex and not capable of simple derivation from the ternary graphs. The system is illustrated in Figures 124 and 125 with photographs of a plaster-of-Paris model. These are paralleled by a line drawing in Figure 122. The drawing is a front elevation of an opaque solid so that the water corner is invisible. These illustrations show conclusively that the presence of a partially miscible pair, water–aniline, resulted in a concave phase boundary or binodal surface (which are identical in a quaternary system with only four pure components) instead of one with straight elements. This surface was divided into three areas of upper layer (shaded) and three of lower layer. The areas were separated by the plait line, PL, and by two twin density lines.

Fig. 124. Oblique photograph of tetrahedral model of system water–methanol–aniline–benzene.   (Courtesy of *Ind. Eng. Chem.*)

Fig. 125. Second photograph of tetrahedral model. (Courtesy of *Ind. Eng. Chem.*)

Within the heterogeneous volume (below the surface) were two separate "twin density surfaces," which define quaternary compositions separating into two liquid phases of equal density. These also were located with precision.

The tables of observations are illustrated also in Figure 123 with uniform concentrations of methanol in a triangular prism model of the water–aniline–benzene ternary system. This is essentially a method suggested by Brancker *et al.* (69) and by Crespi (114). Methanol was selected as the vertical component because it is completely miscible with each of the other three components. Otherwise, this method of illustration might have been confusing, as noted by Treybal (694, p. 32). One such component usually can be selected in proposed quaternary systems.

Two interesting systems in which the selection of a completely miscible component as the vertical component is not possible are water–acetonitrile or sulfolane–benzene–heptane (247). Three liquid phases appear in quaternary compositions but not in any of the four ternary compositions. The shapes of the three-phase composition volumes are complex. Mertslin and co-workers (433, 435, 525A) proposed the possibility of the same type of system. They presented quaternary systems (water–sulfur–hexane–phenol or aniline) with four liquid phases (434, 439) over a limited temperature range at about 96 °C.

If the two solvents are almost immiscible with each other in an extraction, limited miscibility with the charge stock may result in three liquid layers in equilibrium. And if the selectivities of the two solvents are opposite, i.e., if one component of the charge dissolves by preference in one solvent and the other component dissolves preferentially in the other solvent, there results a happy combination for solvent extraction. The selectivities are additive. Most solvents are selective for aromatic hydrocarbons; but a few, such as liquid carbon dioxide and fluorocarbons, have reverse selectivities. Examples of such three-phase extractions have been patented (188, 199).

The Duo Sol process (200, p. 234), employing liquid propane and "Selecto" (phenol-cresol mixture), is not quite of this type because it does not give three liquid phases. However, its aim and result are similar. Propane facilitates extraction by reducing the viscosity of the oil by dilution and by controlling the solvent power of the "Selecto." Propane is almost neutral in selectivity except with respect to polycyclic hydrocarbons and asphaltines, which it rejects and drives into the "Selecto."

The presence of multiple layers in equilibrium, with appropriate increase in number of components, has intrigued several investigators, such as Smith (639), Carrière (92), Hildebrand (255A), and Kittsley and Goeden (330). Recently Hildebrand and Scott have shown a photograph of 10 liquid phases in equilibrium (256, inside cover). Hildebrand explained the requirements for immiscibility in these systems (255A).

10 | COMPILATION OF LIQUID–LIQUID EQUILIBRIUMS

Tables I (pp. 124–194) and II (pp. 195–220) present lists of published systems which separate into two or more liquid phases in equilibrium. Most of them are ternary systems. Unary systems are interesting for elementary phase relations; but with possibly one exception, phosphoric oxide (645), they do not include two liquid phases. That system may have allotropic forms and be a pseudo-unary system.

Binary systems have been compiled (in large measure) in an independent book, *Critical Solution Temperatures* (178). They are not included in the present lists except for the few CST's in Table III (pp. 221–236) which have appeared more recently or have come to the author's attention through Volumes II through IV by Timmermans (685, 686, 687) or have been noted elsewhere in the literature (especially the work by Fischer and Neupauer (154), not previously available).

Quaternary systems and those with still more components are included in Tables I and II. Because each of them involves about four ternary systems and because the extra components might be considered as modifiers of ternary systems, it would be an unnecessary complication to list them in a separate table.

The lists are more extensive than previous compilations (140, 179, 180, 261, 641) because new systems are continually being published. Furthermore, there is here no arbitrary qualification, sometimes used (261, 641), of systems for which at least two tie lines are published. While tie lines are important in solvent extraction, an explanation of solvent extraction is not the only purpose in this book. Moreover, the shape and orientation of a binodal curve and the position of the plait point, if shown, permit a good approximation to the tie lines, which can be verified by the most appropriate experiments. It seemed to the author that even a little information about a system is better than none.

The purpose in including the compilation in this book is the same as that in Seidell's *Solubilities of Inorganic and Organic Compounds* (604): to have it readily available for discussion on any aspect of liquid–liquid equilibrium. Moreover, a proposed study of any system should consider previous investigations of that or similar systems. One system, water–ethyl alcohol–benzene, has been studied at least 30 times—an unnecessary duplication unless there are inaccuracies or omissions.

It is impractical now to draw graphs for so many systems, especially since the majority of them are of two common types. However, many systems with an unusual feature are illustrated for purposes of discussion. Moreover, many items call attention to an isopycnic, iso-optic, solutrope, island curve, two separate binodal curves, or other unusual feature in the system. Lack of such a notation does not necessarily mean a feature's absence, however. Iso-optics would be as common as isopycnics, but they are seldom noted because of less importance and lack of data.

The items in Tables I and II are usually listed under *each* component to facilitate location of a system. However, salts are often omitted as primary components when their only function seems to be "salting out." And not every possible arrangement of components is given, especially for nonaqueous and quaternary systems. Some saving in space results from cross references. Likewise, hydrocarbons are usually omitted as primary components (upper case) in Table II. Also omitted are the numerous individual components studied in the carbon dioxide systems (165, 173) and some other systems (116, 124A, 143, 154, 154A, 223, 451, 455, 582, 600, 610, 611, 674, 689).

The tables are not subdivided into systems with one hydrocarbon or two hydrocarbons, etc., as is sometimes done (179, 261, 641), because the divisions are often superficial, i.e., hydrocarbons are not fundamentally different in solubility characteristics from many other water-immiscible solvents. The division into aqueous and nonaqueous systems merely lists separately that portion which would be segregated anyway and saves naming water as a component in 70% of the systems (see Table I). The listing of one component with upper-case letters in Table II helps to distinguish these systems from the aqueous ones. Some systems are listed in both Table I and Table II. These include quaternary aqueous systems, with and without water.

Omitted from this compilation are: systems involving alloys or liquid-metal components (with a few exceptions); those with only one liquid phase at equilibrium; and about 1500 unpublished systems (mostly nonaqueous) observed by the present author. Some of the last group may be published eventually—but probably only those involving unusual features or those included in special categories, such as systems of ammonia, sulfur dioxide, or aceto-nitrile, the three components most extensively studied.

Bibliography

The bibliography (pp. 237–284) is extensive. To prevent doubling its length, references in the tables to those systems illustrated in Seidell's *Solubilities of Inorganic and Organic Compounds* (604) are given only to pages in that volume or in the earlier edition (602, 603); the original references are omitted, unless needed in discussion. Consequently, most of the references are later than 1949. Furthermore, publications of substantially the same subject matter by the same authors in the same or different journals are sometimes combined as one reference. "A," "B," or "C" after a reference number has no significance except to indicate a different reference. References with a letter attached to the reference number were added after the original numbering required for the compilation and text; and it was impractical to change all of the numbers repeatedly. Literature coverage was continued up to the issue of *Chemical Abstracts* for May 27, 1963.

Included in the bibliography are short "abstracts." These notations were almost a necessity in setting up the bibliography, especially when the addition of many new references required the renumbering of the entire list. The idea of the notations was copied from certain bibliographies in the Landolt-Börnstein *Tables* (384) and was used also in *Critical Solution Temperatures* (178). The notations are of those portions of publications pertinent to this book—not necessarily the most important portions.

In these notations and in the tables and text the arrangement of components is usually: first, water or other polar solvent; second, the consolute component (the one distributed between two immiscible phases); and last, the hydrocarbon or other least polar component. However, when a salt is used to salt out an organic compound, water is the consolute component. As in the text, dashes indicate different primary components present together. Additional components are separated by commas. Additional components may be alternative components indicating different systems; such components usually are arranged alphabetically. Or, additional components may be present together forming a composite component, especially in systems involving radioactive or rare earth reagents. In some of these latter systems there are so many substances present that the arrangement is equivocal and the compilation of the systems is not exhaustive. Some additional ones are indexed in the *Russian Journal of Inorganic Chemistry* under "Extraction."

The original publications or complete translations were consulted except for about forty references of which the originals are apparently not available in this country.

Acknowledgments

The author acknowledges with thanks the courtesies extended to him in several libraries. Two of the libraries were those of the Mobil Chemical Company Research and Technical Laboratories in Edison Township, New Jersey, and the Mobil Oil Company Research and Development Laboratories in Paulsboro, New Jersey. Other libraries were: Rutgers University Main Library in New Brunswick, New Jersey, Rutgers University Chemistry Library in University Heights; Princeton University Chemistry Library; Columbia University Chemistry and Physics Libraries; Chemists' Club Library in New York City; Stanford University Chemistry Library in Palo Alto, California; University of Southern California Science Library in Los Angeles; Ohio State University Chemistry Library; and Chemical Abstracts Library in Columbus, Ohio. Arrangements for the last were facilitated by Dr. L. J. Hillenbrand of Battelle Memorial Institute in Columbus, who had previously made available to the author copies of over 30 references from the Battelle Library.

The author appreciates the review of the text and helpful suggestions by Dr. J. K. Peterson and Dr. W. C. L. Wu of the Mobil Chemical Company.

He thanks the Mobil Oil Company, who provided facilities for his research in this field (and others) over a period of 30 years in their Research and Development Laboratories in Paulsboro, New Jersey; he also thanks the Mobil Chemical Company Research and Technical Laboratories, Edison Township, New Jersey, who facilitated the preparation of this manuscript, including typing by Mrs. M. J. Manley, and released it.

TABLE I

Aqueous Systems Separating into Two Liquid Phases

System	References
Acetaldehyde–Acetone–Vinyl acetate	68
Amyl alcohol–Benzene, Toluene, or	
Furfural	180 (pp. 885–886), 489
Vinyl acetate	516, 636
Acetamide–Cuprous chloride–Hydro-	
gen chloride–Olefins	203
Acetanilide–Acetone	736
Acetic acid–Acetic anhydride	335, 414, 695
Acetone–Chloroform	69, 71, 113, 180 (pp. 849–850), 272
Amyl acetate	180 (pp. 888, 900), 344C
Aniline	180 (pp. 890, 901), 335
Benzaldehyde	8
Benzene	1B, 31, 64, 97, 180 (pp. 890, 901), 209, 262, 281, 377, 396, 451, 517, 518, 664, 691, 732
Benzene–Carbon tetrachloride	517, 518
Benzene–Sodium chloride	241, 562
Benzene–Toluene	97
n-Butane	138
2-Butanone	396, 633
n-Butyl acetate	84, 180 (pp. 888–892, 900), 467, 531, 654, 691
n-Butyl alcohol	633
n-Butylamine	499
Butyl Carbitol acetate	180 (pp. 891–892, 900)
n-Butyl ether	180 (pp. 891–892, 900)
Butyl lactate	180 (pp. 891–892, 900)
Butyl diacetone ether	180 (pp. 891–892)
Caproic acid	180 (p. 895), 488, Fig. 119
Caprylic acid	554
Carbon dioxide	173
Carbon disulfide	180 (pp. 845, 901), 393
Carbon tetrachloride	180 (p. 839), 345, 393, 517, 518, 580, 625
Chlorobenzene	499
Chloroform	31, 69, 71, 88A, 90, 109, 113, 114, 180 (pp. 849–850), 272, 354, 393, 487, 731
Cottonseed oil	550
Creosote	580

(continued)

TABLE I: Aqueous Systems (*continued*)

System	References
Acetic acid (*continued*)	
Cyclohexane	309
Cyclohexanol	633
Cyclohexyl acetate	180 (pp. 891–892)
Diethylaniline	14
Dimethylaniline	14, 211
2,6-Dimethyl-4-heptanone (Di-isobutyl ketone)	180 (pp. 891–892, 900)
2,4-Dimethyl-3-pentanol (Di-isopropyl carbinol)	180 (pp. 891–892)
Epichlorohydrin (C_3H_5OCl)	180 (pp. 886, 901)
Ethyl acetate (solutrope)	180 (p. 888), 396, 446, 532, 646, 654, 691, 758
Ethyl benzoate	533
Ethyl butyrate	532, 654
2-Ethylbutyric acid	180 (p. 895), 488
Ethylene	143
Ethylene chloride	691
Ethyl ether	65, 95, 180 (pp. 889, 900), 281, 451, 531, 636, 691, 732
2-Ethylhexoic acid	180 (p. 895), 488
Ethylene diacetate or Ethylidine diacetate	180 (pp. 891–893)
Ethyl propionate	532, 654
Fenchone	180 (pp. 891–892)
Furfural	252, 500, 633
Gasoline (straight run)	179 (p. 247), 180 (pp. 899, 901)
n-Heptadecyl alcohol	706
n-Heptane–Toluene	180 (p. 1077), 489, Figs. 112, 113
3-Heptanol	492
"Hexalin" acetate (Cyclohexyl acetate)	180 (pp. 891–892)
n-Hexane	180 (p. 901), 451, 537
Isoamyl acetate	180 (pp. 891–892)
Isoamyl alcohol	507
Isocaproic acid	180 (p. 895), 488
Isophoron	180 (pp. 891–892, 901)
Isopropyl ether	180 (pp. 891–892, 896, 901), 655, 661
Lube oil–Chloroform	69
Mesityl oxide	180 (pp. 888, 900)
Methyl acetate	467
Methylcyclohexanone	180 (pp. 891–892)
Methylene chloride	95
4-Methyl-2-pentanol	535

(*continued*)

TABLE I: Aqueous Systems (*continued*)

System	References
Acetic acid (*continued*)	
4-Methyl-2-pentanone (Methyl isobutyl ketone)	36, 180 (pp. 891–894, 900)
4-Methyl-2-pentanone–Sulfuric acid	403
Nitrobenzene	180 (pp. 889, 901)
Nitromethane	633
o-Nitrotoluene	180 (pp. 896, 901)
Octyl acetate	180 (pp. 891–892)
Oleic acid–five vegetable oils	737
About 60 organic compounds (distribution)	180 (pp. 901–902), 554
Petroleum ether	452
Phenol	180 (p. 890), 234, 709
Phenyl ether	523
Propyl acetate	467
Propylene	179 (p. 256), 180 (p. 886)
13 Solvents	309
Toluene	31, 97, 180 (p. 897), 200 (p. 199), 253, 281, 451, 489, 558, 564, 691, Figs. 112, 113
o-Toluidine (isopycnic below 24.5°C) ("closed" curve)	10, 163, 180 (p. 897), 603 (pp. 555–557)
m-Toluidine (isopycnic below 7°C) ("closed" curve)	163, 180 (p. 898)
Triacetin	180 (pp. 891–892)
Trichloroethylene	345, 580
Urea–Hydrocarbons	189
Five vegetable oils	737
Vinyl acetate	180 (p. 887)
Xylene	180 (pp. 899, 901), 691
Acetic anhydride–Acetic acid	335, 414, 695
Acetone	452, 696
Acetone–Glycerol	511
Allyl isothiocyanate, Chloral, Diphenylamine, Ethylene diamine, Piperidine	127
Aniline–Acetic acid	335
Carbon disulfide (three layers)	180 (p. 847), 448, Figs. 97, 98, 99
Dioxane	342
Gasoline or Petroleum ether	180 (p. 979), 452
Glycerol	511
Poly(vinylpyrrolidinone)	128

(*continued*)

TABLE I: Aqueous Systems (*continued*)

System	References
Acetone–Acetaldehyde–Vinyl acetate	68
Acetanilide	736
Acetic acid–Chloroform	69, 71, 113, 114, 115, 180 (pp. 849–850), 272
Acetic anhydride	452, 696
Acetic anhydride–Glycerol	511
Allyl alcohol	133
Ammonium chloride or sulfate	180 (p. 946)
Amyl acetate	728
Amyl alcohol	180 (p. 950)
Anethole (isopycnic)	163, 180 (p. 957)
Aniline (isopycnic)	180 (p. 953), 450
Barium nitrate	432
Benzene (solutrope at 15°C)	23, 73, 180 (p. 952), 267, 732
Bromobenzene	180 (p. 951), Fig. 24
1,3-Butadiene	440
2-Butanone	336, 486
n-Butyl acetate	320, 467
n-Butyl alcohol	180 (p. 949), 233, 646A, 729
n-Butyl ether	180 (p. 956)
Cadmium sulfate	49
Calcium chloride	180 (p. 944)
Carbon dioxide	173
Carbon disulfide (isopycnic, solutrope)	163, 180 (p. 845), 267, 393
Carbon tetrachloride (solutrope)	80, 180 (p. 840), 267, 306, 336, 393
Cellulose nitrate	495
Chlorobenzene (solutrope)	180 (p. 951), 244A
Chloroform	1 (pp. 58–61), 31, 42, 69, 113, 180 (p. 851), 272, 393
Cobalt chloride (island curve)	466
Cottonseed oil	550
Cyclohexane	451, 452
DDT (Dichlorodiphenyltrichloroethane)	297
Dextrose	180 (p. 954)
2,2′-Dichloroethyl sulfide (Mustard gas)	267
3,3-Dimethyl-2-butanone (Methyl *tert*-butyl ketone)	180 (pp. 954, 1039)
Ethyl acetate	180, (p. 949), 336, 467, 728
Ethyl alcohol–Butyl alcohol	646A
Ethyl butyrate	728
Ethylene	143

(*continued*)

TABLE I: Aqueous Systems (*continued*)

System	References
Acetone (*continued*)	
Ethyl ether	180 (p. 950), 345, 451, 452, 732
Ethyl propionate	728
Furfural	180 (p. 950)
Gasoline	345
Glycerol	180 (p. 948), 511
n-Heptane	180 (p. 955), 244A
n-Heptyl alcohol (solutrope)	534
Hexachlorocyclohexane	297
n-Hexane	180 (p. 954), 451
n-Hexyl alcohol	729
Isobutyl alcohol	180 (p. 950), 205B
Isobutyl alcohol–Tetrachloroethane (iso-pycnic)	180 (p. 879), 205B
Kerosine	628
Kollidone (polymer of vinyl pyrrolidone)	180 (p. 1037)
Lithium, Potassium, or Sodium hy-droxides	132, 180 (pp. 945, 947), 230, 386, 689
Lithium or Manganese sulfates	180 (p. 945)
Maltose	180 (p. 957)
Methyl acetate	728
4-Methyl-2-pentanone (Methyl isobutyl ketone)	180 (p. 953)
3,3-Dimethyl-2-butanone (Methyl *tert*-butyl ketone)	180 (p. 954)
Mustard gas (2,2′-Dichloroethyl sulfide)	267
Naphthalene	180 (p. 957), 200 (p. 208), Fig. 50
Nicotine	394
Nitrocellulose	180 (p. 1073)
n-Octyl alcohol (solutrope)	534
Pentane	451
Petroleum ether	452
Phenol (isopycnic, island curve above 66°C)	163, 180 (p. 952), 702, 733, Fig. 91
Pinacolin	180 (pp. 954, 1039)
Poly(vinyl acetate)	319, 469
Potassium carbonate, chloride, fluoride, or hydroxide	132, 133, 180 (pp. 944–945), 689
Potassium hydroxide	230, 386
n-Propyl acetate	728
Quinone iodobismuthate	180 (p. 957)

(*continued*)

TABLE I: Aqueous Systems (*continued*)

System	References
Acetone (*continued*)	
Salicylic acid	736
Sodium carbonate, chloride, hydroxide, nitrate, or sulfate	132, 133, 180 (pp. 944–945), 230, 386
Solvent oil	345
Sucrose	180 (p. 957)
1,1,2,2-Tetrachloroethane (isopycnic)	180 (pp. 878–879), 205B
Tetrachloroethylene	539, 603 (p. 181)
Toluene	180 (p. 954)
1,1,2-Trichloroethane	180 (p. 881), 281, 244A
Trichloroethylene (solutrope)	180 (p. 875), 636
Vinyl acetate	516
Vinyl acetate–Acetaldehyde	68
m-Xylene	180 (p. 956)
Zinc sulfate	180 (p. 948)
Acetonitrile–Benzene–*n*-Heptane (three liquid phases)	247
Ethylene	143
Trichloroethylene (solutrope)	180 (p. 874), 636
Acetophenone–Chlorides of hydrogen, aluminum, gallium, hafnium, iron, or zirconium	339A
Diacetyl cellulose acetate (+Mg(ClO$_4$)$_2$)	128
Acrolein–Hydroquinone or Gallic acid	603 (p. 165)
Acrylic acid–Poly(vinylpyrrolidinone) (island curve)	472
Acrylonitrile–Styrene	180 (p. 942)
Adipic acid–Amyl acetate, Amyl alcohol, Butyl acetate, 4-Methyl-2-pentanol, 4-Methyl-2-pentanone	530
Cyclohexanol	71D
Adiponitrile–Ammonia	780
Alcohols, seven–Benzene or Ethyl acetate	180 (pp. 984–986, 1023)
Alkylamines–Alkali carbonates or chlorides, or Sodium hydroxide	19, 293
Alkylphosphoric acid compounds– Uranium salts	56, 58
Allene–Sodium chloride or iodide (isooptics)	171

(*continued*)

TABLE I: Aqueous Systems (*continued*)

System	References
Allyl alcohol–Acetone	133
Allyl ether (solutrope)	180 (p. 958), 636
Carbon tetrachloride	180 (p. 840), 244
Potassium chloride or fluoride	689
Trichloroethylene	180 (p. 875), 244
Allyl isothiocyanate–Acetic	
anhydride	127
Aluminum sulfate–Ethyl alcohol	180 (p. 904)
Aminopyrine (Pyramidon)–Chloral	
hydrate	764, Fig. 90
Diantipyrylmethylmethylamine (two	
separate curves)	765
Diethylamine	373
Isobutyric acid	776
Salicylic acid (Binodal curve and separate	
island, 90–138°C)	358
Triethylamine	765
Ammonia–Adiponitrile	780
n-Butane	171
1-Butene (iso-optic)	171, 180 (p. 837)
Butyl alcohol	154
Cuprous acetate–Olefins	513
Cyclohexane–*n*-Hexane	148, 283
Phenols	286
Potassium carbonate or hydroxide	180 (p. 836)
Sodium hydroxide	180 (p. 837)
Xylenes	521
Zinc sulfate	180 (p. 837)
Ammonium Chloride–Acetone	180 (p. 946)
Manganous chloride	102
Ammonium fluoride–Ethyl alcohol	760
Ammonium sulfate–Acetone	180 (p. 946)
Ethyl alcohol	602 (pp. 1129–1130)
Ethyl alcohol–Benzene	525A
Glycerol, Glycol, or Methanol	46
n-Propyl alcohol	180 (p. 963)
Pyridine	264
Ammonium thiocyanate–Phenol	431
Thorium nitrate–Cyclohexanol or Isoamyl	
alcohol	99A
Amsco–Thorium nitrate–Tributyl	
phosphate	598

(*continued*)

TABLE I: Aqueous Systems (*continued*)

System	References
n-Amyl acetate–Acetic acid	180 (pp. 888, 900), 344C
Acetone	728
Adipic acid	530
Butyric, Formic, or Propionic acid	344C
Ethyl alcohol	180 (pp. 908, 930–931)
Methanol	541
Propyl alcohol	542
n-Amyl alcohol–Acetaldehyde	180 (pp. 885–886), 489
Acetone	180 (p. 950)
Adipic acid	530
Chloroacetic acid	180 (p. 882)
Cobalt thiocyanate	553
Dicyanoauric acid	788
Dimethylmalonic acid	180 (p. 1014), Fig. 44
Ethyl alcohol	180 (p. 916), 354
Ethylene glycol	180 (p. 941), 379, Fig. 118
Methanol	180 (p. 862)
Nickel thiocyanate	553
Nitrates of cobalt, copper, nickel or zinc	408
Phenol (isopycnic)	163, 180 (p. 1017)
Poly(vinylpyrrolidinone)	128
n-Propyl alcohol	180 (p. 964)
Trichloroacetic acid (isopycnic)	163, 180 (p. 876)
tert-Amyl alcohol–Bromal or Chloral	137B
Glycerol	180 (p. 975), Fig. 31
Isoamyl alcohol	353
Amylamine–Carbonates or Chlorides of sodium or potassium	19
Sodium hydroxide	293
Amyl formate–Ethyl alcohol	180 (pp. 908, 924–925)
Anabasine–Benzene	528, 604 (p. 725)
Ten other solvents	604 (p. 725)
Anethole–Acetone (isopycnic)	180 (p. 957)
Ethyl alcohol (isopycnic)	163, 180 (p. 938)
Aniline (isopycnic)	Fig. 8
Aniline–Acetic acid	180 (pp. 890, 901), 335
Acetic acid–Acetic anhydride	335
Acetic anhydride	335
Acetone (isopycnic)	180 (p. 953), 450
Aniline hydrochloride	180 (p. 1034), 660
Benzene (isopycnic)	163, 164, 180 (p. 1024), 200 (p. 216)

(*continued*)

TABLE I: Aqueous Systems (*continued*)

System	References
Aniline (*continued*)	
Benzylamine	437
Butyric acid (isopycnic)	12, 163, 180 (p. 988), Fig. 100
Cyclohexane	410, 426
Ethyl alcohol	180 (p. 922), 451, 452, 639, 710
Formic acid	180 (p. 857), Fig. 45
Glycerol (isopycnic)	163, 180 (p. 975)
n-Heptane (three layers)	180 (pp. 1035–1036), 766
n-Hexane (three layers)	439, 481, 766
Iso-octane	616
Isopropyl alcohol (isopycnic)	163, 180 (p. 970), 450
Lactic acid	180 (p. 962), 603 (p. 414)
Methanol	164, 180 (p. 866), 393
Methanol–Benzene (isopycnic, twin density surface)	164, 201 (p. 440) Figs. 117, 122–125
Methylcyclohexane (three layers)	180 (p. 1035)
Nitrobenzene	284, 604 (p. 650), 642
Nitrobenzene–Hexane (three layers)	478
17 Organic compounds	180 (p. 1033)
Phenol (isopycnic above 77°C)	163, 180 (p. 1027)
Phenol–Ethyl alcohol	710
Phenylhydrazine	437
Piperidine	437, 603 (p. 307)
Propionic acid (isopycnic above 50°C)	163, 180 (p. 960)
n-Propyl alcohol	180 (p. 966)
Pyridine	180 (p. 1012), 437
Quinoline	370
Sulfur (col at 82.5°C)	439, 480, 683
Sulfur–Hexane (four layers)	439
Toluene (isopycnic)	163, 180 (p. 1034)
o-Toluidine	353
Trimethylethylene	683
2,2,4-Trimethylpentane	616
Anisole–Caproic acid (isopycnic below 13°C)	163, 180 (p. 1039)
Anthranilic acid–Ethyl alcohol	368
Gasoline (three layers)	365
Phenol (two separate binodal curves)	364
Pyridine (island curve)	180 (p. 1013), 762
Salicylic acid (metastable col)	371

(*continued*)

TABLE I: Aqueous Systems (continued)

System	References
Anthraquinone–Phenol	34, 683
Antipyrine–Benzoic acid	362
Catechol (island curve)	772
Chloral hydrate (island curve)	357, 772
Phenol (island curve)	363
Resorcinol (island curve)	772
Salicylic acid (island curve)	355, 358
Aphilidine–Benzene	528
Azobenzene–Butyric acid, Phenol,	
Succinonitrile, or Triethylamine	34, 683
Barium nitrate–Acetone	432
Benzaldehyde–Acetic acid	8
Dioxane	180 (p. 992), 625
Ethyl alcohol	180 (p. 926)
Benzene–Acetaldehyde	180 (p. 885), 489
Acetic acid	1B, 31, 97, 180 (pp. 890, 901), 209, 262, 281, 377, 396, 664, 691, 732
Acetic acid–Carbon tetrachloride	517, 518
Acetic acid–Sodium chloride	241, 562
Acetic acid–Toluene	97
Acetone (solutrope at 15°C)	23, 73, 180 (p. 952), 267, 732
Acetonitrile–n-Heptane (three layers)	247
Seven Alcohols	180 (p. 1023)
Anabasine or Aphilidine	528, 604 (p. 725)
Aniline (isopycnic)	163, 164, 180 (p. 1024), 200 (p. 216)
Bromine–Potassium bromide	398B
Butyl acetate	717
n-Butyl alcohol	180 (pp. 996, 1023), 281, 407, 636, Fig. 25
sec-Butyl alcohol	124, 180 (p. 1023)
tert-Butyl alcohol	180 (pp. 1001, 1023), 636
Butyric acid	344, 348, 377, 393, 396
Caproic acid	603 (pp. 438–439)
ϵ-Caprolactam (+ Ammonium sulfate)	315, 457, 677
Carbon dioxide	171
Carbon tetrachloride–Acetic acid	517, 518
Chloroacetic acid	180 (p. 882)
m-Cresol (isopycnic)	163, 180 (p. 1024)
Diethylene glycol–Cyclohexane, Cyclohexene	390

(continued)

TABLE I: Aqueous Systems (*continued*)

System	References
Benzene (*continued*)	
Diethylene glycol–*n*-Heptane	238, 307, 390
Diethylene glycol–*n*-Hexane	390, 391
Diethylformamide	711
1,1-Difluoro-1-chloroethane (iso-optic)	171
1,1-Difluoroethane (iso-optic)	171
Dimethylformamide–Cyclohexane,	
n-Hexane, or Paraffin oil	567, 666, 711
Dioxane	45, 180 (p. 992), 281
Ephedrine–Sodium chloride or hydroxide	562
Ethane (iso-optic)	171
Ethyl alcohol (isopycnic below 19°C)	31, 42, 62, 90, 97, 163, 180 (pp. 920–921, 1023), 267, 281, 450–452, 456, 732, Fig. 30
Ethyl alcohol–Lube oil	179 (p. 250), 180 (p. 1080), 201 (p. 440), Fig. 114
Ethyl alcohol–Toluene	97
Ethylene (iso-optic)	171
Ethylene glycol–Benzene–*n*-Hexane	390, 391
Ethylenediamine–*n*-Hexane	121
Ethyl isovalerate–Ethyl alcohol	97
Formic acid	1B, 90, 180 (p. 857), 396, 701A
Freons 12, 22, and 114 (iso-optics)	171
Furfural	656
Hexamethyleneimine	781
Hydrogen	296A
Hydrogen chloride	180 (p. 1022), 651
Isobutane (iso-optics)	171
Isobutyl alcohol	180 (pp. 999, 1000, 1023)
Isopropyl alcohol (solutrope)	45A, 61, 180 (pp. 970, 1023). 281 450, 636, 659
Isovaleric acid	180 (p. 1016)
Magnesium bromide–Ether	238A
Metal chelates of $XOCH_2COCF_3$	87
Methanol (isopycnic)	163, 164, 180 (p. 865), 331, 393, 450, 451, 732
Methanol–Aniline (isopycnic, twin density surface)	163, 164, 201 (p. 440), Figs. 117, 122–125
Methanol–Cyclohexane, Cyclohexene, *n*-Heptane, or *n*-Hexane	337, 389, 391
Methyl ether (iso-optic)	171
Morpholin	665

(*continued*)

TABLE I: Aqueous Systems (*continued*)

System	References
Benzene (*continued*)	
Nitric acid–Thenoyltrifluoroacetone	573
70 Organic compounds (distribution)	180 (p. 1022)
Perchloric acid	624
Phenol (isopycnic)	90, 180 (p. 1023), 262, 663, 785
Phenol–Heptane or Gasoline	26
Phenol–Hexane, Decalin, or Paraffin oil	667
2-Picoline–Nonaromatic hydrocarbons	98
Picric acid	90
Piperidine	435C
Plutonium nitrate–Trifluoroacetylacetone	111
Propane or Propylene (iso-optics)	171
Propionic acid (double solutrope)	54, 180 (p. 960), 344, 348, 349, 377, 396, 536
n-Propyl alcohol	61, 180 (p. 966, 1023), 407
Pseudoephedrine–Sodium chloride or hydroxide	562
Pyridine (solutrope)	90, 180 (pp. 1011–1012), 267, 529, 625, 643, 739, 740, Fig. 34
8-Quinolinol	759
Resorcinol	785
Silver perchlorate	258
Sodium chloride	241, 562
Stannic iodide	219A
Succinonitrile	683
Sulfolane–*n*-Heptane (three layers)	247
Sulfur	683
Thenoyltrifluoroacetone	573
Thorium nitrate–Tributyl phosphate	147
Tributyl phosphate	624
Triethylamine	310
Triethylene glycol–*n*-Heptane	238, 549
Triethylene glycol dimethyl ether	465
Trifluoroacetyl acetone–Plutonium nitrate	111
Trimethylamine (solutrope)	310
1,2,4-Benzenetriole–Phenol	16A
Benzil–Phenol, Succinonitrile, or Triethylamine	34, 683
Benzilic acid–Ethyl ether or Xylene	90
Benzoic acid–Antipyrine	362
Phenol	34, 429, 683
Pyridine (island curve)	180 (p. 1013), 354, 761

(*continued*)

TABLE I: Aqueous Systems (*continued*)

System	References
Benzoic acid (*continued*)	
Salicylic acid	372
15 Solvents (distribution)	180 (p. 1043)
Benzophenone–Butyric acid or Phenol	34, 683
Benzyl acetate–Ethyl alcohol	180 (p. 937)
Benzyl alcohol–Ethyl alcohol	180 (p. 928)
Glycerol (isopycnic)	163, 180 (p. 975)
Hydrogen chloride and many other acids	59A
Seven Hydrocarbons	622
Trichloroacetic acid	180 (p. 876)
Benzylamine–Aniline or Phenylhydrazine	437
Benzyl chloride	683
Benzylic acid–Ethyl ether	90
Benzyl ethyl ether–Ethyl alcohol	
(isopycnic)	163, 180 (p. 937)
Boric acid–Ethyl ether–Uranium salts	376
Bromal–Bromal hydrate (three liquid	
phases)	773
Butyl chloral (two LCST's)	773
Ethyl or *tert*-Amyl alcohols	137B
Bromine–Carbon tetrachloride	90, 180 (p. 838)
Hydrogen bromide (two separate binodal	
curves)	428, 602 (p. 207)
Potassium bromide (and 21 other solutes)	180 (p. 835)
Potassium bromide–Benzene	398B
Bromobenzenes–Acetone	180 (p. 951), Fig. 24
Caproic acid (isopycnic)	180 (p. 1039)
Ethyl alcohol	180 (p. 917)
Methanol	180 (p. 863)
n-Propyl alcohol (isopycnic, solutrope)	180 (p. 965)
Bromoform–Chloroacetic acid	180 (p. 848)
1-Bromonaphthalene–Ethyl	
alcohol	180 (p. 938)
o-Bromotoluene–Ethyl alcohol	180 (p. 926)
n-Propyl alcohol	180 (p. 967)
1,3-Butadiene–Acetone	440
Furfural (three layers)	409
Sodium chloride or iodide (iso-optics)	171

(*continued*)

TABLE I: Aqueous Systems (*continued*)

System	References
Butane–Acetic acid	138
Ammonia (iso-optics)	171
1-Butene	744
Butanes and Butenes–Furfural	
(three layers)	180 (p. 1009), 200 (p. 207), 239, 312, 409
2-Butanone (Methyl ethyl ketone)	Fig. 5
Acetic acid	396, 633
Acetone	336, 486
Butyl Cellosolve	180 (p. 982)
Butyric acid	396
Calcium chloride	427
Carbon dioxide	173
Carbon disulfide	180 (p. 847)
Chlorobenzene (isopycnic)	163, 180 (p. 982), 244A
Cyclohexane	537
Ethyl alcohol	603 (p. 243)
Ethyl alcohol–Kerosine	215
Ethylene	143
Ethylene glycol	537
Formic acid	396
Gasoline	51, 180 (p. 983)
Glycerol	180 (p. 975)
n-Heptane	180 (p. 983), 244A
n-Hexane	180 (p. 983), 311
Hydrogen chloride (two separate curves)	175
Nicotine	88
Phenol	86
Potassium fluoride or Sodium chloride	180 (p. 984)
Propionic acid	396
Thiodiacetic acid	180 (p. 980)
Trichloroethane (isopycnic)	163, 180 (p. 982), 244A
Trichloroethylene (isopycnic)	163, 180 (p. 982)
2,2,4-Trimethylpentane	180 (p. 983)
1-Butene–Ammonia (iso-optic)	171, 180 (p. 837)
Butane	744
cis- or trans-2-Butene–Sodium chloride	
(iso-optics)	171
2,3-Butene glycol–Butene diacetate	
n-Butyl acetate, n-Butyl alcohol, or	
Methyl vinyl carbinol acetate	180 (pp. 1006–1007)

(*continued*)

TABLE I: Aqueous Systems (*continued*)

System	References
n-Butyl acetate–Acetic acid	84, 180 (pp. 888, 891–892, 900), 467, 531, 654, 691
Acetone	320, 467
Adipic acid	530
Benzene	717
2,3-Butene glycol	180 (pp. 1006–1007)
n-Butyl alcohol	180 (p. 996)
Ethyl alcohol	180 (pp. 908, 924–925), 320
Formic acid	540
Gallium or Sodium chloride–Sulfuric acid	340
Methanol	541, 604 (p. 579), 653
Phenol	469A, 566, 597, 785
n-Propionic acid or Butyric acid	531
n-Propyl alcohol	542
Resorcinol	785
Sulfuric acid	340
n-Butyl alcohol–Acetic acid	633
Acetone	180 (p. 949), 233, 646A, 729
Ammonia	154
Benzene	180 (pp. 996, 1023), 281, 407, 636, Fig. 25
2,3-Butene glycol	180 (pp. 1006–1007)
n-Butyl acetate	180 (p. 996)
Butyl ether	387
Three Chloroacetic acids	231
Diethylene glycol	420
Ethyl acetate	61, 180 (p. 985)
Ethyl alcohol	180 (p. 912), 451, 646A
Ethylene glycol	382, 420, 537
Glycerol	180 (p. 975), 422
Hexane or Heptane–Benzene	407
2-Hexanone	311
Hydrogen	296
Hydrogen bromide	175, Fig. 105
Hydrogen chloride	175, 180 (p. 994), Fig. 105
Hydrogen peroxide	154
Isopropyl alcohol	180 (p. 995)
Lactic acid	506
Malonic acid	604 (p. 603)
Methanol	180 (p. 861), 271, 281, 442

(*continued*)

TABLE I: Aqueous Systems (*continued*)

System	References
n-Butyl alcohol (*continued*)	
Nitrates of cobalt, copper, nickel, or zinc	408, 587
Nitrates of copper, thorium, or uranium	742
Phenyl ether	523
Polymethacrylic acid–Heptane	705
n-Propyl alcohol	180 (p. 995)
Sodium thiocyanate and other salts	180 (p. 994)
Sulfuric acid–Cobalt, Iron, or	
Nickel sulfates	589
Toluene	180 (p. 997)
Triethylene glycol	420
sec-Butyl alcohol–Benzene	124, 180 (p. 1023)
Carbon dioxide	173
Ethyl acetate	61, 180 (p. 985)
Isobutyric acid	415
Succinonitrile	683
tert-Butyl alcohol–Benzene (solutropes)	180 (pp. 1001, 1023), 636
tert-Butyl hypochlorite	747
Carbon tetrachloride	423
Cobaltous chloride	317
Ethyl acetate	61, 180 (p. 985)
Ethylene	143
Hydrogen bromide	197, Figs. 102–104
40 Salts	180 (pp. 1000–1001)
n-Butylamine–Acetic acid	499
Chlorobenzene (isopycnic)	163, 499
Salts	19
Sodium hydroxide	291
Butyl Carbitol acetate–Acetic	
acid	180 (pp. 891–892, 900)
Butyl Cellosolve–2-Butanone	180 (p. 982)
Butyl chloral–Bromal (two LCST's)	773
Butyl diacetone ether–Acetic acid	180 (pp. 891–892)
n-Butyl ether–Acetic acid	180 (pp. 891–892, 900)
Acetone	180 (p. 956)
n-Butyl alcohol	387
Ethyl alcohol	180 (p. 936)
Nitric acid	157, 719, 722
Uranyl nitrate	207, 723
n-Butyl formate–Ethyl alcohol	180 (pp. 908, 915)

(*continued*)

TABLE I: Aqueous Systems (*continued*)

System	References
tert-Butyl hypochlorite–*tert*-Butyl alcohol	747
n-Butyl lactate–Acetic acid	180 (pp. 891–892, 900)
tert-Butylphenol–Cetane or	
Methylnaphthalene	180 (pp. 1116–117), 520, Fig. 116
Butyltoluene–Ethyl alcohol	
(isopycnic)	163, 180 (p. 939), 450
Isopropyl alcohol (isopycnic)	163, 180 (p. 974), 450
Methanol (isopycnic)	163, 180 (p. 872), 450
n-Butyraldehyde–Ethyl acetate	311
n-Butyric acid–Amyl acetate	344C
Aniline (isopycnic)	12, 163, 180 (p. 988), Fig. 100
Azobenzene	34, 683
Benzene	344, 348, 377, 393, 396
Benzophenone or Camphor	34, 683
2-Butanone	396
Butyl acetate	531
Carbon disulfide	180 (p. 847), 393
Carbon tetrachloride	180 (p. 842), 393, Fig. 23
Chloroform (solutrope)	180 (p. 852), 393
Diethylaniline or Dimethylaniline	14
Ethyl acetate	344, 396, 758
Ethyl benzoate	533
Ethyl ether	344
n-Hexyl alcohol	96A
Mannite	683
4-Methyl-2-pentanol	535
4-Methyl-2-pentanone	36
Naphthalene	683
Phenyl ether	523
Three salts or Sucrose	683
Sodium chloride	180 (p. 987), 749
Toluene	393
Toluidines (isopycnics)	163, 180 (p. 989)
Trichloroethylene or Xylene	393
Cadmium sulfate–Acetone	49
Isopropyl alcohol	50, 509
Calcium chloride–Acetone	180 (p. 944)
2-Butanone	427
Dioxane	565

(*continued*)

TABLE I: Aqueous Systems (*continued*)

System	References
Camphor–*n*-Butyric acid, Phenol, Succinonitrile, or Triethylamine	683
Cresols	170
Phenol	34, 170, 603 (p. 389), 683
Caoutchouc–Ethyl ether	90
Caproic acid–Acetic acid	180 (p. 895), 488, Fig. 119
Anisole (isopycnic below 13°C)	163, 180 (p. 1039)
Benzene	603 (pp. 438–439)
Carbon tetrachloride (isopycnic)	163, 180 (p. 844)
Decalin	180 (p. 1039)
Eight solvents (four isopycnics)	163, 180 (p. 1039)
e-Caprolactam–Benzene or Carbontetrachloride	315, 457, 677
Chloroform	354, 375, 677
Cyclohexane	315
Cyclohexanol or Nitrobenzene	677
Ethylene chloride	354, 375, 457
Methylene chloride	375
Trichloroethylene	315, 677
Capryl alcohol–Cobalt and Nickel chlorides	212
Carvacrol–Potassium hydroxide	603 (p. 675)
m-Cresol–Potassium hydroxide	603 (p. 550)
Caprylic acid–Acetic acid or Furfural	554
Carbon dioxide–Acetic acid, Acetone, 2-Butanone, *sec*-Butyl or Isopropyl alcohols, Furfural, Methanol, Phenol or Succinonitrile	173
Benzene or Carbon disulfide (iso-optic)	171
Ethyl alcohol	38, 173
Carbon disulfide–Acetic acid	180 (pp. 845, 901), 393
Acetic anhydride (three layers)	180 (p. 847), 448, Figs. 97, 98, 99
Acetone (isopycnic, solutrope)	163, 180 (p. 845), 267, 393
2-Butanone	180 (p. 847)
Butyric acid	180 (p. 847), 393
Carbon dioxide or Difluoroethane (iso-optics)	171
Chloroacetic acid (isopycnic)	163, 180 (p. 845)
Ethane (iso-optic)	171
Ethyl alcohol	180 (p. 845), 267, 393, 451

(*continued*)

System	References
Carbon disulfide (*continued*)	
Ethylene (iso-optic)	171
Freon 114 [(CClF$_2$)$_2$] (iso-optic)	171
Iodine	90
Isobutyl alcohol (isopycnic)	180 (p. 847)
Isopropyl alcohol (isopycnic)	180 (p. 846), 393
Methanol	180 (p. 844), 393
Nitromethane–*n*-Hexane	683
Phenol (solutrope)	180 (p. 848), 275 (p. 428)
Propane (iso-optic)	171
Propionic acid	180 (p. 845), 393
n-Propyl alcohol (isopycnic)	163, 180 (p. 846), 393
Pyridine	180 (p. 847), 267, 393
Succinonitrile	683
Carbon tetrachloride–Acetic acid	180 (p. 839), 345, 393, 580, 625
Acetic acid–Benzene	517, 518
Acetone (solutrope)	80, 180 (p. 840), 267, 306, 336, 393
Allyl alcohol	180 (p. 840), 244
Bromine	90, 180 (p. 838)
tert-Butyl alcohol	423
Butyric acid (solutrope)	180 (p. 842), 393, Fig. 23
Caproic acid (isopycnic)	163, 180 (pp. 843–844)
ε-Caprolactam (+ Ammonium sulfate)	315, 457, 677
Catechol–Phenol	180 (p. 1026)
Ceric nitrate–Tributyl phosphate	
Chloroacetic acids	180 (p. 838)
Creosote	580
Dialkylfluorophosphates	483
Diethylamine	712
Ethyl alcohol (solutrope)	180 (p. 840), 267, 393, 422A, 451
Ethyl hypochlorite	603 (p. 120)
Formic acid	180 (p. 838)
Heptylic acid (isopycnic)	163, 180 (p. 844)
Isobutyric acid (isopycnic, solutrope)	163, 180 (p. 842)
Isopropyl alcohol (solutrope)	180 (p. 842), 300, 393, 422A, 658
Isovaleric acid (isopycnic, solutrope)	163, 180 (p. 843)
Methanol	180 (p. 838), 393
Nicotine	158, 159
Nitrous oxide (iso-optic)	171
Phenol (solutrope)	603 (p. 386)

(*continued*)

TABLE I: Aqueous Systems (*continued*)

System	References
Carbon tetrachloride (*continued*)	
Phosphate esters–Uranyl or Thorium salts	255
Propionic acid	180 (p. 841), 306, 393
n-Propyl alcohol (isopycnic)	163, 180 (p. 841), 393, 422A
Pyridine (solutrope)	180 (p. 843), 267, 393, 421, 527
8-Quinolinol	759
n-Valeric acid (isopycnic)	163, 180 (p. 848)
Carbonyl sulfide–Sodium chloride	
(iso-optic)	171
Carvacrol–Capryl alcohol, Heptane,	
or Toluene–Potassium hydroxide	603 (p. 675)
Castor oil–Ethyl alcohol	399A
Catechol–Antipyrine	772
Phenol	180 (p. 1026)
Cellulose acetate–Dioxane or	
Methoxyethanol	254
Cellulose nitrate–Acetone	495
Cetyltrimethylammonium bromide–	
Phenol (island and separate curve)	519
Chloral–Acetic anhydride	127
Ethyl or *tert*-Amyl alcohols	137B
Chloral hydrate–Aminopyrine	764, Fig. 90
Antipyrine (island curve)	357, 772
Diethylamine	367, 368B, 769, Figs. 106, 107
Pyridine (island curve)	772
Chlorine–Calcium or Sodium chloride	
(iso-optic)	171
Chloroacetic acid–Amyl alcohol or	
Benzene	180 (p. 882)
Bromoform	180 (p. 848)
n-Butyl alcohol	231
Carbon disulfide (isopycnic)	163, 180 (p. 845)
Carbon tetrachloride	180 (p. 838)
Chloroform	180 (p. 849)
m-Cresol	231
n- and Isoamyl alcohols, Benzene, Ethyl	
bromide, Isobutyl alcohol, or Toluene	
(two isopycnics)	180 (p. 882)
Methyl iodide	180 (p. 859)
Nitrobenzene or *o*-Nitrotoluene (iso-	
pycnics)	163, 180 (p. 883)

(*continued*)

TABLE I: Aqueous Systems (*continued*)

System	References
Chlorobenzene–Acetic acid	499
Acetone	180 (p. 951)
2-Butanone (isopycnic)	163, 180 (p. 982), 244A
n-Butylamine (isopycnic)	163, 499
Dichloroacetic acid (isopycnic)	163, 499
Ethyl or n- or Isopropyl alcohols	423
Methanol	180 (p. 863), 625
Propionic acid	349
Pyridine (solutrope)	499
Chlorodifluoroethane (Genetron 142B)–Benzene (iso-optic)	171
2-Chloroethanol–47 Organic compounds	153A, 154, 180 (p. 903)
Inorganic salts	545
Chloroform–Acetic acid	31, 69, 71, 88A, 90, 109, 113, 114, 180 (pp. 849–850), 272, 354, 393, 487, 731
Acetone (solutrope)	1A (pp. 58–61), 31, 42, 69, 113, 180 p. 851), 272, 393
n-Butyric acid (solutrope)	180 (p. 852), 393
ε-Caprolactam	354, 375, 677
Chloroacetic acid	180 (p. 849)
Diacetylcellulose acetate + Magnesium perchlorate	128
Dichloroacetic acid	180 (pp. 849, 880)
Diethylene glycol	423
Ethyl alcohol (solutrope)	31, 180 (p. 850), 393
Ethylene glycol	423
Formic acid	109, 487
Isopropyl alcohol (solutrope)	177, 180 (p. 852), 201 (p. 447), 300, 393, Fig. 33
Lube oil–Acetic acid	69
Malonic acid	604 (p. 603)
Methanol	180 (p. 849), 393
Methyl acetate	401
Methylene chloride	354
70 Organic substances (mostly acids, distribution) (at least seven systems with solutropes)	154, 180 (pp. 853–855), 604 (pp. 574, 617, 619, 665, 667), 603 (p. 386)

(*continued*)

TABLE I: Aqueous Systems (*continued*)

System	References
Cyclohexanone (*continued*)	
Ethylene glycol	584
Hydrogen chloride	602 (p. 574)
Sulfuric or Thiocyanic acid	268A
Uranium(VI)	390
Cyclohexene–Ethyl alcohol	180 (p. 923)
Ethylene chloride	390
Isopropyl alcohol (solutrope)	180 (p. 970), 636
Methanol	180 (p. 866), 389, 391
Propionic acid	536
Cyclohexyl acetate–Acetic acid	180 (pp. 891–892)
Cyclopentanone–Succinic acid	52
DDT (Dichlorodiphenyltrichloroethane)–	
Acetone or Dioxane	297
Phenol	592
Decalin–Caproic acid	180 (p. 1039)
Phenol	667
Propionic acid	180 (p. 962)
Decyl alcohol–Sodium caprylate	138B
Deuterium oxide–Deuteriophenol	91, 525
Ethyl acetate	525
Phenol	91, 525, 603 (p. 375)
Sulfur trioxide, Cupric oxide,	
or Uranium oxide	417B
Triethylamine	341, 630
Nine Deuterio compounds	525
Dextrose–Acetone	180 (p. 954)
Diacetone alcohol–Ethylbenzene	
or Styrene	117
Diacetylcellulose acetate–	
Magnesium perchlorate–Acetophenone,	
Chloroform, or Isoamyl alcohol	128
Dialkylfluorophosphates–	
Carbon tetrachloride or Whale oil	483
Diantipyrylmethylmethylamine–	
Aminopyrine	765
Dibutylamine–Sodium hydroxide	293
Dibutyl phosphate in kerosine–	
Uranyl phosphate	678
Dichloroacetic acid–*n*-Butyl alcohol	231
Carbon tetrachloride	180 (p. 838)

(*continued*)

TABLE I: Aqueous Systems (*continued*)

System	References
Dichloroacetic acid (*continued*)	
Chlorobenzene (isopycnic)	163, 499
Chloroform, Ethyl bromide, Nitro-	
benzene, *o*-Nitrotoluene, or Toluene	
(two solutropes)	180 (p. 880)
n-Cresol	231
Ethyl bromide	180 (p. 880)
Phenol	180 (p. 877)
1,1-Dichloroethylene–Ethyl alcohol	180 (p. 878)
2,2-Dichloroethyl sulfide	
(Mustard gas)–Acetone,	
Ethyl alcohol, Pyridine	267
Dicyanoauric acid–Alcohols or Ketones	788
Diethylamine–Aminopyrine	373
Carbon tetrachloride	712
Chloral hydrate	367, 368B, 769, Figs. 106, 107
Salts	294
Sodium hydroxide	287
Toluene	180 (p. 1008), 208
Diethylaniline–Formic to	
Butyric acids	14
Diethylene glycol–Benzene–*n*-Heptane and	
other nonaromatics	238, 307, 390, 391
n-Butyl alcohol	420
Chloroform	423
Diethylene glycol dibutyl ether–	
Nitric acid	715
Diethylformamide–Benzene	711
Di(2-ethylhexyl)phosphoric acid–	
Uranium salts	58
Diethyl ketone (3-Pentanone)–Ethyl alcohol	180 (p. 914)
1,1-Difluoro-1-chloroethane–benzene	
(iso-optic)	171
1,1-Difluoroethane–Benzene (iso-optic)	171
Di-isoamylmethyl phosphonate–	
Sulfuric acid	647, 647A
Di-isobutene–Ethyl alcohol	180 (p. 935)
Di-isobutyl ketone (2,6-Dimethyl-	
4-heptanone)–Acetic acid	180 (pp. 891–892, 900), 508
Hydrogen chloride	508
Di-isopropylcarbinol (2,4-	
Dimethyl-3-pentanol)–Acetic acid	180 (pp. 891–892)

(*continued*)

TABLE I: Aqueous Systems (*continued*)

System	References
Dimethylacetamide or Dimethyl-formamide–Cuprous chloride–Hydrogen chloride–Olefins	203
Dimethylaniline–Acetic acid	211
Formic to Butyric acids	14
2,3-Dimethylbutane–Ethyl alcohol	180 (p. 925)
3,3-Dimethyl-2-butanone (Pinacoline)–Acetone	180 (p. 954, 1039)
Dimethylformamide–Benzene,	
Hexane, Cyclohexane, or Paraffin oil	567, 666, 711
Poly(*p*-iodostyrene)	459B
Dimethylmalonic acid–Amyl alcohol or Ethyl ether	180 (p. 1014), Fig. 44
2,4-Dimethyl-3-pentanol–Acetic acid	180 (pp. 890, 891)
Dimethylpyrone (island curve)	752
Dinitroglycerol–Nitric acid	180 (p. 963)
Di-*n*-octylamine in *o*-xylene–Nitric acid	441
Dioxane–Acetic anhydride	342
Benzaldehyde	180, (p. 992), 625
Benzene	45, 180 (pp. 991–992), 281
Calcium chloride	565
Cellulose acetate	254
Cobalt or Nickel chloride	593
DDT	297
Ferric chloride	496
Hexachlorocyclohexane	297
Hydrogen bromide (island curve)	169, 240
Hydrogen chloride (island curve and separate curve)	175, 180 (p. 991), 240, 333, 565, Fig. 89
Lithium or Potassium chlorides	333
Lithium, Potassium, or Sodium hydroxide	132, 230, 386, 689
Potassium carbonate (and 16 other salts)	604 (p. 272)
Salicyclic acid	180 (p. 993)
Sodium chloride–Organic compounds	45
Sodium nitrate	47, 180 (p. 992)
Sulfuric acid	333
Diphenylamine–Acetic anhydride	127
Diphenyl ether (see Phenyl ether)	523

(*continued*)

TABLE I: Aqueous Systems (*continued*)

System	References
Di-*n*-propylamine–Ethyl alcohol	180 (p. 925)
Sodium hydroxide and chloride	293
Di-*n*-propylketone (4-Heptanone)–	
Ethyl alcohol	180 (p. 930)
Dodecyl(trialkylmethyl)amine–Salts of	
Al, As, Bi, Fe, Sb, or Ti	468
Dodecylphosphoric acid in kerosine–	
Uranium salts	568
Ephedrine–Benzene–Sodium chloride	
or hydroxide	562
Epichlohydrin (C_3H_5OCl)–Acetic	
acid	180 (p. 886, 901)
Toluene or Phenol	429
Ethane–Benzene or Carbon disulfide	
(iso-optics)	171
Ethanolamine–Cuprous chloride–	
Hydrogen chloride–Olefins	203
Phenols	1
Ether (see Ethyl ether)	Fig. 6
Ethoxyethanol (Cellosolve)–	
Ethylbenzene or Styrene	374
Potassium fluoride	689
Ethyl acetate–Acetic acid	
(solutrope)	180 (p. 888), 396, 446, 532, 646, 654, 691, 758
Acetone	180 (p. 949), 336, 467, 728
Six alcohols	180 (p. 985)
Three Butyl alcohols	61, 180 (p. 985)
n-Butyraldehyde	311
Butyric acid	344, 396, 758
Deuterium oxide	525
Ethyl alcohol	61, 180 (pp. 908, 911), 322, 336, 446, 451
Formic acid	396, 540
Furfural (isopycnic)	163, 180 (p. 986), 251, 656, Fig. 27
Isobutyl alcohol	180 (p. 985)
Isopropyl alcohol	61, 180 (p. 985)
Malonic acid	604 (p. 603)
Methanol	61, 180 (pp. 861–862), 653

(*continued*)

TABLE I: Aqueous Systems (*continued*)

System	References
Ethyl acetate (*continued*)	
Nitrates of copper, thorium, or uranium	99A, 742
Propionic acid	344, 396, 532, 758
n-Propyl alcohol	61, 180 (p. 985)
40 Salts and four Sugars	603 (pp. 246–247)
Urea	180 (p. 873)
Vinylpyrrolidone	180 (p. 1037)
Ethyl alcohol–Acetone–Butyl alcohol	646A
Aluminum sulfate	180 (p. 904)
Ammonium acid fluoride	760
Ammonium sulfate	602 (pp. 1129–1130)
n- or Isoamyl acetate	180 (pp. 908, 930–931)
n-Amyl alcohol	180 (p. 916), 354
Amyl formate	180 (pp. 908, 924–925)
Anethole (isopycnic)	163, 180 (p. 938)
Aniline	180 (p. 922), 451, 452, 639, 710
Aniline–Phenol	710
Anthranilic acid	368
Benzaldehyde	180 (p. 926)
Benzene (isopycnic below 19°C)	31, 42, 62, 90, 97, 163, 180 (pp. 920–921, 1023), 267, 281, 435A, 450, 451, 452, 456, 732, Fig. 30
Benzene–Ammonium sulfate	525A
Benzene–Ethyl isovalerate	97
Benzene–Lube oil	179 (p. 250), 180 (p. 1080), Fig. 114
Benzene–Toluene	97
Benzyl acetate	180 (p. 937)
Benzyl alcohol	180 (p. 928)
Benzyl ethyl ether (isopycnic)	163, 180 (p. 937)
Bromobenzene	180 (p. 917)
Bromonaphthalene	180 (p. 938)
o-Bromotoluene	180 (p. 926)
2-Butanone	603 (p. 243)
2-Butanone–Kerosine	215
Butyl acetate	180 (pp. 908, 924–925), 320
n-Butyl alcohol	180 (p. 912), 451, 646A
Butyl ether	180 (p.936)

(*continued*)

TABLE I: Aqueous Systems (*continued*)

System	References
Ethyl alcohol (*continued*)	
n-Butyl formate	180 (pp. 908, 915)
Butyltoluene (isopycnic)	163, 180 (p. 939), 450
Carbon dioxide	38, 173
Carbon disulfide	180 (p. 845), 267, 393, 451
Carbon tetrachloride (solutrope)	180 (p. 840), 267, 393, 421, 422A, 451
Castor oil	399A
Chloral hydrate	137B
Chlorobenzene	423
Chloroform (solutrope)	31, 180, (p. 850), 393
Cottonseed oil (isopycnic)	163, 180 (p. 941)
o-Cresol	180 (p. 928)
Cyclohexane or Cyclohexene	180 (p. 923)
1,1-Dichloroethylene	180 (p. 878)
2,2′-Dichloroethyl sulfide (Mustard oil)	267
Diethyl ketone (3-Pentanone)	180 (p. 914)
Di-isobutene	180 (p. 935)
2,2-Dimethylbutane	180 (p. 925)
Di-*n*-propylamine	180 (p. 925)
25 Esters	180 (p. 908)
Ethyl acetate	61, 180 (pp. 908, 911), 322, 336, 446, 451
Ethyl bromide	180 (p. 902)
Ethyl butyrate	180 (pp. 908, 924)
Ethyl chloroacetates	180 (pp. 908, 910)
Ethylene chloride	62, 180 (p. 884), 336, 703
Ethyl ether (solutrope at 25°C)	180 (p. 913), 322, 336, 451, 452, 732
Ethyl formate	451
Ethylidine chloride	180 (p. 885)
Ethyl isovalerate	97, 180 (pp. 908, 931)
Ethyl isovalerate–Benzene or Toluene	97
Ethyl propionate	180 (pp. 908, 914–915)
Ethyl silicate	180 (p. 913)
Ethyl valerate	180 (pp. 908, 931)
Ethyl vinyl ether	180 (p. 910), 625
Eugenol	180 (p. 938)
Furfural	130, 397
Gasoline	180 (p. 932)

(continued)

TABLE I: Aqueous Systems (*continued*)

System	References
Ethyl alcohol (*continued*)	
Glycerol–six Freons	314
n-Heptadecyl alcohol	706
n-Heptane	180 (p. 931, 1048), 599
3-Heptanol	492
4-Heptanone	180 (p. 930)
n-Hexane	180 (p. 925), 435C, 451, 639
n-Hexyl alcohol	346, 347
Hydrazine monohydrochloride	220
Isoamyl acetate	180 (pp. 908, 930–931)
Isoamyl alcohol	15, 78A, 180 (pp. 908, 917)
Isoamyl bromide	180 (p. 915)
Isoamyl ether	180 (p. 939)
Isobutyl alcohol	78A, 180 (p. 912)
Isobutyl alcohol or bromide	180 (p. 912–913)
Iso-octane	180 (p. 936), 482
Isopentane	180 (p. 916)
Kerosine (isopycnic)	163, 180 (p. 940), 215
Lube oil (only 95% Ethyl alcohol)–	
Benzene	179 (p. 250), 180 (p. 1080), 201 (p. 440), Fig. 114
Magnesium or Manganese sulfates	180 (p. 906)
Mesitylene (isopycnic)	163, 180 (p. 937)
Methylaniline (isopycnic)	163, 180 (p. 929)
Methyl n-butyrate	180 (pp. 908, 914)
Methylcyclohexane	180 (p. 930)
Methyl isovalerate	180 (p. 923)
Methyl propionate	180 (p. 908)
Methyl salicylate (isopycnic)	163, 180 (p. 932)
Methylene chloride	266
Mustard gas (2,2′-Dichloroethyl sulfide)	267
Nitrobenzene	180 (p. 918)
Three Nitrophenols	180 (pp. 918–919), Fig. 53
o-Nitrotoluene	180 (p. 927)
1-Octene	482
sec-Octyl alcohol (solutrope)	347
Oleic acid	153A, 180 (p. 940), 639
Oleic acid–Triolein	180 (p. 1081), 555, 603 (p. 150)
n-Pentane	180 (p. 916), 451, 452
3-Pentanone (Diethyl ketone)	180 (p. 914)
Petroleum ether	180 (p. 916), 451, 452

(*continued*)

TABLE I: Aqueous Systems (*continued*)

System	References
Ethyl alcohol (*continued*)	
Phenetole (isopycnic)	163, 180 (p. 935)
Phenol	180 (p. 922), 710
Phenyl ether	180 (p. 940), 523
2-Picoline	154
Pinene (isopycnic)	163, 180 (p. 939)
Potassium citrate	180 (pp. 919, 1021)
Potassium carbonate, fluoride, hydroxide, nitrate, or sulfantimonate	180 (pp. 904–905)
n-Propyl acetate	180 (pp. 908, 914)
n-Propyl alcohol	78A
n-Propyl bromide	180 (p. 909)
n-Propyl butyrate	180 (pp. 908, 931)
Propylene glycol–Alcohols, Esters, or Ketones	125A
Propylene glycol–Benzene, Hexane, or Cyclohexane	125
n-Propyl formate	180 (p. 908)
n-Propyl propionate	180 (pp. 908, 924)
Pyridine–Carbon tetrachloride	421
Salicylic acid	369
Sodium carbonate, hydroxide, sulfoantimonate	180 (pp. 906–907)
Sodium hydroxide	639
Sodium sulfate	180 (p. 907)
Sodium thiosulfate	48, 180 (p. 907)
Succinonitrile (two separate binodal curves, classical example)	180 (p. 909), 595, Fig. 59
Toluene (isopycnic)	31, 97, 163, 180 (pp. 927–928), 435A, 450, 451, 452
o-Toluidine (isopycnic above 24.5°C)	163, 180 (p. 929)
Trichloroethylene	180 (p. 874), 424A
Triethylamine	180 (p. 926)
Triolein	180 (p. 940), 543, 555
Trimethylpentane	180 (p. 936), 482
Six Vegetable oils	180 (p. 938), 543
Vinylidine chlorides	180 (p. 878)
Three Xylenes (isopycnics)	163, 180 (pp. 933–934), 450–452
Ethylbenzene–Diacetone alcohol	117
Ethoxyethanol	374
Isopropyl alcohol	179 (p. 262)
Silver nitrate–Styrene	202

(*continued*)

TABLE I: Aqueous Systems (*continued*)

System	References
Ethyl benzoate–C$_1$ to C$_4$ acids	533
Ethyl benzylaniline–Ethyl	
benzylaniline sulfate	447A
Ethyl bromide–Chloroacetic acid	180 (p. 882)
Dichloroacetic acid	180 (p. 880)
Ethyl alcohol	180 (p. 902)
Isovaleric acid	180 (p. 1016)
Methanol	180 (p. 860)
Propionic acid (solutrope)	603 (p. 188)
n-Propyl alcohol	180 (p. 902)
Trichloroacetic acid (solutrope)	180 (p. 876)
Ethyl butyrate–Acetic acid	532, 654
Acetone	728
Ethyl alcohol	180 (pp. 908, 924)
Methanol	541
Propionic acid	532
n-Propyl alcohol	542
Ethylbutyric acid–Acetic acid	180 (p. 895), 488
Ethyl chloride–Sodium chloride	
(iso-optic)	171
Ethyl chloroacetates	180 (pp. 908, 910)
Ethylene–Benzene or Carbon disulfide	
(iso-optic)	171
26 Organic liquids	143
Ethylene chloride–Acetic acid	691
ε-Caprolactam	354, 375, 457
Chlorides of hydrogen, aluminum, iron,	
gallium, hafnium, and zirconium	339A
Ethyl alcohol	62, 180 (p. 884), 336, 703
Formic acid	701
Glycerol or Glycol	46
Isopropyl alcohol	299, 493, Fig. 35
Methanol	46, 301, 493, 628A
8-Quinolinol	759
Ethylene diacetate–Acetic acid	180 (pp. 891–892)
Ethylenediamine–Acetic anhydride	127
Benzene–n-Hexane	121
Sodium hydroxide	753
Ethylene glycol–Ammonium sulfate	46
n-Amyl alcohol	180 (p. 941), 379, Fig. 118
Benzene–n-Hexane	390, 391

(*continued*)

TABLE I: Aqueous Systems (*continued*)

System	References
Ethylene glycol (*continued*)	
2-Butanone	537
n-Butyl alcohol	382, 420, 537
Chloroform	423
Cyclohexane	390, 391
Cyclohexanol	583
Cyclohexanone	584
Cyclohexene	390
Ethylene chloride	46
Ethyl formate	584
Furfural	180 (pp. 1008–1009)
Glycolic or Salicylic acids–Metal nitrates	105
n-Heptane or *n*-Hexane	390, 391
2-Heptanone	180 (p. 942)
n-Hexyl alcohol	180 (p. 941)
Isobutyl alcohol	382
Isobutyraldehyde	583
Methyl acetate	584
4-Methyl-2-pentanone (Methyl isobutyl ketone)	584
Potassium carbonate	604 (p. 272)
Triethyl amine	583
Ethylene oxide–Sodium chloride (iso-optic)	171
Ethyl ether	Fig. 6
Acetic acid	65, 95, 180 (pp. 889, 900), 281, 451, 452, 531, 636, 691, 732
Acetone	180 (p. 950), 345, 451, 452, 732
Benzoic acid	603 (p. 509)
Benzylic acid	90
Boric acid–Uranium salts	376
Butyric acid	344
Caoutchouc	90
Cyanoform (three layers)	180 (p. 976), 683
Dimethylmalonic acid	180 (p. 1014), Fig. 44
Ethyl alcohol (solutrope at 25°C)	180 (p. 913), 322, 336, 451, 452, 732
Ferric ammonium chloride	205A
Ferric bromide–Hydrogen bromide	232
Ferric chloride	4, 216, 476
Ferric thiocyanate	90

(*continued*)

TABLE I: Aqueous Systems (*continued*)

System	References
Ethyl ether (*continued*)	
Formamide	604 (p. 576)
Formic acid	180 (p. 856), 451
Furfural	656
Hydrogen bromide–Ferric bromide	232
Hydrogen chloride	4, 175, 180 (p. 1002), 216, 476
Inorganic nitrates	474
Isobutyl alcohol	180 (p. 999), 205B
Isopropyl alcohol	451
Lithium chloride	4
Magnesium bromide	570A
Magnesium bromide–Benzene	238A
Mercuric and Potassium iodides (three layers)	602 (p. 644)
Methanol	180 (p. 862), 451, 452, 653, 732
Nitrates of europium, thorium, and uranium	742
Nitric acid	90
Nitric acid–Nitrates of rare earths	63, 644
About 300 Organic compounds (distribution)	106, 180 (p. 1005), 604 (p. 603)
Perchloric acid	180 (p. 1003)
Phenylacetic acid	604 (p. 701)
Phosphoric acid	108 (p. 1003)
Propionic acid	344, 531
n-Propyl alcohol	451, 452
Quinoline	370
Radioisotopes of antimony, indium, iron, or zinc	459
40 Salts (distribution) (six solutropes)	180 (p. 1002)
Silicomolybdic acid	644
Succinonitrile (three layers)	180 (p. 977), 436, 594, 683
Sulfuric acid	180 (p. 1003), 681, Fig. 101
Tetrachloroethylene	681, Fig. 111
Triethylamine	354
Uranyl nitrate	77, 376, 454, 644
Uranyl nitrate–Nitric acid	644
Vinyl pyrrolidone	180 (p. 1037)
Ethyl formate–Ethyl alcohol or Methanol	451
Ethylene glycol	584

(*continued*)

TABLE I: Aqueous Systems (*continued*)

System	References
Ethylhexoic acid–Acetic acid	180 (p. 895), 488
Ethyl hypochlorite	603 (p. 120)
Ethylidine chloride–Ethyl alcohol	180 (p. 885)
Ethylidine diacetate–Acetic acid	180 (p. 893)
Ethyl isovalerate–Benzene or Toluene	97
Ethyl alcohol	97, 180 (pp. 908, 931)
Ethyl propionate–Acetic acid	532, 654
Acetone	728
Ethyl alcohol	180 (pp. 908, 914–915)
Methanol	541
Propionic acid	532
n-Propyl alcohol	542
Ethyl propyl ether–Nitric acid	419A
Ethyl silicate–Ethyl alcohol	180 (p. 913)
Ethyl valerate–Ethyl alcohol	180 (p. 908, 931)
Ethyl vinyl ether–Ethyl alcohol	180 (p. 910), 625
Eugenol–Ethyl alcohol	180 (p. 938)
Fenchone–Acetic acid	180 (pp. 891–892)
Ferric bromide–Hydrogen bromide–	
Ethyl ether	232
Ferric chloride–Dioxane	496
Ethyl ether	4, 216, 476
Ferric sulfate–Butyl alcohol–	
Sulfuric acid	589
Ferric thiocyanate–Ethyl ether	90
Formamide–Cuprous and	
Hydrogen chlorides–Olefins	203
Ethyl ether	604 (p. 576)
Formic acid–Aniline	180 (p. 857), Fig. 45
Benzene	1B, 90, 180 (p. 857), 396, 701A
2-Butanone	396
Butyl acetate	540
Carbon tetrachloride	180 (p. 838)
Chloroform	109, 487
Diethylaniline or Dimethylaniline	14
Ethyl acetate	396, 540
Ethyl benzoate	533
Ethylene chloride	701
Ethyl ether (plait point at apex of	
curve, possibly double solutrope)	36, 180 (p. 856), 451

(*continued*)

TABLE I: Aqueous Systems (*continued*)

System	References
Formic acid (*continued*)	
Isopropyl ether	655
4-Methyl-2-pentanol	535
4-Methyl-2-pentanone	36, 733, 750
4-Methyl-2-pentanone–	
Hydrochloric acid	403
Nitrobenzene	180 (p. 856)
o-Nitrotoluene (isopycnic)	163, 180 (p. 858)
Phenol	180 (p. 857), 234
Propyl acetate	540
Propyl formate	559
Xylene	180 (p. 858)
Freon 11 or 21-Sodium chloride	
(iso-optics)	171
Freon 12 or 22-Benzene (iso-optics)	171
Freon 114-Benzene or Carbon disulfide	
(iso-optics)	171
Furfural-Acetaldehyde	180 (p. 885), 489
Acetic acid	252, 500, 633
Acetone	180 (p. 950)
Benzene	656
1,3-Butadiene (three phases)	409
Butanes (three phases)	180 (p. 1009), 200 (p. 207) 239,
	312, 409
Butenes (three phases)	239, 312, 409
Caprylic acid and 20 Organic liquids	554
Carbon dioxide	173, 192
Deuterium oxide	525
Ethyl acetate (isopycnic)	163, 180 (p. 986), 251, 656, Fig. 27
Ethyl alcohol	130, 397
Ethylene glycol	180 (pp. 1008–1009)
Ethyl ether	656
Glycolic or Salicylic acids–	
Metal nitrates	105
Isoamyl acetate (isopycnic)	163, 180 (p. 1010)
Isopropyl ether	656
Methyl esters of Castor oil–Hexane	380
4-Methyl-2-pentanone (Methyl	
isobutyl ketone) (isopycnic)	110, 163
Propane and Propylene	239

(*continued*)

TABLE I: Aqueous Systems (*continued*)

System	References
Furfural (*continued*)	
Propionic acid	252
Salicylic acid–Metal nitrates	105
Tetralin	552, 554
Toluene (isopycnic)	163, 180 (p. 1010)
Tributyl phosphate	247A
Zinc chloride or sulfate	213
Galium chloride–Hydrogen	
chloride–Seven Ethers	74
Sulfuric acid–Butyl acetate	340
Gasoline–Acetic acid	179 (p. 247), 180 (pp. 899, 901)
Acetic anhydride	180 (p. 979)
Acetone	345
Anthranilic acid (three layers,	
metastable)	365
2-Butanone (MEK)	51, 180 (p. 983)
Ethyl alcohol	180 (p. 932)
Phenol	26, 180 (p. 1031)
Salicylic acid (three layers)	360
Genetron 142B (CH_3CClF_2)–	
Benzene (iso-optic)	171
Germanium chloride–	
Hydrogen chloride	44, 463
Glycerol–Acetic anhydride–Acetone	511
Acetone	180 (p. 948), 511
Ammonium sulfate	46
tert-Amyl alcohol	180 (p. 975), Fig. 31
Aniline or Benzyl alcohol (isopycnics)	163, 180 (p. 975)
2-Butanone (MEK) or *tert*-Amyl or	
n-Butyl alcohol	180 (p. 975), 422
Cyclohexanol	180 (p. 975)
Cyclohexanol–Cyclohexanone	632
Ethyl alcohol–Six Freons	314
Ethylene chloride	46
Isopropyl alcohol–Six Freons	314
Methanol–Six Freons	314
Phenol (solutrope)	120, 180 (p. 976), 424, Fig. 19
Phenols	120
Glycol (see Ethylene glycol)	
Glycol ethers–Sodium sulfonates	96

(*continued*)

TABLE I: Aqueous Systems (*continued*)

System	References
Glycolic acid–Furfural–Metalnitrates	105
Gold cyanide–*n*-Trioctylamine in	
Kerosine	385A
n-Heptadecyl alcohol–	
Acetic acid or Ethyl alcohol	706
n-Heptane–Acetic acid–Toluene	180 (p. 1077), 489, Figs. 112, 113
Acetone	180 (p. 955)
Acetonitrile or Sulfolane–Benzene	
(three liquid phases)	247
Seven Alcohols	180 (p. 1048)
Aniline (three layers)	180 (pp. 1035–1036), 766
2-Butanone (MEK)	180 (p. 983)
Carvacrol—Potassium hydroxide	603 (p. 675)
m-Cresol–Potassium hydroxide	603 (p. 550)
Diethylene glycol–Benzene	238, 307, 390, 391
Ethyl alcohol	180 (pp. 931, 1048), 599
Hydrogen bromide (band solutrope)	200 (p. 202)
Methanol	389, 391, 622
Nitrobenzene	631
Phenol	26, 180 (p. 1030), 480
n-Propyl or *n*-Butyl alcohols	180 (p. 1048), 407
Triethylamine	631
3-Heptanol–Acetic acid or	
Ethyl alcohol	492
2-Heptanone–Ethylene glycol	180 (p. 942)
Hydrogen chloride	508
3-Heptanone–Hydrogen chloride	508
n-Heptyl alcohol–Acetone	
(solutrope)	534
n-Heptylamine–Salts	
Sodium hydroxide	291
Heptylic acid–Carbon	
tetrachloride (isopycnic)	163, 180 (p. 844)
Hexachlorocyclohexane–	
Acetone or Dioxane	297
Hexadecane–Methanol–*p*-Cresol	520
Hexadecyltrimethyl-	
ammonium bromide–Nicotine	
or Triethylamine	385
"Hexalin" Acetate (Cyclohexyl	
acetate)–Acetic acid	180 (pp. 891–892)

(*continued*)

TABLE I: Aqueous Systems (*continued*)

System	References
Hexamethyldisiloxane–*n*-Propyl alcohol	100
Hexamethylenimine–Benzene	781
Sodium chloride or hydroxide	782
Hexamethylmellitic acid– Phenol	683
n-Hexane–Acetic acid	180 (p. 901), 451, 537
Acetone	180 (p. 954), 451
Aniline (three layers)	481, 766
Aniline–Nitrobenzene	478
Aniline–Sulfur (four layers)	439
Benzene–Ethylene diamine	121
2-Butanone (MEK)	180 (p. 983), 311
Diethylene glycol	390, 391
Ethyl alcohol	180 (p. 925), 435C, 451, 639
Ethylene diamine	121
Furfural or Nitromethane–Methyl esters or Castor oil	380
Isopropyl alcohol	179 (p. 257), 180 (pp. 971–972), 246
Methanol	180 (p. 867), 389, 391. 622, 652
Nitromethane	683
Phenol	180 (p. 1029), 200 (p. 208), 434, 439, 479, 667, Fig. 81
Phenol–Sulfur (four layers below 96°C)	434, 439
Phenyl ether	180 (p. 540), 523
Propionic acid	536
n-Propyl or *n*-Butyl alcohols	407
Pyridine–Sulfur	435D
Silver nitrate–Propylene	123
Soap	406
Succininonitrile	683
2-Hexanone–*n*-Butyl alcohol	311
Hexoic acid-4-Methyl-2-Pentanone	36
n-Hexyl alcohol–Acetone	729
Ethyl alcohol	346, 347
Ethylene glycol	180 (p. 941)
Hydrogen chloride (band solutrope and iso-optics)	175, Fig. 36
Methanol	346
Nitrates of calcium, cobalt, lanthanum, magnesium, and zinc	672
Propionic or Butyric acids	96A

(*continued*)

TABLE I: Aqueous Systems (*continued*)

System	References
n-Hexylamine–Salts	19
Hydrazine–Sodium hydroxide	180 (p. 837)
Hydrazine monohydrochloride–	
Ethyl alcohol	220
Hydrochloric acid (see	
Hydrogen chloride)	
Hydrogen–Butyl alcohol	296
Benzene or Isoamyl alcohol	296A
Hydrogen bromide–Bromine	
(island curve)	50A
(two separate binodal curves)	428, 602 (p. 207)
n-Butyl alcohol (two separate curves)	175, Fig. 105
tert-Butyl alcohol (reversibly ternary	
system)	197, Figs. 102–104
Dioxane (island curve)	169, 240
n-Heptane (band solutrope)	200 (p. 202)
Hydrogen cyanide	176
Isoamyl alcohol (two separate binodal	
curves)	169, 175, 180 (p. 1018)
Isobutyl alcohol (two separate binodal	
curves)	169, 180 (p. 997)
Phenol	154
Sulfur dioxide	275, (p. 403)
Tributyl phosphate	325
Hydrogen chloride–Benzene	50A, 180 (p. 1022), 651
Benzyl alcohol and other substances	59A
2-Butanone (MEK) (two separate	
binodal curves)	175
n-Butyl alcohol (two separate binodal	
curves)	175, 180 (p. 994), Fig. 105
m-Cresol	603 (p. 548)
Cuprous chloride–Alkylamides–Olefins	203
Cyclohexanone	268A, 602 (p. 574)
2,6-Dimethyl-4-heptanone	
(Di-isobutyl ketone)	508
Dioxane (island curve and separate	
curve)	175, 180 (p. 991), 240, 333, 565, Fig. 89
Ethyl ether	4, 175, 180 (p. 1002), 216, 476
Gallium chloride–Seven Ethers	74
Germanium chloride	44, 463
3-Heptanone	508

(*continued*)

TABLE I: Aqueous Systems (*continued*)

System	References
Hydrogen chloride (*continued*)	
n-Hexyl alcohol (band solutrope and iso-optics)	175, Fig. 36
Hydrogen cyanide (island curve and separate curve)	176, Fig. 88
Indium chloride	74
Isoamyl alcohol (two separate curves)	169, 175, 180 (pp. 1018)
Isobutyl alcohol (two separate curves)	169, 180 (p. 997)
Isopropyl ether	89, 169, 699
4-Methyl-2-pentanone	403, 508
Nitrobenzene	602 (p. 575)
5-Nonanone	508
32 Organic solvents	116, 600
Phenol (isopycnic)	154, 163, 180 (p. 1025)
Hydrogen cyanide–Benzene	176
Hydrogen bromide	176
Hydrogen chloride (island curve and separate curve)	176, Fig. 88
Hydrogen fluoride–	
4-Methyl-2-pentanone	508
Hydrogen iodide–Isobutyl alcohol	180 (p. 997)
Isoamyl alcohol	180 (p. 1018)
Hydrogen peroxide–19 Liquids	602 (pp. 590–591)
n-Butyl alcohol	154
Hydrogen sulfide–Sodium chloride (iso-optic)	171
Hydroquinone (Quinol)–Phenol	180 (p. 1026)
Indium chloride–Hydrogen chloride–Seven Ethers	74
Iodine-17 liquids	180 (p. 836)
Carbon disulfide	90
Isoamyl acetate–Acetic acid	180 (pp. 891–892)
Ethyl alcohol	180 (pp. 908, 930–931)
Furfural (isopycnic)	163, 180 (p. 1010)
Phenol	469B
Isoamyl alcohol–Acetic acid	507
Nine acids and 15 Salts (distribution)	180 (p. 1018)
tert-Amyl alcohol	353
Chlorides of aluminum, cadmium, calcium, cobalt, iron, lead, nickel, and zinc	221

continued)

TABLE I: Aqueous Systems (*continued*)

System	References
Isoamyl alcohol (*continued*)	
Chloroacetic acid	180 (p. 882)
Citric acid	180 (p. 1018)
Cobalt compounds	474
Diacetyl cellulose acetate	128
Ethyl alcohol	15, 78A, 180 (p. 908, 917)
Hydrogen	296A
Hydrogen bromide (two separate binodal curves)	168, 175, 180 (p. 1018)
Hydrogen chloride (two separate binodal curves)	169, 175, 180 (p. 1018)
Hydrogen iodide	180 (p. 1018)
Isobutyl alcohol	180 (p. 999)
Isocaproic acid	180 (p. 895)
Isopropyl alcohol	25
Isovaleric acid	180 (pp. 1015–1018)
Methanol	180 (p. 863)
50 Organic compounds	108
Perchloric acid	59A
Pertechnetic acid	694A
n-Propyl alcohol	180 (p. 965)
15 Salts (distribution or salting out)	180 (p. 1018)
Thorium nitrate–Ammonium thiocyanate	99A
Trichloroacetic acid (isopycnic)	180 (p. 876)
Triethylamine	607, 786
Isoamyl bromide–Ethyl alcohol	180 (p. 915)
Isoamyl ether–Ethyl alcohol	180 (p. 939)
Isobutane–Ammonia or Benzene (iso-optic)	171
Isobutene–Sodium chloride (iso-optic)	171
Isobutyl alcohol–Acetone	180 (p. 950), 205B
Acetone–Tetrachloroethane	205B
Benzene	180 (pp. 999–1000, 1023)
Carbon disulfide (isopycnic)	180 (p. 847)
Chloroacetic acid	180 (p. 882)
Ethyl acetate	61, 180 (p. 985)
Ethyl alcohol	78A, 180 (pp. 912–913)
Ethylene glycol	382
Ethyl ether	180 (p. 999), 205B
Hydrogen bromide, chloride (two separate curves)	169, 180 (p. 997)
Hydrogen iodide	180 (p. 997)

(*continued*)

TABLE I: Aqueous Systems (*continued*)

System	References
Isobutyl alcohol (*continued*)	
Isoamyl alcohol	180 (p. 999)
Methanol	180 (p. 861), 637
Phenol	668
Picric acid	90
Sodium chloride	180 (p. 998), 205B
148 Substances	107, 180 (p. 999)
Tetrachloroethane (isopycnic)	163, 180 (p. 879), 205B
Isobutyl bromide–Ethyl alcohol	180 (p. 912)
Isobutyraldehyde–Ethylene glycol	583
Isobutyric acid–Aminopyrine	776
sec-Butyl alcohol	415
Carbon tetrachloride (isopycnic, solutrope)	163, 180 (p. 842)
Phenol	368A, 767
Potassium isobutyrate	180 (p. 990)
Sodium chloride	180 (p. 990)
Iso-octane (2,2,4-Trimethylpentane)– Aniline	616
Ethyl alcohol	180 (p. 936), 482
Methanol	81, 622
Phosphate esters in Carbon tetrachloride or Kerosine–Uranium salts	255
Pyridine	775
Isopentane–Ethyl alcohol	180 (p. 916)
Isophoron–Acetic or Lactic acids	180 (pp. 891–892, 901)
Isopropoxyethanol–Potassium chloride	689
Isopropyl alcohol–salts	133, 180 (p. 969)
Aniline (isopycnic)	163, 180 (p. 970), 450
Benzene (solutrope)	45A, 61, 180 (pp. 970, 1023), 281, 450, 636, 659
n-Butyl alcohol	180 (p. 995)
Butyltoluene (isopycnic)	180 (p. 974), 450
Cadmium sulfate	50, 509
Carbon dioxide	173
Carbon disulfide	180 (p. 846), 393
Carbon tetrachloride	180 (p. 842), 300, 393, 422A, 658
Chlorobenzene	423
Chloroform (solutrope)	177, 180 (p. 852), 201 (p. 447), 300, 393, Fig. 33
Cottonseed oil (isopycnic)	163, 180 (p. 974), 246

(*continued*)

TABLE I: Aqueous Systems (*continued*)

System	References
Isopropyl alcohol (*continued*)	
Cottonseed oil–Oleic acid	246
Cyclohexane or Cyclohexene (solutrope)	180 (pp. 970–971), 636
Ethyl acetate	61, 180 (p. 985)
Ethylbenzene	179 (p. 262)
Ethylene chloride	299, 493, Fig. 35
Ethyl ether	451
Glycerol-Six Freons	314
n-Hexane	179 (p. 257), 180 (pp. 971–972), 246
Isoamyl alcohol	25
Isopropyl ether (solutrope)	72, 180 (pp. 972–973), 354, 636
Isopropyl ether–Sulfuric acid	197, Fig. 109
Lithium sulfate	50, 509
Nitromethane	180 (p. 859), 336
Oleic acid–Cottonseed oil or Hexane	246
Phenol	575, 576
Phenyl ether	180 (p. 940), 523
Potassium chloride	45A, 689
Propane	81B
Propylene	179 (p. 256), 180 (p. 944)
Salts	133, 180 (p. 969)
Sodium hydroxide	444
Sodium sulfate	445
Tall oil–Naphtha	100B
Tetrachloroethylene	180 (p. 873)
Toluene (solutrope)	180 (p. 973), 450, 636, 657
o-Toluidine (isopycnic)	163, 180 (p. 974), 450
Xylene (isopycnic)	180 (p. 974), 450
Isopropyl ether–Acetic acid	180 (pp. 891–892, 896, 901), 655, 661
Formic acid	655
Furfural	656
Hydrogen chloride (two separate curves)	89, 169, 699
Isopropyl alcohol (solutrope)	72, 180 (pp. 972–973), 354, 636
Isopropyl alcohol–Sulfuric acid	197, Fig. 109
Propionic acid	655
Isovaleric acid–Carbon tetrachloride (isopycnic)	163, 180 (p. 843)
Benzene, Ethyl bromide, Isobutyl or Isoamyl alcohol, Nitrobenzene, o-Nitrotoluene, Toluene, or Xylene	180 (pp. 1015–1016)

(*continued*)

TABLE I: Aqueous Systems (*continued*)

System	References
Kerosine–Acetone	628
Ethyl alcohol (isopycnic)	163, 180 (p. 940), 215
Ethyl alcohol–2-Butanone	215
Nicotine	33, 180 (p. 1056), 266A
Kollidone (polymer of Vinylpyrrol-	
idone)–Acetone	180 (p. 1037)
Lactic acid–Aniline	180 (p. 962), 603 (p. 414)
n-Butyl alcohol	506
57 Organic compounds (distribution)	180 (pp. 900–901, 962)
o-Toluidine	603 (p. 195)
Lanthanum nitrate–Tributyl	
phosphate–Nitric acid	612
Levulinic acid–4-Methyl-2-pentanone	530A
Lithium chloride–Dioxane	333
Ethyl ether	4
Lithium hydroxide–Acetone or	
Dioxane	132, 230, 386
Lithium nitrate–Trioctylamine in	
Benzene	7
Lithium sulfate–Isopropyl alcohol	50, 509
2,6-Lutidine–Sodium hydroxide	661A
Magnesium bromide–Ethyl ether	570A
Magnesium perchlorate–	
Diacetylcellulose	128
Magnesium or Manganese	
sulfates	180 (p. 906)
Malonic acid–Four solvents	604 (p. 603)
Maltose–Acetone	180 (p. 957)
Manganous chloride–Ammonium	
chloride	102
Mannite–Butyric acid, Succinonitrile,	
or Triethylamine	683
Mercuric cyanide	34
Mesitylene–Ethyl alcohol (isopycnic)	163, 180 (p. 937)
Methanol (isopycnic)	163, 180 (p. 872), 393
Mesityl oxide–Acetic acid	180 (pp. 888, 900)
Metal chelates of $XOCH_2COCF$–	
Benzene	87
Metal chlorides–Isoamyl alcohol	
or Octanoic acid	221
Metal sulfates–Butyl alcohol–	
Sulfuric acid	589
Methanethiol (Methyl mercaptan)–	
Sodium chloride or Sucrose (iso-optic)	171

(*continued*)

TABLE I: Aqueous Systems (*continued*)

System	References
Methanol–Ammonium sulfate	46
Amyl acetate	541
Amyl alcohol	180 (p. 862)
Aniline	164, 180 (p. 866), 393
Aniline–Benzene	164, 201 (p. 440), Figs. 117, 122, 123
Aromatics–Paraffins	331
Benzene (isopycnic)	163, 164, 180 (p. 865), 393, 450, 451, 732
Benzene–Cyclohexane, Cyclohexene Heptane, or Hexane	337, 389, 391
Bromobenzene	180 (p. 863)
n-Butyl acetate	541, 604 (p. 579), 653
n-Butyl alcohol–Hydrocarbons	180 (p. 861), 271, 281, 442
p-tert-Butylphenol–Methylnaphthalene or Cetane	180 (p. 1116), 520
Butyltoluene (isopycnic)	163, 180 (p. 872), 450
Carbon dioxide	173
Carbon disulfide	180 (p. 844), 393
Carbon tetrachloride	180 (p. 838), 393
Chlorobenzene	180 (p. 863), 625
Chloroform	180 (p. 849), 393
m- or p-Cresols–Ligroin	551
o- and p-Cresols	180 (p. 869)
p-Cresol–Cetane–Methylnaphthalene	180 (p. 866), 520, Fig. 116
Cyclohexane	180 (pp. 866–867), 389, 391, 622
Cyclohexene	180 (p. 866), 389, 391
Ethyl acetate	61, 180 (pp. 861–862), 653
Ethyl bromide	180 (p. 860)
Ethyl butyrate	541
Ethylene chloride	46, 301, 493, 628A
Ethyl ether	180 (p. 862), 451, 452, 653, 732
Ethyl formate	451
Ethyl propionate	541
Gasoline-Benzene	180 (p. 1072), Fig. 115
Glycerol–Six Freons	314
n-Heptane	389, 391, 622
n-Hexane	180 (p. 867), 389, 391, 622, 652
n-Hexyl alcohol	346
Seven Hydrocarbons	180 (p. 867)
Isoamyl alcohol	180 (p. 863)
Isobutyl alcohol	180 (p. 861), 637
Iso-octane	81, 622

(*continued*)

TABLE I: Aqueous Systems (*continued*)

System	References
Methanol (*continued*)	
Mesitylene (isopycnic)	163, 180 (p. 872), 393
Methyl cellulose–Phenol	128
Methyl acetate	112, 336
Methyl benzoate	180 (p. 870)
Methylcyclohexane	622
Three Methylcyclohexanols	180 (p. 870), 393
Methyl methacrylate	180 (p. 862)
1-Methylnaphthalene–Cetane or Iso-octane	180 (p. 872)
Methyl *p*-toluate	249
Methyl *p*-toluate–*p*-Xylene	248
2-Naphthol–Methylnaphthalene or *n*-Hexadecane (Cetane)	180 (p. 1116), 520
Nitrobenzene	180 (p. 863), 393
o- and *p*-Nitrophenol	180 (p. 864)
o-Nitrotoluene	180 (p. 868), 393
n-Octane	622
sec-Octyl alcohol	346
Oleic acid–Ground Nut oil	727
Oleic acid–Triolein (Olive oil)	555
Paraffins	60, 337
n-Pentane or Pentenes	179 (p. 258), 180 (p. 862),
Phenol	180 (p. 866), 520
27 Phenols	675
Phenol–*p*-Cresol–Iso-octane or 1-Methylnaphthalene	520
Phenyl ether	523
Poly(vinyl acetate)	319
Potassium carbonate or sulfantimonate	180 (p. 860), Fig. 51
Propylene (iso-optic)	171
Styrene	180 (pp. 868–870), 450
Tall oil–Naphtha	100B
Toluene (isopycnic)	163, 180 (p. 868), 393, 450
o-Toluidine (isopycnic above 24.5°C)	163, 180 (p. 869), 393
m-Toluidine (isopycnic)	163, 180 (p. 869), 450
Trichloroethylene	345, 567
2,2,4-Trimethylpentane (Iso-octane)	81, 622
Triolein (Olive oil)	555
Triptane	622
Three Xylenes (isopycnics)	163, 180 (p. 871), 393, 450
m-Xylidine (isopycnic)	163, 180 (p. 871), 450

(*continued*)

TABLE I: Aqueous Systems (*continued*)

System	References
Methoxyethanol (Methyl	
Cellosolve)–Cellulose acetate	254
Methyl acetate–Acetic acid	467
Acetone	728
Chloroform	401
Deuterium oxide	525
Ethylene glycol	584
Methanol	112, 336
Methylacetylene (Propyne)–	
Sodium chloride (iso-optic)	171
Methylaniline–Ethyl alcohol	
(isopycnic)	163, 180 (p. 929)
Methyl benzoate–Methanol	180 (p. 870)
Methyl bromide–Sucrose (iso-optic)	171
1-Methyl-2-butene–Aniline or	
Nitrobenzene–Hexane	683
Methyl *tert*-butyl ketone (3,3-	
Dimethyl-2-butanone)–Acetone	180 (p. 954)
Methyl *n*-butyrate–	
Ethyl alcohol	180 (pp. 908, 914)
Methylcellulose–Phenol	128
Methyl chloride–Sodium chloride	
(iso-optic)	171
Methylcyclohexane–Aniline	
(three layers)	180 (p. 1035)
Ethyl alcohol	180 (p. 930)
Methanol	622
Phenol	180 (p. 1030)
Three Methylcyclohexanols–	
Methanol	180 (p. 870), 393
Methylcyclohexanone–	
Acetic acid	180 (pp. 891–892)
Picrolonic acid–Strontium and yttrium	
compounds	471
Methylene chloride–Acetic acid	95
ε-Caprolactam	375
Ethyl alcohol	266
Vinylpyrrolidone	180 (p. 1037)
Methyl esters of castor oil–	
Furfural or Nitromethane–*n*-Hexane	380
Methyl ether–Benzene (iso-optic)	171

(*continued*)

TABLE I: Aqueous Systems (*continued*)

System	References
Methyl ethyl ketone (see 2-Butanone)	
Methyl iodide–Caproic acid (isopycnic)	163, 180 (p. 1039)
Chloroacetic acids	180 (p. 859)
Methyl isobutyl carbinol (see 4-Methyl-2-pentanol)	
Methyl isobutyl ketone (see 4-Methyl-2-pentanone)	
Methyl isovalerate–Ethyl alcohol	180 (p. 923)
Methyl methacrylate–Methanol	180 (p. 862)
1-Methylnaphthalene–*p*-Cresol, Phenol, 2-Naphthol, Butylphenol	180 (pp. 1032, 1046, 1116), 520, Fig. 116
4-Methyl-2-pentanol–C₁ to C₄	
Acids	535
Adipic acid	530
4-Methyl-2-pentanone (Methyl isobutyl ketone)–Acetic acid	36, 180 (pp. 891–894, 900)
Acetone	180 (p. 953)
Acetic and Sulfuric acids	403
Adipic acid	530
Butyric acid	36
Ethylene glycol	584
Formic acid	36, 403, 735, 750
Furfural (isopycnic)	110, 163
Hexoic acid	36
Hydrochloric acid	403, 508
Hydrogen fluoride	508
Inorganic nitrates	474
Nitrates of copper, thorium, uranium	742
Pertechnitic acid	694A
Phenol	469B
Propionic acid	36, 245
Propylene glycol	125A
Sulfuric acid	245, 403, 750
Uranyl nitrate	149, 742
Valeric acid	36
Methyl propionate–Ethyl alcohol	180 (p. 908)
Methyl pyridine (see 2-Picoline)	
Methyl salicylate–Ethyl alcohol (isopycnic)	163, 180 (p. 932)
Methylstyrene–Phenol	85, 613
Methyl *p*-toluate–Methanol	249
p-Xylene	248

(*continued*)

TABLE I: Aqueous Systems (*continued*)

System	References
Methyl vinyl carbinol acetate–Butene glycol	180 (pp. 1006–1007)
Methyl vinyl ether– Sodium chloride (iso-optic)	171
Morpholin–Benzene	665
Mustard gas (2,2′-Dichloroethyl sulfide)–Acetone	267
Naphthalene–Acetone	180 (p. 957), 200 (p. 208), Fig. 50
Butyric acid, Phenol, Succinonitrile, or Triethylamine	683
Ten Organic compounds	180 (p. 1055)
Phenol	34, 429, 683
2-Naphthol–1-Methylnaphthalene	180 (p. 1116), 520
Nickel chloride–Capryl alcohol	212
Octanoic acid or Isoamyl alcohol	221
Nickel sulfate–Butyl alcohol– Sulfuric acid	589
Nickel thiocyanate–Amyl alcohol	553
Nicotine–Acetone	394
2-Butanone	88
Carbon tetrachloride	158, 159
Hexadecyltrimethylammonium bromide	385
Kerosine	33, 266A
Kerosine or Lube oil	180 (p. 1056)
Petroleum and Vegetable oils	604 (p. 724)
Six Salts	21, 385
Soaps	385
Sodium hydroxide	290
Sulfuric acid	158, 159, Fig. 55
Trichloroethylene (solutrope)	180 (p. 875)
Nitric acid–Amyl or Butyl alcohols, 2-Butanone, or Ethyl ether	90, 602 (p. 583)
Benzene, Cyclohexanone, 4-Methyl-2-pentanone	157
Butyl alcohol–Nitrates of cobalt or nickel	587
Butyl ether	157, 719, 722
Diethylene glycol dibutyl ether	715
Dinitroglycerol	180 (p. 963)
Di-*n*-octylamine in *o*-Xylene	441
Ethyl ether	90
Ethyl ether–Nitrates of rare earths	63, 644
Nitrogen dioxide	745
Propyl ether or Ethyl propyl ether	419A
Thenoyltrifluoroacetone–Benzene	573

(*continued*)

TABLE I: Aqueous Systems (*continued*)

System	References
Nitric acid (*continued*)	
Tributyl phosphate–Salts of 74 elements	270, 295, 324, 476A, 574, 598, 612
Tributyl phosphate–Nitrates of calcium, thorium, or uranium	308
Tridecyl- or Trinonylamine	718
Uranyl nitrate	48A, 718
Nitrobenzene–Acetic acid	180 (pp. 889, 901)
Aniline	284, 604 (p. 650), 642
Aniline–*n*-Hexane (three layers)	478
Caproic acid (isopycnic)	163, 180 (p. 1039)
ε-Caprolactam	677
Chloroacetic acid (isopycnic)	163, 180 (p. 883)
Dichloroacetic acid (solutrope)	180 (p. 880)
Ethyl alcohol	180 (p. 918)
Formic acid	180 (p. 856)
n-Heptane	631
Hydrogen chloride	602 (p. 575)
Isovaleric acid (isopycnic)	163, 180 (p. 1016)
Methanol	180 (p. 863), 393
Sulfuric acid (isopycnic)	163, 180 (p. 1020)
Trichloroacetic acid	180 (p. 876)
Trimethylethylene	683
m-Nitrobenzoic acid–Phenylacetic acid	368A, 767
Nitrocellulose–Acetone	180 (p. 1073)
Nitrogen dioxide–Nitric acid	745
Nitromethane–Acetic acid	633
Benzene–*n*-Heptane	172
Carbon disulfide or Hexane	683
Deuterium oxide	525
Isopropyl alcohol	180 (p. 859), 336
Methyl esters of Castor oil–*n*-Hexane	380
Nitrates of copper, thorium, or uranium	742
n-Propyl alcohol	180 (p. 859)
Nitrophenols–Ethyl alcohol	180 (pp. 918–919), Fig. 53
Methanol	180 (p. 864)
o-Nitrotoluene–Acetic acid	180 (pp. 896, 901)
Chloroacetic acid (isopycnic)	163, 180 (p. 883)
Dichloroacetic acid (solutrope)	180 (p. 880)
Ethyl alcohol	180 (p. 927)
Formic acid (isopycnic)	163, 180 (p. 858)

(*continued*)

TABLE I: Aqueous Systems (*continued*)

System	References
o-Nitrotoluene (*continued*)	
Isovaleric acid (isopycnic)	163, 180 (pp. 1015–1016)
Methanol	180 (p. 868), 393
Nitrous oxide–Carbon tetrachloride	
(iso-optic)	171
5-Nonanone–Hydrogen chloride	508
Nonyl alcohol–Triethylamine	609
n-Octane–Methanol	622
Octanoic acid–Chlorides of	
aluminum, cadmium, calcium, cobalt,	
copper, iron, lead, nickel, zinc	221
1-Octene–Ethyl alcohol–Iso-octane	482
Octyl acetate–Acetic acid	180 (pp. 891–892)
n-Octyl alcohol–Acetone	
(solutrope)	534
Octyl alcohol–50 Organic	
compounds	108
sec-Octyl alcohol–Ethyl alcohol	347
Methanol	346
Olefins–Silver nitrate	123, 180 (p. 943), 186, 190, Figs. 47, 48
Oleic acid–Acetic acid–Five Vegetable	
oils	737
2-Chloroethanol	153A
Ethyl alcohol	180 (pp. 940, 1081), 639
Isopropyl alcohol–Cottonseed oil	246
Methanol–Ground Nut oil	727
2-Picoline	154
Triolein–95% Ethyl alcohol	180 (p. 1081), 555, 603 (p. 150)
Triolein–Methanol (90% and 95%)	555
Oleyl alcohol–50 Organic	
compounds	108
Olive oil (see Triolein)	
Oxalic acid–Phenol (island curve)	180 (p. 881), 709
Palmitic acid–Sodium palmitate	419
Paraffins–Methanol	60, 337
Silver nitrate	123
Pentachloroethane–Phenol	
(solutrope)	603 (p. 386)
n-Pentane–Acetone	451
Ethyl alcohol	180 (p. 916), 451, 452
Methanol	179 (p. 258), 180 (p. 862), 451

(*continued*)

TABLE I: Aqueous Systems (*continued*)

System	References
2-Pentanone and other solvents–	
Fumaric or Succinic acid	604 (pp. 617, 619)
3-Pentanone–Ethyl alcohol	180 (p. 914)
Pentenes–Phenol	179 (pp. 245, 253), 180 (pp. 1015, 1093), 200 (p. 208)
Pentyl acetate–Fatty acids	344C
Perchloric acid–Benzene	624
Ethyl ether	180 (p. 1003)
Isoamyl alcohol	59A
Pertechnitic acid–Isoamyl	
alcohol or 4-Methyl-2-pentanone	694A
Petroleum ether–Acetic acid	452
Acetic anhydride	180 (p. 979), 452
Acetone	452
Ethyl alcohol (isopycnic)	180 (p. 916), 451, 452
Phenetole–Ethyl alcohol (isopycnic)	163, 180 (p. 935)
Phenol (binary system)	Figs. 7, 13
Phenol–Acetic acid	180 (p. 890), 234, 709
Acetone (island curve, isopycnic)	163, 180 (p. 952), 702, 733, Fig. 91
Acetophenone, CCl_4, $CHCl_3$, Polymers	128
Ammonium thiocyanate	431
n-Amyl alcohol (isopycnic)	163, 180 (p. 1017)
Aniline (isopycnic above 77°C)	163, 180 (p. 1027)
Aniline–Ethyl alcohol	710
Anthranilic acid (two separate curves)	364
Anthraquinone	34,683
Antipyrene (island curve)	363
Azobenzene	34, 683
Benzene (isopycnic)	90, 163, 180 (p. 1023), 262, 663, 785
Benzene–Heptane or Gasoline	26
Benzene–Decalin, Hexane, or Paraffin oil	667
1,2,4-Benzenetriol	16A
Benzil	34, 683
Benzoic acid	34, 429, 683
Benzophenone	34, 683
Boric acid	34, 683
2-Butanone (MEK)	86
n-Butyl acetate	469A, 566, 597, 785
Camphor	34, 170, 603 (p. 389), 683
Carbon dioxide	173
Carbon disulfide (solutrope)	180 (p. 848), 275 (p. 428)

(*continued*)

TABLE I: Aqueous Systems (*continued*)

System	References
Phenol (*continued*)	
Carbon tetrachloride (solutrope)	603 (p. 386)
Catechol	180 (p. 1026)
Cetyltrimethylammonium bromide (island and separate curve)	519
Chloroform	603 (p. 386)
Cobalt salts	343
o-Cresol	321A, 603 (p. 375)
DDT (Dichlorodiphenyltrichloroethane)	592
Decalin	667
Deuterium oxide	91, 525, 603 (p. 375)
Dichloroacetic acid	180 (p. 877)
Epichlorohydrin	429
Ethyl alcohol	180 (p. 922), 710
Formic acid	180 (p. 857), 234
Gasoline (three layers)	26, 180 (p. 1031)
Glycerol (solutrope)	120, 180 (p. 976), 424, Fig. 19
n-Heptane (three layers)	26, 180 (p. 1030), 480
Hexamethylmellitic acid	683
n-Hexane (three layers, col at 89°C)	180 (p. 1029), 434, 200 (p. 208), 479, 667, Fig. 81
Hexane–Sulfur	434, 435E, 439
Hydrogen bromide	154
Hydrogen chloride (isopycnic)	154, 163, 180 (p. 1025)
Isoamyl acetate	469B
Isobutyl alcohol	668
Isobutyric acid	368A, 767
Isopropyl alcohol	575, 576
Malonic acid	603 (p. 375)
Mercuric cyanide	34
Methanol	180 (p. 866), 520
Methylcellulose	128
Methylcyclohexane (three layers)	180 (p. 1030)
1-Methylnaphthalene	180 (pp. 1032, 1116), 520
4-Methyl-2-pentanone	469B
Methylstyrene	85, 613
Naphthalene (three layers)	34, 429, 683
11 Organic compounds (distribution)	180 (p. 1025)
Oxalic acid (island curve)	180 (p. 881), 709
Pentachloroethane (solutrope)	603 (p. 386)
n-Pentane–Pentanes (three layers)	179 (pp. 245, 253), 180 (pp. 1015, 1093), 200 (p. 208)
m-Phenylenediamine (island curve)	180 (p. 1028)

(*continued*)

TABLE I: Aqueous Systems (*continued*)

System	References
Phenol (*continued*)	
Phenylhydrazine	180 (p. 1028)
Phloroglucinol	16
Phosphoric acid (isopycnic) (triangular island from 68–100°C)	163, 180 (p. 1026), 350, 709
Phosphorous acid (isopycnic) (triangular island above 68°C)	163, 180 (p. 1026)
Picric acid	180 (p. 1019), 709
Piperidine	180 (p. 1016), 430
Polyacrylamide, Poly(vinyl pyrrolidinone) and other polymers	128
Pyridine (island curve)	180 (p. 1012), 435D, 470
Pyrogallol	34, 180 (p. 1026)
Quinol or Resorcinol	180 (p. 1026)
Quinoline	361
Quinone	603 (p. 375)
Salicylic acid (two separate metastable curves)	34, 35, 180 (p. 1030), 364, 683
34 Salts	34, 94, 153A, 180 (p. 1025), 242, 431, 494, 603 (p. 375), Fig. 13
Soap	43
Sodium hydroxide	398
Sodium oleate	34, 180 (p. 1032), 504, 683
Sodium oleate–Toluene	34, 755
Succinic acid	34, 603 (p. 375), 683
Sulfur (col at 71°C)	470, 479, Fig. 66
Sulfur–n-Hexane (four layers at 96°C)	434, 439
Sulfuric acid (island curve)	621, 709
Tartaric acid (isopycnic)	180 (p. 980), 683
Tetrachloroethane or Tetrachloroethylene	603 (p. 386)
Thorium nitrate	67
Thymol (isopycnic)	163, 180 (p. 1032)
Toluene (isopycnic)	55, 163, 180 (p. 1030), 603 (p. 386), 667
Trichloroacetic acid	180 (p. 877), 709
Trichloroethylene (solutrope)	603 (p. 386)
Triethylamine (isopycnic)	163, 180 (p. 1029), 416, 649
Triethylene glycol (solutrope)	120
Uranium salts	67
Urea	604 (p. 582)
Xylene (isopycnic)	163, 180 (p. 1031), 603 (p. 386)

(*continued*)

TABLE I: Aqueous Systems (*continued*)

System	References
Phenols–Ammonia	286
Glycerol or Triethylene glycol	120
Phenylacetic acid–Ether	604 (p. 701)
m-Nitrobenzoic acid	368A, 767
m-Phenylenediamine–Phenol (island curve)	180 (p. 1028)
Resorcinol (island curve)	772
Phenyl ether–Five Alcohols, Three Acids	523
Phenylhydrazine–Aniline	
Benzylamine, Piperidine, or Pyridine	437
Phenol	180 (p. 1028)
Succinonitrile	368A, 767
Phloroglucinol–Phenol	16
Phosphate esters in Carbon tetrachloride–Uranium or Thorium salts	255
Phosphomolybdic acid–Ethyl ether	644
Phosphoric acid–Ethyl ether–Nitric acid	180 (p. 1003)
Phenol (isopycnic) (triangular island from 68 to 100° C)	163, 180 (p. 1026), 350, 709
27 Organic solvents	600
Phosphorous acid–Phenol (isopycnic, island curve)	163, 180 (p. 1026)
2-Picoline–Benzene, Di-isobutene, n-Heptane, or Methylcyclopentane	98
Sodium chloride	153A
Sodium hydroxide	289
Other Salts	20, 153A
Picric acid–Benzene, Isobutyl alcohol	90
Phenol	180 (p. 1019), 709
Salicylic acid	352
Picrolonic acid–Strontium and Yttrium complexes–Methylcyclohexane	471
Pinacolin (3,3-Dimethyl-2-butanone)–Acetone	180 (pp. 954, 1039)
Pinene–Ethyl alcohol (isopycnic)	163, 180 (p. 939)
Piperidine–Acetic anhydride	127
Aniline	437, 603 (p. 307)
Benzene	435C
Phenol	180 (p. 1016), 430
Phenylhydrazine	437

(*continued*)

TABLE I: Aqueous Systems (*continued*)

System	References
Plutonium nitrate–Benzene or Trifluoroacetylacetone	111, 624A
Phosphorus compounds in carbon tetrachloride	82
Polyacrylamide–Phenol	128
Poly(methacrylic acid)–*n*-Butyl alcohol	705
Poly(vinyl acetate)–Acetone or Methanol	319, 469
Poly(vinylpyrrolidinone)–Acetic anhydride, Amyl alcohol, or Phenol	128
Acrylic acid	472
Potassium carbonate or hydroxide–Ammonia	180 (p. 836)
Potassium carbonate or chloride–Alkylamines	19
Potassium carbonate or fluoride–Allyl alcohol	689
2-Butanone	180 (p. 984)
Dioxane	604 (p. 272)
Ethyl alcohol	180 (pp. 904–905)
Ethylene glycol	604 (p. 272)
Potassium ethyldipropyl maleate	180 (p. 1058)
n-Propyl or isopropyl alcohol	133, 180 (pp. 963, 969)
Potassium citrate–Ethyl alcohol	180 (pp. 919, 1021)
Potassium hydroxide–Acetone or Dioxane or Pyridine	132, 180 (p. 945), 230, 386
Ethyl alcohol	180 (p. 905), 604 (p. 312)
Triethylamine	288
Potassium isobutyrate–Isobutyric acid	180 (p. 990)
Potassium nitrate–Thallium nitrate	90
Potassium perrhenate–Tributyl phosphate or Tri-isooctylamine	324
Potassium sulfoantimonate–Ethyl alcohol	180 (p. 905)
Methanol	180 (p. 860)
Praseodymium nitrate–Tributyl phosphate	612
Propadiene (Allene)–Sodium chloride (iso-optic)	171

(*continued*)

TABLE I: Aqueous Systems (*continued*)

System	References
Propane–Benzene or Carbon disulfide	
(iso-optic)	171
Butane or Carbon disulfide (iso-optic)	171
Furfural	239
Hydrogen fluoride	604 (p. 222)
Isopropyl alcohol	81B
Propanol (see *n*-Propyl alcohol)	
Propionic acid–Amyl acetate	344C
Aniline (isopycnic)	163, 180 (p. 960)
Benzene (double solutrope, plait point	
near top)	54, 180 (p. 960), 344, 348, 349, 377, 396, 536
2-Butanone	396
n-Butyl acetate	531
Carbon disulfide	180 (p. 845), 393
Carbon tetrachloride	180 (p. 841), 306, 393
Chlorobenzene	349
Chloroform (solutrope)	180 (p. 851), 393
Cyclohexane	536
Cyclohexene	536
Decalin	180 (p. 962)
Diethylaniline or Dimethylaniline	14
Ethyl acetate	344, 396, 532, 758
Ethyl benzoate	533
Ethyl bromide	603 (p. 188)
Ethyl butyrate	532
Ethyl ether	344, 531
Ethyl propionate	532
Furfural	252
n-Hexane	536
n-Hexyl alcohol	96A
Isopropyl ether	655
4-Methyl-2-pentanol	535
4-Methyl-2-pentanone	36, 245
25 Organic liquids (distribution)	180 (pp. 608, 959)
Phenyl ether	523
Tetrachloroethylene	536
Toluene (solutrope)	180 (p. 961), 348, 536
o-Toluidine (double isopycnic)	163, 177, 180 (p. 961), Fig. 40
m-Toluidine (isopycnic)	180 (pp. 961–962)
Trichloroethylene	349
Xylene	180 (p. 962), 348

(*continued*)

TABLE I: Aqueous Systems (*continued*)

System	References
Propoxyethanol–Potassium chloride or fluoride	689
n-Propyl acetate–Acetic acid	467
Acetone	728
Ethyl alcohol	180 (pp. 908, 914)
Formic acid	540
n-Propyl alcohol	180 (p. 964), 542, 634, Fig. 22
n-Propyl alcohol salts	180 (p. 964)
Acetone–Salts	133
Ammonium sulfate	180 (p. 963)
Amyl acetate	542
n-Amyl alcohol	180 (p. 964)
Aniline	180 (p. 966)
Benzene	61, 180 (pp. 966, 1023), 407
Bromobenzene (isopycnic, solutrope)	180 (p. 965)
o-Bromotoluene	180 (p. 967)
n-Butyl acetate	542
n-Butyl alcohol	180 (p. 995)
Carbon disulfide (isopycnic)	163, 180 (p. 846), 393
Carbon tetrachloride (isopycnic)	163, 180 (p. 841), 393, 422A
Chlorobenzene	423
Chloroform (isopycnic, solutrope)	163, 180 (p. 852), 393
Cyclohexane	180 (p. 967), 200 (p. 201), 636, Fig. 29
Ethyl acetate	61, 180 (p. 985)
Ethyl alcohol	78A
Ethyl bromide	180 (p. 902)
Ethyl butyrate	542
Ethylene	143
Ethyl ether	451, 452
Ethyl propionate	542
n-Heptane	407
Hexamethyldisiloxane	100
n-Hexane	407
Isoamyl alcohol	180 (p. 965)
Nitromethane	180 (p. 859), 336
Phenyl ether	523
Potassium carbonate or fluoride	133, 180 (p. 963)
n-Propyl acetate	180 (p. 964), 542, 634, Fig. 22
n-Propyl ether	354

(*continued*)

TABLE I: Aqueous Systems (*continued*)

System	References
n-Propyl alcohol (*continued*)	
Sodium carbonate or chloride	133, 180 (p. 964)
Twelve other Salts	683
Toluene	37, 180 (p. 968)
o-Toluidine	180 (p. 974), 450
Xylene	180 (p. 968)
n-Propylamine–Salts–Propylamine	19
Sodium hydroxide	293
Propyl bromide–Ethyl alcohol	180 (p. 909)
Propyl butyrate–Ethyl alcohol	180 (pp. 908, 931)
Propylene–Acetic acid	179 (p. 256), 180 (p. 886)
Ammonia or Benzene (iso-optics)	171
Cuprous chloride–Alkylamides	203
Furfural	239
Isopropyl alcohol	179 (p. 256), 180 (p. 944)
Methanol (iso-optic)	171
Silver nitrate	123, 180 (p. 943), 186, 190, Figs. 46, 47
Silver nitrate–Hexane	123
Propylene glycol–Alcohols, Esters, Ketones	125A
Ethyl alcohol–Benzene, Hexane, or Cyclohexane	125
n-Propyl ether–Nitric acid	419A
n-Propyl alcohol	354
Propyl formate–Ethyl alcohol	180 (p. 908)
Formic acid	559
Propyl propionate–Ethyl alcohol	180 (pp. 908, 924)
Propyne (Methylacetylene)–Sodium chloride (iso-optic)	171
Pseudoephedrine–Benzene–Sodium chloride or hydroxide	562
Pyramidone (see Aminopyrine)	
Pyridine–Ammonium sulfate	264
Aniline	180 (p. 1012), 437
Anthranilic acid (island curve)	180 (p. 1013), 762
Benzene (solutrope)	90, 180 (pp. 1011–1012), 267, 529, 625, 643, 739, 740, Fig. 34
Benzoic acid (island curve)	180 (p. 1013), 354, 761
Carbon disulfide	180 (p. 847), 267, 393

(*continued*)

TABLE I: Aqueous Systems (*continued*)

System	References
Pyridine (*continued*)	
Carbon tetrachloride (solutrope)	180 (p. 843), 267, 393, 421, 527
Chloral hydrate (island curve)	772
Chlorobenzene (solutrope)	499
Chloroform	180 (p. 853), 393
Cuprous chloride–Amides–	
Hydrogen chloride–Olefins	203
2,2′-Dichloroethyl sulfide (Mustard gas)	267
Hexane–Sulfur	435D
Iso-octane	774
Lithium, Potassium, or Sodium	
hydroxides	132, 386
Phenol (island curve)	180 (p. 1012), 435D, 470
Phenylhydrazine or Piperidine	437
Eight Salts	20, 683
Sodium formate	126A
Sodium hydroxide	292, 661A
Sodium mercuric iodide and acids	59A
Sulfur	435D, 470, 591
Sulfuric acid (liquid–liquid and solid–	
liquid curves)	180 (p. 1011), Fig. 54
Toluene or Xylene (solutropes)	180 (pp. 1012–1013), 393, 480A, 739
Quinine iodobismuthate–Acetone	180 (p. 957)
Quinol (Hydroquinone)–Phenol	180 (p. 1026)
Quinoline–Aniline or Ethyl ether	370
Phenol	361
8-Quinolinol–Benzene, Chloroform,	
Carbon tetrachloride, Dichloroethane,	
Toluene	759
Quinone–Phenol	603 (p. 375)
Rare earth nitrates–Nitric acid–	
Ethyl ether	63
Resorcinol–Antipyrine or	
m-Phenylenediamine (island curves)	772
Benzene or Butyl acetate	785
Phenol	180 (p. 1026)
Salicylic acid–Acetone	736
Aminopyridine (Pyramidone) (island	
curve and separate binodal curve)	358
Anthranilic acid (three liquid phases,	
metastable; two separate curves)	371
Antipyrine	355, 358

(*continued*)

TABLE I: Aqueous Systems (*continued*)

System	References
Salicylic acid (*continued*)	
Benzoic acid	372
Dioxane	180 (p. 993)
Ethyl alcohol	369
Furfural–Metal nitrates	105
Gasoline (three liquid phases)	360
Phenol (two separate metastable curves)	34, 35, 180 (p. 1030), 364, 683
Picric acid	352
Pyramidone (island curve)	358
Silica–Sodium hydroxide	700
Silicomolybdic acid–Ethyl ether	644
Silver cyanide–*n*-Trioctylamine in	
Kerosine	385A
Silver nitrate–Olefins or Paraffins	123, 180 (p. 943), 186, 190, **Figs.** 46, 47
Ethylbenzene–Styrene	202
Succinonitrile	683
Silver perchlorate–Benzene	258
Toluene	260
Soap–Hexane	406
Nicotine or Triethylamine	385
Phenol	43
Sodium caprylate–Decyl alcohol	138B
Sodium carbonate or	
chloride–Alkylamines	19, 293
n-Propyl alcohol	133, 180 (p. 964)
Sodium chloride or iodide–	
Liquefied gases (iso-optics)	171
Sodium chloride–Alkylamines	19, 293
Benzene–Acetic acid	241, 562
2-Butanone	180 (p. 984)
Butyric or Isobutyric acids	180 (pp. 987, 990), 749
Diethylamine	294
Dioxane	45, 47
Hexamethyleneimine	782
Isobutyl alcohol	180 (p. 998), 205B
2-Picoline	153A
Sodium laurate or palmitate	404, 405
Sodium dodecyl sulfate	385
Sodium formate–Pyridine	126A
Sodium hydroxide–Acetone	132, 180 (p. 947), 230, 386
Alkylamines	293
Ammonia	180 (p. 837)

(*continued*)

TABLE I: Aqueous Systems (*continued*)

System	References
Sodium hydroxide (*continued*)	
Butyl- or Heptylamine	291
Cresols	392, 741
Dibutylamine	293
Diethylamine	287
Dioxane	132, 230, 386
Dipropylamine	293
Ethylenediamine	753
Hexamethyleneimine	782
Hydrazine	180 (p. 837)
Isobutyl alcohol	180 (p. 998), 205B
Isopropyl alcohol	444
2,6-Lutidine	661A
Nicotine	290
Phenol	398
2-Picoline	289
Pyridine	292, 661A
Pyridine–Sulfur	591
Silica	700
Triethylamine	288
Sodium laurate–Sodium chloride	404
Sodium mercuric iodide–	
Pyridine	59A
Sodium nitrate–Dioxane	47, 180 (p. 992)
Sodium oleate–Three Cresols	34, 180 (p. 1045)
Phenol	34, 180 (p. 1032), 504, 683
Phenol–Toluene	34, 755
40 Solvents	515
Sodium palmitate or stearate–	
40 Solvents	405, 515
Sodium sulfate–Acetic acid–	
Isopropyl ether	661
Diethylamine	294
Ethyl alcohol	180 (p. 994)
Isopropyl alcohol	445
Triethylamine	787
Sodium sulfonates–Glycol ethers	96
Sodium thiocyanate–*n*-Butyl	
alcohol	180 (p. 994)
Sodium thiosulfate–Ethyl alcohol	48, 180 (p. 907)
Solvent oil–Acetone	345
Stannic acid–Benzene	219A
Strontium complexes–	
Picrolinic acid	471

(*continued*)

TABLE I: Aqueous Systems (*continued*)

System	References
Styrene–Acrylonitrile	180 (p. 942)
Diacetone alcohol	117
Ethoxyethylene	374
Ethylbenzene–Silver nitrate	202
Methanol	180 (p. 870), 450
Succinic acid–Cyclopentanone	52
Phenol	34, 603 (p. 375), 683
Succinonitrile–Azobenzene, Benzene, Benzil, *sec*-Butanol, or Camphor	683
Carbon dioxide (three layers)	173
Carbon disulfide	683
Ethyl alcohol (two separate binodal curves)	180 (p. 909), 595, Fig. 59
Ethyl ether (three layers)	180 (p. 977), 436, 594, 683
Hexane, Mannite, Naphthalene, Phenylhydrazine, two Salts, or Triethylamine	683
Phenylhydrazine	368A, 767
Sucrose–Acetone	180 (p. 957)
Butyric acid, Succinonitrile, or Triethylamine	683
Sulfolane–Benzene–*n*-Heptane (three layers)	247
Sulfonic acids (aromatic)– Sulfuric acid–Xylenes	650
Sulfur–Aniline	439, 480, 683
Aniline–Hexane (four layers)	439
Benzene, Benzyl chloride, or Hexane	683
Phenol	470, 479, Fig. 66
Phenol–Hexane (four layers)	434, 439
Phenol–Pyridine	470
Pyridine–Sodium hydroxide	591
Sulfur dioxide	84A
Ethylene glycol–Hydrocarbons	196
Hydrogen bromide	275 (p. 403)
Sulfur hexafluoride– hydrocarbons (iso-optics)	171
Sulfuric acid–Aromatic sulfonic acids–Xylenes	650
Butyl acetate–Gallium chloride	340
Butyl alcohol–Sulfates of Cobalt, Iron, or Nickel	589

(*continued*)

System	References
Sulfuric acid (*continued*)	
Cobalt, Iron or Nickel sulfates–23	
Organic liquids	589
Cyclohexanone	268A
Di-isoamylmethylphosphonate	647
Dioxane	333
Ethylbenzylaniline sulfate	447A
Ethyl ether	180 (p. 1003), 681, Fig. 101
Isopropyl alcohol–Isopropyl ether	197, Fig. 109
4-Methyl-2-pentanone	245, 403, 750
Nicotine	159, Fig. 55
Nitrobenzene (isopycnic)	163, 180 (p. 1020)
Phenol (island curve)	621, 709
Pyridine	180 (p. 1011), Fig. 54
Tetrachloroethylene	681, Fig. 111
Tributyl phosphate	71A
Uranium nitrate	48A
Tall oil–Naphtha–Isopropyl alcohol	
or Methanol	100B
Tartaric acid–Phenol (isopycnic)	163, 180 (p. 980), 683
Tetrabutylethylene	
diphosphate in kerosine–	
Nitrates of cerium, europium–	
promethium, thorium, uranium,	
yttrium, zirconium	579
1,1,2,2-Tetrachloroethane–	
Acetone or Isobutyl alcohol (isopycnic)	163, 180 (pp. 878–879), 205B
Phenol	603 (p. 386)
Tetrachloroethylene–Acetone	539, 603 (p. 181)
Ether–Sulfuric acid	681, Fig. 111
Iodine	602 (p. 668)
Isopropyl alcohol	180 (p. 873)
Phenol	603 (p. 386)
Propionic acid	536
Tetrahydrofurfuryl	
alcohol–Salts	545
Tetralin–Furfural or Acetic acid	552, 554
Tetramethylammonium iodide–	
Triethylamine	607
Thenoyltrifluoroacetone–	
Benzene–Nitric acid	573
Thallium nitrate–Potassium	
nitrate	90

(*continued*)

TABLE I: Aqueous Systems (*continued*)

System	References
Thiocyanic acid–Cyclohexanone	268A
Thiodiacetic acid–2-Butanone	
(three layers)	180 (p. 980)
Thorium nitrate–Phenol	67
Ammonium thiocyanate–Cyclohexanol,	
Ethyl acetate, or Isoamyl alcohol	99A
Tributyl phosphate–Nitric acid	83, 147, 255, 502, 598
Other Organic liquids	475, 742
Thymol–Phenol (isopycnic)	163, 180 (p. 1032)
Toluene–Acetaldehyde	180 (p. 885), 489
Acetic acid	31, 97, 180 (p. 897), 200 (p. 199) 253, 281, 489, 558, 564, 691
Acetic acid–n-Heptane	180 (p. 1077), 489, Figs. 112, 113
Acetone	180 (p. 954)
Seven Alcohols	180 (p. 1045)
Aniline (isopycnic)	163, 180 (p. 1034)
n-Butyl alcohol	180 (p. 997)
Butyric acid	348, 393
Caproic acid	180 (p. 1039)
Carvacrol	603 (p. 675)
Chloroacetic acid	180 (p. 882)
m-Cresol	603 (p. 550)
Dichloroacetic acid	180 (p. 880)
Diethylamine	180 (p. 1008), 208
Epichlorohydrin	429
Ethyl alcohol (isopycnic)	31, 97, 163, 180 (pp. 927–928), 450, 451, 452
Ethyl isovalerate	97
Furfural (isopycnic)	163, 180 (p. 1010)
Isoamyl alcohol	180 (pp. 1015–1016)
Isopropyl alcohol (solutrope)	180 (p. 973), 450, 636, 657
Methanol (isopycnic)	163, 180 (p. 868), 393, 450
59 Organic substances (distribution)	180 (p. 1044)
Phenol (isopycnic)	55, 163, 180 (p. 1030), 603 (p. 386), 667
Phenol–Sodium oleate	34, 755
Propionic acid	180 (p. 961), 348, 536
n-Propyl alcohol	37, 180 (p. 968)
Pyridine (solutrope)	180 (p. 1012), 393, 480A, 739
8-Quinolinol	759
Silver perchlorate	260
Trichloroacetic acid	180 (p. 876)
Xylenol	603 (p. 607)

(*continued*)

TABLE I: Aqueous Systems (*continued*)

System	References
o- and *p*-Toluene sulfonamide	81A
o-Toluidine–Acetic acid (isopycnic)	
("closed curve")	10, 163, 180 (p. 897), 603 (pp. 555–557)
Aniline	353
Butyric acid (isopycnic)	12, 163, 180 (p. 989)
Ethyl alcohol (isopycnic above 24.5°C)	163, 180 (p. 929), 450
Isopropyl alcohol (isopycnic)	163, 180 (p. 974), 450
Lactic acid	603 (p. 195)
Methanol (isopycnic above 24.5°C)	163, 180 (p. 869), 393
Propionic acid (double isopycnic)	163, 177, 180 (p. 961), Fig. 40
m-Toluidine	
Acetic acid ("closed curve") (isopycnic below 7°C)	163, 180 (p. 898)
n-Butyric acid	180 (p. 989)
Methanol (isopycnic)	163, 180 (p. 869), 450
Propionic acid	180 (pp. 961–962)
Triacetin–Acetic acid	180 (pp. 891–892)
Trialkylphosphine oxides–	
Uranium and Vanadium salts	57
Tributyl phosphate–Benzene	624
Cerium nitrate	476A
Cobalt chloride	716
Furfural	247A
Germanium chloride	44, 463
Hydrogen bromide	325
Hydrogen chloride	18A
Nitrates of calcium, thorium, or uranium	308, 598
Nitric acid–Nitrates of lanthanum or praseodymium	270, 612
74 Nitrates of Elements	295
Potassium perrhenate	324
Sulfuric acid	71A
Thorium nitrate	83, 147, 255, 502, 598
Uranium salts	58, 151, 298, 476A, 574, 598, 623, 719
Trichloroacetic acid–Amyl	163, 180 (p. 876)
alcohols (isopycnic)	163, 180 (p. 876)
Benzyl alcohol, Chloroform, Cumene, Ethyl bromide, Nitrobenzene, *o*-Nitrotoluene, or Toluene (two isopycnics)	180 (p. 876)
n-Butyl alcohol or *m*-Cresol	231

(*continued*)

TABLE I: Aqueous Systems (*continued*)

System	References
Trichloroacetic acid (*continued*)	
Carbon tetrachloride	180 (p. 838)
Methyl iodide	180 (p. 859)
Phenol	180 (p. 877), 709
1,1,2-Trichloroethane–Acetone	180 (p. 881), 281
2-Butanone (isopycnic)	163, 180 (p. 982)
Trichloroethylene–Acetic acid	345, 580
Acetone (solutrope)	180 (p. 875), 636
Acetonitrile (solutrope)	180 (p. 874), 636
Allyl alcohol	180 (p. 875), 244
2-Butanone (isopycnic)	163, 180 (p. 982)
Butyric acid	348
ϵ-Caprolactam (+ Ammonium sulfate)	315, 677
Ethyl alcohol	180 (p. 874), 424A
Methanol	345, 567
Nicotine (solutrope)	180 (p. 875)
Phenol (solutrope)	603 (p. 386)
Propionic acid	349
Tridecylamine–Uranyl nitrate–	
Nitric acid	718
Triethylamine–Aminopyrine	765
Azobenzene, Benzil, or Camphor	683
Benzene	310
Deuterium oxide	341, 630
Ethyl alcohol	180 (p. 926)
Ethylene glycol	583
Ethyl ether	354
n-Heptane	631
Hexadecyltrimethylammonium bromide	385
Isoamyl alcohol	607, 786
Mannite or Naphthalene	683
n-Nonyl alcohol	609
Phenol (isopycnic)	163, 180 (p. 1029), 416, 649
Potassium hydroxide	288
Pyramidone (Aminopyrine)	765
16 Salts	334, 385
Five Salts, Succinonitrile, or Sucrose	683
Soaps	385
Sodium dodecyl sulfate	385
Sodium hydroxide	288
Sodium sulfate	787
Twelve Substances	180 (p. 1041)
Tetramethylammonium iodide	607

(*continued*)

TABLE I: Aqueous Systems (*continued*)

System	References
Triethylene glycol–Benzene,	
Toluene, or Ethylbenzene–*n*-Heptane	238, 549
n-Butyl alcohol	420
Phenols (solutropes)	120
Triethylene glycol dimethyl ether–	
Benzene	465
Trifluoroacetyl acetone–	
Benzene–Plutonium nitrate	111
Tri-isooctylamine–Potassium	
perrhenate	324
Trimethylamine–Benzene	
(solutrope)	310
Trimethylethylene	683
2,2,4-Trimethylpentane (Iso-	
octane)–Aniline	616
2-Butanone (MEK)	180 (p. 983)
Ethyl alcohol	180 (p. 936), 482
Methanol	81, 622
Trinonylamine–Uranyl nitrate	718
Trioctylamine salts in Benzene–	
Nitrates of Cerium, Lithium, or	
Praseodymium	7
Uranium salts	6
Trioctylamine in kerosine–	
Gold or Silver cyanide	385A
Tri-olein (olive oil)–Oleic acid–	
Ethyl alcohol	180 (p. 940), 543, 555
Methanol	555
79 Organic substances (distribution)	180 (p. 1062)
Triptane–Methanol	622
Uranium acetate–Phenol	67
Uranium chloride–Hydrogen	
chloride–Tributyl phosphate in	
Kerosine (three layers)	298
Uranium salts–Dibutyl phosphate	476A, 624A, 647A, 678
Dodecyl phosphoric acid	568
Uranyl chloride–Tributyl	
phosphate	719
Hydrogen fluoride–Chlorine	
Uranyl fluoride–trifluoride	577

(*continued*)

TABLE I: Aqueous Systems (*continued*)

System	References
Uranyl nitrate–Butyl ether	207, 723
Cyclohexanone	39
Ethyl ether	77, 376, 454, 644, 742
Hexyl ether or 2-Hexanone	318
4-Methyl-2-pentanone	149, 742
Other Organic solvents	229, 318, 742
Sulfuric acid	48A
Trialkylphosphine oxides	57
Tributyl phosphates in Amyl acetate or alcohol, Benzene, or Carbon tetrachloride	82, 255, 476A, 574, 623
Tributyl phosphate–Cyclohexane or Hexane	150
Tridecyl or Trinonylamine–Nitric acid	718
Trioctylamine sulfate	6
Uranyl sulfate–Amines	76
Phenol	67
Sulfuric acid, Cupric oxide, Nickel oxide	309A, 417A
Urea–Acetic acid–*n*-Decane, 2,3-Dimethyloctane, *n*-Octadecane, or *n*-Octane	189
Cuprous chloride–Hydrogen chloride–Olefins	203
Ethyl acetate	180 (p. 873)
Phenol	604 (p. 582)
Valeric acid–Carbon tetrachloride (isopycnic)	163, 180 (p. 843)
4-Methyl-2-pentanone	36
Vanadium salts–Trialkylphosphine oxides	57
Vegetable oils–Acetic acid	737
Chloroethanol or Chloroform	153A
Ethyl alcohol	153A, 180 (p. 938), 543
Nicotine	604 (p. 724)
2-Picoline	153A
Vinyl acetate–Acetaldehyde (solutrope)	516, 636
Acetaldehyde–Acetone	68
Acetic acid	180 (p. 887)
Acetone	180 (p. 949), 516

(*continued*)

TABLE I: Aqueous Systems (*continued*)

System	References
Vinyl bromide–Ethylene glycol or	
Sucrose (iso-optics)	171
Vinyl chloride–Sodium chloride	
(iso-optic)	171
Vinylidine chloride–Ethyl alcohol	180 (p. 878)
Vinylpyrrolidone–Ethyl acetate,	
Ethyl ether, or Methylene chloride	180 (p. 1037)
Whale oil–Dialkylfluorophosphates	483
Xylenes–Acetic acid	180 (p. 899, 901), 691
Acetone	180 (p. 956)
Ammonia	521
Benzilic acid	90
Butyric acid	348, 393
Ethyl alcohol (isopycnic)	163, 180 (pp. 933–934), 450–452
Formic acid	180 (p. 858)
Isopropyl alcohol (isopycnic)	163, 180 (p. 974), 450
Methanol (isopycnic)	163, 180 (p. 871), 393, 450
Methanol–Methyl-*p*-toluate	248
60 Organic compounds (distribution)	180 (pp. 1050–1051)
Phenol (isopycnic)	163, 180 (p. 1031), 603 (p. 386)
Propionic acid	180 (p. 962), 348
n-Propyl alcohol	180 (p. 968)
Pyridine (solutrope)	180 (p. 1013), 393, 739
Sulfuric acid–Aromatic sulfonic acids .	650
Xylenol–Capryl alcohol or Toluene	603 (p. 607)
m-Xylidine–Methanol (isopycnic)	163, 180 (p. 871), 450
Yttrium complexes–Picrolonic acid	471
Zinc chloride or sulfate–Furfural	213
Zinc sulfate–Acetone	180 (p. 948)
Ammonia	180 (p. 837)

TABLE II
Nonaqueous Systems Separating into Two Liquid Phases
(Hydrocarbons usually omitted as primary solvent, upper case)

System	References
ABIETIC ACID–Oleic acid–Propane	180 (pp. 1087–1088)
ACETALDEHYDE–Acetone–Vinyl acetate	68
ACETAMIDE–Cuprous chloride–Propylene or	
Propane	203
ACETIC ACID–Aniline–Iso-octane	
(two island curves)	777, Fig. 94
Aniline–Benzene–Gasoline	64
Aniline–Cyclohexane (island curve)	180 (p. 1099)
Aniline–Gasoline (100–125°C) (island curve)	180 (p. 1076), 770
Chloroform–Glycerol	275 (p. 434)
Chloroform–Lube oil	69
Dimethylaniline–Benzene–Gasoline	512
Dimethylaniline–Gasoline	
(island curve below 41.7°C)	180 (p. 1076), 771
Glycerol–Benzene	180 (p. 1075), 625
n-Heptane–o-Toluidine	175, Fig. 96
Hydrogen bromide–Benzene, n-Heptane,	
1-Methyl-naphthalene, or m-Xylene	
(island curve)	175
2,6-Lutidine–Decane	778
Methylaniline–Benzene–Gasoline	
(island curves)	512, 771
Methylaniline–n-Heptane or Gasoline	
(island curve)	180 (pp. 826, 1076), 200
	(p. 211), 201 (p. 445),
	Fig. 92
Nitrobenzene–n-Heptane (two separate binodal	
curves)	169
Oleic acid–Peanut oil	725
Pyridine–n-Octane (island curve)	779
Toluene–n-Heptane (homogeneous when	
anhydrous, see Table I)	179 (p. 251), 180 (p. 1077),
	489, Figs. 112, 113
o-Toluidine–n-Heptane	175 (Fig. 96)
Vegetable oils–Oleic acid	737
ACETIC ANHYDRIDE–Acetic acid–Carbon	
disulfide	180 (p. 847), 448
Acetic acid–Gasoline, Cyclohexane, or Decanes	180 (pp. 979, 1076)
Acetone–Glycerol	180 (p. 1086), 511
Acetone–Hexane or Petroleum ether	451, 452

(*continued*)

System	References
ACETIC ANHYDRIDE (*continued*)	
Decalin–Nine aromatics	13
Hydrogen bromide–*m*-Xylene	175
Toluene–*n*-Heptane	179 (p. 267), 180 (p. 1105)
Triptane–Other paraffins	185
Xylene–Gasoline	179 (p. 268), 180 (p. 1107)
ACETONE–Acetaldehyde–Vinyl acetate	68
Acetic anhydride–Glycerol	180 (p. 1086), 511
Acetic anhydride–Hexane or Petroleum ether	451, 452
Benzene–Formamide	714
Butyl alcohol–Ethyl alcohol	646A
Butyl alcohol–Polymethylmethacrylate	303
Carbon tetrachloride–Formamide	713
Ethyl acetate–Triolein	556
Ethyl alcohol–Triolein	498
Ethylene glycol–Benzene, Bromobenzene, Chlorobenzene, C_4 Olefins, Toluene, Xylene	180 (pp. 1081–1083)
Ethylene glycol–Nitrobenzene (isopycnic)	163, 180 (pp. 1082–1083)
Ethylene glycol–Cyclohexane (solutrope) or four esters	538
Formamide–Benzene or Carbon tetrachloride	713, 714
Formamide–Chloroform or Toluene	59
Glycerol–26 Organic acids–7 Amines, or 11 Acid phthalates	180 (p. 1085)
Glycerol–Triolein (Olive oil)	556
Hydrogen bromide–Xylene or *n*-Decane (island curves)	175
Isobutyl alcohol–Tetrachloroethane	205B
Methanol–Gasoline	180 (p. 1072)
Olive oil	556
Oleic acid–Palmitic acid	627
Oleic acid–Stearic acid–Hexane	626
Perfluoroheptane–Hydroperfluoroheptane	133A
n-Propyl alcohol–Polymethylmethacrylate	303
Triolein–Ethyl alcohol	498
ACETONITRILE–Benzene–*n*-Heptane	199, 224, 247
Carbon disulfide–Aromatics–Lube oil	196B
n-Decyl alcohol–Ethylene glycol	174
Ethane–Ethylene	142, 143
Fluorocarbons–Benzene or Heptane	199
n-Heptane and Methylcyclohexane	148, 250

(*continued*)

TABLE II: Nonaqueous Systems (*continued*)

System	References
ACETONITRILE (*continued*)	
Lauryl alcohol–Ethylene glycol	174
2-Methyl-2-butene–*n*-Heptane	250
Methylcyclohexane–*n*-Heptane	250
Silicon tetrachloride	3
Silver nitrate–Olefins–Paraffins	190, 205, Fig. 48
Toluene–Methylcyclohexane	148, 250
Triptane–other Paraffins	185
ACETONYLACETONE–*n*-Heptane–	
Methylcyclohexane	148, 250
2-Methyl-2-butene–*n*-Pentane	250
Toluene–Methylcyclohexane	250
ACIDS (Fatty)–Methanol	
Grapeseed, Linseed, or Walnut oil	560
ADIPONITRILE–Decyl alcohol–Ethylene	
glycol	174
ALDOL–Gasoline–Xylene	179 (p. 268), 180 (p. 1107)
ALLYL ISOTHIOCYANATE–Sulfur–Methyl-	
or Dimethylaniline or *o*-Toluidine	180 (pp. 1066–1067), 763, Fig. 93
ALUMINUM BROMIDE–Hydrogen bromide–	
Benzene	139
ALUMINUM CHLORIDE–Hydrogen	
chloride–Acetone, Ether, Ethyl acetate,	
Isopropyl acetate, Isopropyl ether, Methyl	
ether, Nitrobenzene, or Sulfur dioxide–	
Butanes or Pentanes, Olefins	162, 184, 198
Ethylbenzene–Benzene	159B, 162, 201A
Organic oxygen compounds–Isoparaffins	184
Toluene or Mesitylene	398A
AMINOPYRINE–Salicylic acid–Gasoline	
(island curve)	366
AMMONIA–Benzene–Cyclohexane or Hexane	278
Benzene–Cetane	226, 399
Benzene, Toluene, or Xylene–Gasoline	697
Cyclohexane–*n*-Heptane	226, 399
Cyclohexane–*n*-Hexane	226, 283, 399
Di-isopropylbenzene or Isopropylbenzene–	
Cetane	226, 399
n-Hexane–Isobutane (iso-optic)	171
21 Hydrocarbons	279

(*continued*)

TABLE II: Nonaqueous Systems (*continued*)

System	References
AMMONIA (*continued*)	
Methylcyclohexane–*n*-Heptane, *n*-Hexane, or	
4-Methyl-1-cyclohexene	226, 399
1-Methylnaphthalene–Cetane	226, 399
1-Octene–*n*-Heptane or 1-Octane	226, 283, 284
Potassium–Potassium iodide	180 (p. 1066)
Propane	Fig. 3
Pyridine–*n*-Heptane	276
Sodium–Sodium iodide	180 (p. 1066)
Styrene–Ethylbenzene	278
Tar acid–neutral oil	286
Tetralin–Decalin	226, 285, 399
Thiophene–*n*-Heptane	280
Toluene–Cetane	226, 399
Toluene–*n*-Heptane	277, 281, 282, 285, 399
Toluene–Methylcyclohexane	148
2,2,3-Trimethylpentane–*trans*-	
1,2-Dimethylcyclohexane	226, 399
AMYL ACETATE–Acetone–Ethylene glycol	538
ANILINE–Acetic acid–Benzene–Gasoline	64
Acetic acid–Cyclohexane (island curve)	180 (p. 1099)
Acetic acid–Gasoline (island curve)	180 (p. 1076), 770
Acetic acid–Iso-octane (two island curves)	777, Fig. 94
Aromatic hydrocarbons–Cyclohexane,	
Methylcyclohexane, or Iso-octane	180 (pp. 1100–1102)
Aromatic hydrocarbons–Gasoline	697
Benzene or Heptane–Cetane–Cyclohexane	78, 180 (pp. 1097–1100, 1118)
Biphenyl–Cyclohexane, Iso-octane or	
Methylcyclohexane	180 (p. 1103)
Butyric acid–Cyclohexane	180 (p. 1099)
Carbon dioxide–Decalin or Lube oil	173, 200 (p. 212)
Carbon tetrachloride, Cetane–Formamide	163, 180 (p. 1070)
and Nitrobenzene (three layer isopycnic)	
Carbon tetrachloride, Chloroform or	
Ethylene chloride–Heptane or Iso-octane	493, 493A
Chlorobenzene or Chloroform–*n*-Heptane	492B
Cyclohexane–Cetane or Heptane	78, 180 (pp. 1097, 1098, 1118), 200 (p. 199), 224, 501
Cyclohexane–2-Heptene	Fig. 20, 492B
Cyclopentane–2,2-Dimethylbutane	180 (p. 1093)

(*continued*)

TABLE II: Nonaqueous Systems (*continued*)

System	References
ANILINE (*continued*)	
Dichloroethylene–Heptane	24
trans-1,2-Dimethylcyclohexane–	
2,2,3-Trimethylpentane	226, 746
Dioxane–Heptane or Iso-octane	492A
Diphenylthiourea–Sulfur	449
Ethylene glycol–Methylaniline or	
Dimethylaniline	119
Gasoline–Five Aromatic hydrocarbons	180 (p. 1099), 697
n-Heptane–*n*-Hexane	368A, 767
n-Heptane–Iso-octane	492A
n-Heptane–Methylcyclohexane	148, 180 (p. 1100), 250
n-Heptane–Methylcyclopentane	179 (p. 244), 225
n-Hexadecane–1-Hexadecene	Fig. 56
n-Hexane–Benzamide, Benzil,	
Diphenylthiourea, Urethane	130A
n-Hexane–Methylcyclopentane	180 (pp. 1098–1099), 501
264 Higher hydrocarbons (aniline points)	178 (Table II), 588
Iso-octane–Methylcyclohexane	746
Methanol–Benzene	164, Figs. 117, 122, 123
Methanol–Decalin (isopycnic and iso-optic)	163, 200 (p. 204), Fig. 41
Methanol–Methylcyclohexane (two separate	
curves)	169
2-Methyl-2-butene–*n*-Pentane	250
Methylcyclohexane–2,2,3-Trimethylpentane	226, 746
Naphthalene–Cyclohexane, Iso-octane, or	
Methylcyclohexane	180 (p. 1103), Figs. 49, 52
Nitrobenzene–*n*-Hexane	477
Phenol–Iso-octane	774
Phenol–Tridecane	648A
Phenyl isothiocyanate–Sulfur	449
Propionic acid–Cyclohexane	180 (p. 1099)
Toluene–Decane or Octadecane	514
Toluene–*n*-Heptane	1A (p. 19), 179 (p. 267), 180 (p. 1105), 224, 225, 492A
Toluene–*n*-Hexane	225
Toluene–Iso-octane	492A
Toluene–Methylcyclohexane	148, 250
Xylene–Gasoline	179 (p. 268), 180 (p. 1107)
o-**ANISIDINE**–Aromatic hydrocarbon–	
Cyclohexane, Methylcyclohexane, or	
Iso-octane	180 (pp. 1100–1103)

(*continued*)

TABLE II: Nonaqueous Systems (*continued*)

System	References
ANTIMONY CHLORIDE–Toluene–Petroleum	180 (p. 1106)
ANTIPYRINE–Benzoic acid–Ligroin	362
Chloral hydrate–Gasoline	366
Phenol–Ligroin	363
Salicylic acid–Ligroin	355
Urea–Sulfonal	180 (p. 1075)
BARIUM FLUORIDE–Barium oxide–	
Silicon fluoride–Silicon dioxide	484
BENZALDEHYDE–Furfural–Glycerol	353
Hydrogen bromide–*n*-Heptane	175
BENZAMIDE–Aniline–Hexane	130A
BENZIL–Aniline–Hexane	130A
BENZOIC ACID–Antipyrine–Ligroin	362
Nitrobenzene–Hexane	603 (pp. 359, 458)
BENZYL ALCOHOL–*n*-Heptane–Cyclohexane	
or Toluene	136A, 224, Fig. 37
Two Hydrocarbons	28
1,2-BIS(2-CYANOETHOXY)ETHANE–	
Benzene–Heptane	557
BROMOBENZENE–Acetone–Ethylene glycol	180 (pp. 1082, 1083)
BROMOFORM–Formic acid–Benzene	
(isopycnic, isologous tie lines)	29, 163, 180 (p. 1069), 200
	(p. 200), Fig. 26
2-BUTANONE (MEK)–Methanol–Polystyrene	620
Olive oil	556
n-BUTYL ALCOHOL–Hydrogen chloride–	
Cyclohexane or *n*-Heptane (island curves)	175
Glycerol or Glycol–*n*-Heptane	338
tert-BUTYL ALCOHOL–Hydrogen bromide–	
Cyclohexane, *n*-Heptane, or	
Methylcyclohexane (island curves)	175
BUTYL CELLULOSE–Carbon tetrachloride–	
Nitromethane	128
BUTYRIC ACID–Aniline–Cyclohexane	180 (p. 1099)
Nitrobenzene–Heptane	603 (pp. 359, 458)
CALCIUM FLUORIDE–Calcium oxide,	
Silicon fluoride, Silicon dioxide	484
CALCIUM NITRATE–Pyridine–Lube oil	182
CAMPHOR–Methanol–Vaseline oil	603 (p. 679)
Phosphoric or Sulfuric acid–Ligroin	603 (p. 679)
CARBITOL–Methylcyclohexane–Heptane	148
Toluene–Hydrogen chloride	175

(*continued*)

TABLE II: Nonaqueous Systems (*continued*)

System	References
CARBITOL (*continued*)	
Toluene–*n*-Heptane	179 (p. 267), 180 (p. 1105)
Triptane–Other Paraffins	185
Xylene–Gasoline	179 (p. 268), 180 (p. 1107)
CARBON DIOXIDE (454 ternary systems)	
(several examples of unusual types)	165, 173, 186, 188, 192, 200
	(pp. 211, 212) Figs. 82, 83
Crude oil	413
Lube oil–Another solvent	165, 188, 192, Figs. 84–87
Silver nitrate–Propylene	186
CARBON DISULFIDE–Acetonitrile–Lube oil	196B
Methanol–Aromatics–Jet fuel	196A
Methanol–Diphenylamine, Succinic acid,	
Urea, or five Salts	130A
Methanol–Oleic acid–Olive oil	113, 114, 419
CARBON TETRACHLORIDE–Acetone–	
Formamide	713
Aniline–Heptane	493
Aniline–Formamide–Nitrobenzene–Cetane	
(three layer isopycnic)	163
Aniline–Heptane or Iso-octane	493A
Butyl Cellulose–Nitromethane	128
Cyclohexane–Polystyrene	620
Ethyl alcohol–Glycerol	180 (p. 1068)
n-Heptane–Perfluorocyclo-octyl ether	
or Perfluoro–*n*-heptane	378
Methanol–Vaseline oil	603 (p. 5)
Nicotine–Sulfuric acid (isopycnic)	159
Nitromethane–Butyl Cellosolve	128
Nitric acid–Trioctylamine	615
Pairs of polyolefins or Silicone	5
Tri-*n*-octylamine–Mineral acids	53, 615
CASTOR OIL METHYL ESTERS–Furfural–	
Cyclohexane	316
CELLULOSE DIACETATE–Chloroform–	
Ethyl alcohol	126, 495
CELLULOSE TRIACETATE–	
Tetrachloroethane–Petroleum ether	460
CELLOSOLVE (2-Ethoxyethanol)–Hydrogen	
chloride–*n*-Heptane–Methylcyclohexane	175
CHLORAL HYDRATE–Gasoline–Antipyrine	366

(*continued*

TABLE II: Nonaqueous Systems (*continued*)

System	References
CHLOREX (2,2'-Dichloroethyl ether)–	
Nitrobenzene–*n*-Heptane or Iso-octane	169
CHLORINE TRIFLUORIDE–Fluorides of	
hydrogen and uranium	571
CHLOROBENZENE–Acetone–Ethylene glycol	180 (pp. 1082–1083)
Aniline–*n*-Heptane	492B
2-CHLOROETHANOL (Ethylene	
chlorohydrin)–Triptane–other Paraffins	185
15 Vegetable oils	153A
Xylene–Gasoline	179 (p. 268), 180 (p. 1107)
CHLOROFORM–Acetic acid–Glycerol	275 (p. 434)
Acetic acid–Lube oil	69
Acetone–Formamide	59
Aniline–Heptane	492B, 493
Aniline–*n*-Heptane or Iso-octane	493, 493A
Carbon tetrachloride–Hydrogen cyanide	176
Cellulose diacetate–Ethyl alcohol	126, 495
Glycerol–Acetic acid	275 (p. 434)
Glycerol–Isovaleric acid (isopycnic)	603 (p. 306)
Glycerol–Propionic acid	603 (p. 193)
15 Vegetable oils, Ethyl alcohol, Oleic acid	153A
CITRAL–Ethyl alcohol–Lemon oil	275 (p. 434)
COD LIVER OIL–Ethyl alcohol–Fatty acids	180 (p. 1081)
COTTONSEED OIL–Oleic acid–Propane	180 (p. 1087), 563
m- or *p*-CRESOLS–Methanol–Ligroin	551
CUPROUS ACETATE, Ammoniacal–	
Butadiene–Butenes	513
CUPROUS HYDROGEN CHLORIDE	
(CuHCl$_2$)–Ethanolamine and five Amides–	
Propylene	203
Methanol–Ethylene or Propylene–Propane	193, Fig. 110
CYANOETHYL ACETATE–Benzene–Heptane	180 (p. 1096)
CYCLOHEXANOL–Cyclohexanone, Glycerol,	
or Organic acid salts	632
Ethylcyclohexene–Polystyrene	620
n-DECYL ALCOHOL–Ethylene glycol,	
Acetonitrile, Adiponitrile, Nitroethane, or	
Nitromethane (three separate binodal	
curves)	174, Figs. 67–70
DIACETYLCELLULOSE–Chloroform–	
Isoamyl alcohol	128

(*continued*)

TABLE II: Nonaqueous Systems (*continued*)

System	References
DI(2-AMINOETHYL)AMINE–Benzene	
Cyclohexane	180 (p. 1095)
DICHLOROETHYLENE–Aniline–Heptane	24
2,2'-DICHLOROETHYL ETHER	
(CHLOREX)–Nitrobenzene–Heptane or	
Iso-octane	169
DIETHYLAMINE–Glycerol–*o*-Toluidine	353
DIETHYLENE GLYCOL–Benzene–Heptane	201 (p. 443), 238, 307, 557, 629
Cyclohexane, Cyclohexene–Heptane, Hexene	390
Ethylbenzene	629
Ethylbenzene–Styrene	66, Fig. 38
Tetrabromoethane–Di(2-ethylhexyl)phthalate	214
Thiophene–Benzene	197, Fig. 32
Toluene–Heptane	629
DIETHYLENE GLYCOL MONOETHYL	
ETHER (see Carbitol)	
DIETHYLENE GLYCOL MONOMETHYL	
ETHER (METHYL CARBITOL)–*n*-Butane	222, 250
Methylcyclohexane–*n*-Heptane	148, 250, 501
Methylcyclohexane–2-Methyl-2-butene	148, 222, 250
Toluene–Heptane	179 (p. 267), 180 (p. 1105)
Triptane and other Paraffins	185
Xylene–Gasoline	179 (p. 268), 180 (p. 1107)
DIETHYLFORMAMIDE–Formamide–Benzene	522, 712
DI(ETHYLHEXYL)PHTHALATE–Diethylene	
glycol–Tetrabromoethane	214
DIETHYL TARTRATE–Ethylene Bromide–	
Formamide	275 (p. 434)
DIHYDROXYMETHYLTETRA-	
HYDROFURANE–Toluene–Heptane or	
Methylcyclohexane	206
DI(METHOXYETHYL)PHTHALATE–	
Propylene glycol–Tributyrin	214
DIMETHYLACETAMIDE–Cuprous hydrogen	
fluoride–Propylene	203
DIMETHYLANILINE–Acetic acid–Benzene	512
Acetic acid–Gasoline	180 (p. 1076), 771
Allyl isothiocyanate–Sulfur	180 (pp. 1066, 1067), 763
Aniline–Ethylene glycol	119

(*continued*)

TABLE II: Nonaqueous Systems (*continued*)

System	References
DIMETHYLFORMAMIDE–Cyclohexane or	
Toluene–*n*-Heptane	136, 226, 519A
Aromatics–Paraffins (C$_6$ to C$_8$)	519A
DIMETHYLSULFOLANE–Six pairs of	
hydrocarbons	226, 746
Toluene–Petroleum	180 (p. 1106)
2,4-DIMETHYLTHIOCYCLOPENTANE-	
DIOXIDE–Methylcyclohexane–*n*-Heptane	148
DIOXANE–Aniline–Heptane or Iso-octane	492A
m-DINITROBENZENE–Nitrobenzene–Hexane	683
2,4-DINITROCHLOROBENZENE–Toluene–	
n-Heptane (at 55°C)	179 (p. 267), 180 (p. 1105)
DIPHENYLAMINE–Methanol–Carbon disulfide	130A
Resorcinol–Urea	180 (p. 1075)
Sulfur–Naphthylamine	351
Sulfur–Quinoline	359
DIPHENYLTHIOUREA–Aniline–Hexane	130A
Aniline–Sulfur	449
DIPROPYLENE GLYCOL–Benzene,	
Ethylbenzene, or Toluene–*n*-Heptane	549
Six DISULFIDES–Hydrogen fluoride–Heptane	180 (p. 1064)
ETHANE–Mineral oil	730
ETHANOLAMINE–Ethyl ether–Pyridine	180 (p. 1085), 625
ETHOXYETHANOL–Hydrogen chloride–	
Heptane or Methylcyclohexane	175
ETHYL ACETATE–Acetone–Glycol	538
Hydrogen bromide–*n*-Decane or Heptane	175
ETHYL ALCOHOL–Acetone–Triolein	498
Benzene–Lube oil (at 100 and 118°C)	179 (p. 250), 180 (p. 1080), 201 (p. 440), Fig. 114
Cellulose diacetate–Chloroform	126, 495
Citral–Lemon oil	275 (p. 434)
Cod or Hake liver oil–Fatty acids	180 (p. 1081)
Ethylene glycol–2-Heptanone–Benzene,	
Nitrobenzene, Toluene, or Xylene	180 (pp. 1078–1079), 200 (p. 199)
Freons–Paraffins	670
Gasoline–11 Solvents	180 (p. 1079)
Glycerol–Benzene	180 (p. 1079)
Glycerol–Carbon tetrachloride	180 (p. 1068)
Hydrogen bromide–Toluene or Heptane	175, Fig. 57
Oleic acid–Groundnut oil	726
Oleic acid–Olive oil (Triolein)	180 (p. 1081), 555, 563
Paraffin oil–Salts	180 (p. 1078)

(*continued*)

TABLE II: Nonaqueous Systems (*continued*)

System	References
ETHYL ALCOHOL (*continued*)	
Propylene glycol–Benzene, Cyclohexane, or Hexane	125
Soybean oil–Trichloroethylene	424B
Succinonitrile–Ethyl ether	438
Sulfuric acid–Ethyl ether	197, Fig. 108
ETHYL BUTYRATE–Acetone–Ethylene glycol	538
ETHYLENE–Acetonitrile–Ethane	142
ETHYLENE BROMIDE–Diethyl tartrate–Formamide	275 (p. 434)
ETHYLENE CARBONATE–Benzene–Heptane	32
ETHYLENE CHLORIDE–Aniline–Heptane or Iso-octane	493A
ETHYLENE CHLOROHYDRINE (see 2-Chloroethanol)	
ETHYLENEDIAMINE–Benzene, Cyclohexane, or Hexane	75
n-Heptane	415B
ETHYLENE DIFORMATE–Benzene, Cyclohexane, or Heptane	199
ETHYLENE GLYCOL–Acetone–Benzene–Bromobenzene, Chlorobenzene, Toluene, or Xylenes	180 (pp. 1081–1083)
Acetone–Cyclohexane (solutrope) or four Esters	538
Acetone–Nitrobenzene (isopycnic)	180 (pp. 1081–1083)
Aniline–Methylaniline or Dimethylaniline	119
Benzene–Cyclohexane, Cyclohexene, Hexane, or Heptane	390
Butyl alcohol–Heptane	338
Decyl alcohol–Acetonitrile, Adiponitrile, Nitroethane, or Nitromethane (three binodal curves)	174, Figs. 67–70
Ethyl alcohol–Benzene, 2-Heptanone, Nitrobenzene, Toluene, or Xylene	180 (pp. 1078–1079)
2-Ethylhexanol–Nitromethane (three separate curves)	197
Glycol ethers–Aromatic hydrocarbons	191
Isopropyl alcohol–C$_4$ olefins	180 (p. 1081)
Lauryl alcohol–Nitroethane or Nitromethane	174, 415A, Figs. 71–76
Methanol–12 Hydrocarbons	180 (p. 1071)
Methanol–Toluene–Skellysolve B	180 (p. 1117)
Sulfur dioxide–Benzene–Heptane	196

(*continued*)

TABLE II: Nonaqueous Systems (*continued*)

System	References
ETHYLENE GLYCOL MONOPHENYL	
ETHER–Methylcyclohexane–Heptane	148, 250
ETHYL ETHER–Chloroform–Starch triacetate	180 (p. 1073)
Ethanolamine–Pyridine	180 (p. 1085), 625
Ethyl alcohol–Sulfuric acid	197, Fig. 108
Ferric ammonium chloride	205A
Hydrogen chloride–Chlorides of antimony,	
indium, iron, and tin	458A
Mercuric iodide–Potassium iodide	180 (p. 1065)
Succinonitrile–Ethyl alcohol	438
Sulfuric acid–Tetrachloroethylene	
(isopycnic)	163, 180 (p. 1065), 681,
	Fig. 111
2-ETHYLHEXANOL–Ethylene glycol–	
Nitromethane	197
ETHYL PHTHALATE–Hexanes and Heptanes	443
ETHYL PROPIONATE–Acetone–Glycol	538
ETHYL SULFATE–Benzene or Toluene–	
Heptane	473
Freon 21 ($CHCl_2F$)	171
Oleum–Benzene	195
Sulfuric acid–Benzene–Heptane	194
Triptane–other Paraffins	185
FERRIC AMMONIUM CHLORIDE–Ethyl	
ether	205A
FLUORINE–Oxygen–Ozone	648B
FORMAMIDE–Acetone–Benzene or Carbon	
tetrachloride	713, 714
Acetone–Chloroform or Toluene	59
Diethylformamide–Benzene	522, 712
Diethyl tartrate–Ethylene bromide	275 (p. 434)
Nitrobenzene–Cetane (triple isopycnic with	
additions of aniline and Carbon	
tetrachloride)	163, 180 (p. 1070)
Nitrobenzene–Hexane (isopycnic)	163, 180 (p. 1070)
Sulfur dioxide–Benzene	196
FORMIC ACID–Bromoform–Benzene	
(isopycnic)	29, 163, 180 (p. 1069), 200
	(p. 200), Fig. 26
Six pairs of liquids	180 (p. 1070)
FREONS–Alcohols–Paraffins	670
Glycerol–Alcohols	314

(*continued*)

TABLE II: Nonaqueous Systems (*continued*)

System	References
FURFURAL–Aromatics–Paraffins	473, 526
Benzaldehyde–Glycerol	353
Benzene–Cyclohexane	680
Benzene–*n*-Heptane	180 (p. 1091)
Benzene–Iso-octane	323
Butadiene–Isobutene–Naphtha	180 (pp. 1091, 1117)
Butanes–Butenes	312, 409
Castor oil methyl esters–Cyclohexane	316
Cetane–Xylene	1, 224
Cumene–2,2,5-Trimethylhexane	526
Diphenylhexane–Docosane	73, 180 (p. 1092), 201 (p. 438), Fig. 14
Heptane–Cyclohexane	284, 501
Heptane–Hexane	380
Heptane–Methylcyclohexane	148, 250, 501
Hexane–Iso-octane	284, 501
264 higher Hydrocarbons	178 (Table II), 588
Lube oil	73, Fig. 14, 15
2-Methyl-2-butene–*n*-Pentane	250
Methyl oleate–Methyl stearate–Naphtha	114, 561
Oleic acid–Cyclohexane or Heptane	582
Oleic acid–Peanut oil	725
Toluene–Heptane or Methylcyclohexane	148, 210, 250
Toluene–Iso-octane	680
Xylenes–Gasoline	179 (p. 268), 180 (p. 1107)
FURFURYL ALCOHOL–Toluene–*n*-Heptane	179 (p. 267), 180 (p. 1105)
Xylene–Gasoline	179 (p. 268), 180 (p. 1107)
GLYCEROL–Acetic acid–Benzene	180 (p. 1075), 625
Acetic acid–Chloroform	275 (p. 434)
Acetic anhydride–Acetone	180 (p. 1086), 511
Acetone–26 Organic acids, seven Amines, or 11 Acid phthalates	180 (p. 1085)
Acetone–Triolein (Olive oil)	556
Benzaldehyde–Furfural	353
Butyl alcohol–Heptane	338
Chloroform–Acetic acid	275 (p. 434)
Chloroform–Propionic acid	603 (p. 193)
Chloroform–Isovaleric acids (isopycnic)	603 (p. 306)
Cyclohexanol–Cyclohexanone	632
Diethylaniline–*o*-Toluidine	353
Ethyl alcohol–Benzene	180 (p. 1079)
Ethyl alcohol–Carbon tetrachloride	180 (p. 1068)

(*continued*)

TABLE II: Nonaqueous Systems (*continued*)

System	References
GLYCEROL (*continued*)	
Five Freons–Methanol, Ethyl, or Isopropyl alcohol	314
Furfural–Benzaldehyde	353
Iodine–Carbon tetrachloride, Chloroform, Ether, Benzene	602 (p. 669)
Isoamyl alcohol–Poly(vinylpyrolidine)	128
Isovaleric acid–Chloroform, Nitrobenzene, or Toluene	603 (p. 306)
Nitrobenzene–Phenol–Petroleum	266A
Phenol–Acetophenone–Carbon tetrachloride, Chloroform, Polymers	128
Phenols–Hydrocarbons	120
GLYCOL (see Ethylene Glycol)	
GROUNDNUT OIL–Ethyl alcohol–Oleic acid	726
HEXYL SULFIDE–Heptane–Hydrogen fluoride	180 (p. 1064)
HYDROGEN BROMIDE–Acetic acid–Benzene, Heptane, Methylcyclohexane, 1-Methylnaphthalene, or Xylene (island curves)	175
Acetic anhydride–*m*-Xylene (island curves)	175
Acetone–Decane or *m*-Xylene (island curves)	175
Acetonitrile or Benzyl alcohol (reaction too fast for phase equilibriums)	175
Aluminum bromide–Benzene	139
Benzaldehyde–Heptane (island curves)	175
tert-Butyl alcohol–Heptane, Cyclohexane, or Methylcyclohexane (island curves)	175
Ethyl acetate–Decane or Heptane (island curves)	175
Ethyl alcohol–Toluene or Heptane (island curves)	175, Fig. 57
Methanol–Benzene, Toluene, or 1-Methylnaphthalene (island curves)	175
Propionic acid–Heptane (triangular island)	175, Fig. 95
HYDROGEN CHLORIDE–*n*-Butyl alcohol–Cyclohexane or *n*-Heptane (island curves)	175
Carbitol–Toluene (island curve)	175
Ethoxyethanol–*n*-Heptane or Methylcyclohexane (island curves)	175
Ethyl ether–Chlorides of antimony, indium, iron, and tin	458A
Isopropyl alcohol–Cyclohexane, 1-Decene, *n*-Heptane, or *m*-Xylene (island curves)	175
Methoxyethanol–Benzene (island curve)	175

(*continued*)

TABLE II: Nonaqueous Systems (*continued*)

System	References
HYDROGEN CYANIDE–Benzene–Carbon disulfide, Carbon tetrachloride, Cyclohexane, Decalin, *n*-Hexane, 1-Hexene, Ethylene glycol, Formic acid, 1-Methyl-naphthalene, 1-Octene, or Tetralin	176
Carbon tetrachloride–Acetonitrile, Aniline, Benzene, Chlorex, 2-Chloroethanol, Chloroform, *m*-Cresol, Dioxane, Furfural, Nitrobenzene, or Nitromethane	176
n-Hexane–Butyl or Decyl alcohol	176
Methanol–Perfluorodimethylcyclohexane	176
Propane–Propylene or Sulfur dioxide	176
p-Xylene–*sec*-Butylbenzene, *n*-Hexane, Lauryl alcohol, or *m*-Xylene	176
HYDROGEN FLUORIDE–Chlorine trifluoride–Uranium hexafluoride	577
n-Heptane with six Disulfides, eight Mer-captans, or Hexyl or Propyl sulfides	180 (p. 1064)
Propanes and Butanes	604 (p. 222)
2,2'-IMINODIPROPIONITRILE–Benzene–Cyclohexane	180 (p. 1095)
1-Methylnaphthalene–Dodecane	180 (p. 1109)
IODINE–Glycerol–Benzene, Carbon tetrachloride, Chloroform, Ether	602 (p. 669)
ISOAMYL ALCOHOL–Glycerol–Poly(vinyl-pyrrolidone)	128
ISOBUTANE–Ammonia–Hexane (iso-optic)	171
ISOBUTYL ALCOHOL–Acetone–Tetrachloro-ethane	205B
ISOPROPYL ACETATE–Sulfuric acid–Petroleum ether	179 (p. 266); 180 (p. 1065)
ISOPROPYL ALCOHOL–Hydrogen chloride–Cyclohexane, 1-Hexene, Heptane, or Xylene	175
Six Freons–Paraffins	670
Glycerol–five Freons	314
Glycol–C$_4$ Olefins	180 (p. 1081)
ISOVALERIC ACID–Chloroform–Glycerol (isopycnic)	603 (p. 306)
KETODIOXANE–Benzene–Heptane, Decalin, 1- or 2-Methylnaphthalene	383
Tetralin–Decalin	383

(*continued*)

TABLE II: Nonaqueous Systems (*continued*)

System	References
LAURYL ALCOHOL–Ethylene glycol, Nitromethane, or Nitroethane (three separate binodal curves)	174, 415A, Figs. 71–76
LEMON OIL–Citral–Ethyl alcohol	275 (p. 434)
LITHIUM CHLORIDE–Pyridine–Lube oils	181
LUBE OIL–C_2 to C_6 Paraffins	730
2,6-LUTIDINE–Acetic acid–Decane	778
MAGNESIUM BROMIDE–Ether–Benzene	238A
MAGNESIUM FLUORIDE–Magnesium oxide–Silicon fluoride–Silicon dioxide	144–146
MALEIC ANHYDRIDE–Toluene–Heptane (at 60°C)	179 (p. 267), 180 (p. 1105)
Eight MERCAPTANS–Hydrogen fluoride–Heptane	180 (p. 1064)
MERCURIC ACETATE–Propylene–Saturated Hydrocarbons	168
MERCURIC IODIDE–Ether–Potassium iodide	180 (p. 1065)
METHANOL–Acetone–Gasoline	180 (p. 1072)
Aniline–Benzene	164, Figs. 117, 122–125
Aniline–Decalin (iso-optics and isopycnic)	163, 200 (p. 204), Fig. 41
Aniline–Heptane	652
Aniline–Methylcyclohexane (two separate curves)	169
Benzene–Cyclohexane, Cyclohexene, Hexane, or Heptane (only 80% Methanol)	389
Benzene–Gasoline (96% and 100% Methanol)	180 (p. 1072), Fig. 115
Benzene–Lube oil (at 100°C)	179 (p. 250), 180 (p. 1072)
Benzene–Polystyrene	180 (p. 1073)
2-Butanone–Polystyrene	620
n-Butyl alcohol–Polymethylmethacrylate	303
Butyl benzene–n-Tetradecane	196A
Carbon disulfide–Aromatics–Jet fuel	196A
Carbon disulfide–Diphenylamine, Succinic acid, Urea, or five salts	130A
Carbon disulfide–Oleic acid–Triolein	113, 114, 419
Cetane-1-Methylnaphthalene (90% Methanol) (isopycnic)	163, 180 (p. 1117)
m- or p-Cresol–Ligroin	551
Cuprous chloride–Hydrogen chloride–Ethylene or Propylene	193, Fig. 110
Dibutylbenzene–Paraffins (isopycnics)	196A
Ethylene glycol–C_4 Olefins	180 (p. 1071)
Ethylene glycol–Nine other hydrocarbons	180 (p. 1071)

(*continued*)

TABLE II: Nonaqueous Systems (*continued*)

System	References
METHANOL (*continued*)	
Ethylene glycol–Toluene–Skellysolve B	180 (p. 1117)
Fatty acids–Hexane	603 (p. 53)
Fatty acids–Hake or Cod liver oil	180 (p. 1074)
Fatty acids–three Vegetable oils	560
Five Freons–Glycerol	314
Five Freons–Paraffins	670
Hexane (effects of small amounts of eight other substances on CST)	652
Iso-octane–eight Acids and five Methyl esters	180 (pp. 1071, 1073)
Methylcyclohexane–Heptane	148, 250
Methylnaphthalene–Tetradecane	197, Fig. 16
Morpholin–n-Heptane	662
Nitrobenzene–Cetane–Di-*sec*-butylbenzene	163, Fig. 120
Nitrobenzene–Heptane, Iso-octane, or Pentane (two separate curves)	169, Fig. 58
Nitrobenzene–Iso-octane (two separate curves)	169, 200 (p. 210), 201 (pp. 443–444), Figs. 60, 61
Nitrobenzene–Lubricating oil (twin density and twin index curves)	163, 200 (p. 206), Fig. 121
o-Nitrobiphenyl–Methylcyclohexane (two separate curves)	169
n-Octane	622
Octyltoluene–n-Tetradecane	196A
Oleic acid–Olive oil (Triolein)–Carbon disulfide	113, 114, 180 (p. 1074), 419, 555, 563
Oleic acid–Peanut oil	727
Olive oil–Acetone, Benzene, or 2-Butanone	556
Palmitic acid–Palm oil (tripalmitin)	180 (p. 1074)
Pentanes or Hexane	30
Picoline–Zinc chloride	603 (p. 420)
Propyl alcohol–Polymethylmethacrylate	303
Succinonitrile–Carbon disulfide–Hexane	683
Toluene–Methylcyclohexane	148
Triethanolamine–C_4 olefins	180 (p. 1072)
Triptane and other Paraffins	185, 622
Vaseline oil–Naphthalene	180 (p. 1071)
METHOXYETHANOL (Methylcellosolve)	
Eight Acids and four Esters–Iso-octane	180 (p. 1089)
Benzene–Cyclohexane	680
Benzene–Hydrogen chloride	175
2-Methyl-2-butene–Pentane	250

(*continued*)

TABLE II: Nonaqueous Systems (*continued*)

System	References
METHOXYETHANOL (*continued*)	
Methylcyclohexane–Heptane	148, 250
n-Octane	196A
Toluene or Cumene–Heptane or C_{12}, C_{14}, C_{16}	
Paraffins	179 (p. 267), 180 (p. 1105), 227
Toluene–Methylcyclohexane	148, 250
Triptane–other Paraffins	185
Xylene–Gasoline	179 (p. 268), 180 (p. 1107)
METHYL ACETATE–Butyl or Propyl alcohol	
or *p*-Cymene–Polymethylmethacrylate	303
METHYLANILINE–Acetic acid–Heptane	
(island curve)	180 (pp. 826, 1076), 200 (p. 211), 201 (p. 445), Fig. 92
Acetic acid–Benzene–Gasoline	512
Acetic acid–Gasoline	180 (pp. 826, 1076), 512, 771
Allyl isothiocyanate–Sulfur	763, Fig. 93
Ethylene glycol–Aniline	119
METHYL CARBITOL (see Diethylene glycol	
monomethyl ether)	
METHYL CELLOSOLVE (see	
Methoxyethanol)	
METHYLENE IODIDE–Phenanthrene–	
Cyclohexane	236
METHYL IODIDE–Methyl pyridonium	
iodide	27, 546, Fig. 12
METHYL OLEATE–Furfural–Methyl stearate–	
Naphtha	114, 561
METHYL PERFLUORO-OCTANOATE–	
Toluene–Methylcyclohexane	378
METHYL PYRIDONIUM IODIDE–Methyl	
iodide or pyridine	27, 546, Fig. 12
METHYL RICINOLEATE–Nitromethane–	
Cyclohexane	381
METHYL STEARATE–Furfural–Methyl oleate–	
Naphtha	114, 561
METHYL SULFATE–Benzene–Heptane	179 (p. 248), 180 (p. 1084), Fig. 39
Benzene–Sulfuric acid–Olefins	194
Oleum–Benzene–Heptane, Pentane, or Octane	195
Oleum–Toluene–Paraffins	195
Toluene–Heptane	179 (p. 267), 180 (p. 1105)

(*continued*)

TABLE II: Nonaqueous Systems (*continued*)

System	References
MORPHOLIN–Methanol–Heptane	662
2-NAPHTHYLAMINE–Sulfur–Diphenylamine	351
NICOTINE–Sulfuric acid–Carbon tetrachloride	159
NITRIC ACID–Trioctylamine–Carbon tetrachloride or *o*-Xylene	615
Ten NITRILES–Benzene–Heptane or Cyclohexane	180 (p. 1096), 557
Styrene–Xylene or Ethylbenzene	180 (p. 1096)
Toluene–Heptanes and Octanes	180 (p. 1096)
p-NITROBENZALDEHYDE–Nitrobenzene– Hexane	683
NITROBENZENE–Acetic acid–Heptane (two separate curves)	169
Acetone–Glycol (isopycnic)	163, 180 (pp. 1082–1083)
Aniline–Formamide–Cetane–Carbon tetrachloride (three layer isopycnic)	163, 180 (p. 1070)
Aniline–Hexane	477
Benzoic, Butyric, or Valeric acid–Hexane	603 (pp. 359, 458)
Chlorex–Heptane or Iso-octane (two separate curves)	169
Ethylene glycol–Acetone (isopycnic)	163, 180 (p. 1083)
Formamide–Hexane (isopycnic)	163, 180 (p. 1070)
Glycerol–Phenol–Petroleum	266A
Hexanes or Heptanes	180 (pp. 1070, 1094), 443, 768
o-Nitrophenol or Resorcinol–Hexane	603 (pp. 359, 458, 459)
Methanol–Lube oils (twin density and twin index curves)	163, 200 (p. 206), Figs. 120, 121
Methanol–Pentane, Heptane, or Iso-octane (two separate curves)	169, 200 (p. 210)
Pyrogallol, Quinol, or Resorcinol	683
Sulfuric acid–Olefins	194
Valeric acid–*n*-Hexane	603 (pp. 359, 458)
m-NITROBENZOIC ACID–Nitrobenzene– Hexane	683
NITROBIPHENYL–Methanol– Methylcyclohexane	169
NITROETHANE–Ethylene glycol–Decyl or Lauryl alcohols (three separate curves)	174, Figs. 68–73
Perfluorotributylamine–Iso-octane	738

(*continued*)

TABLE II: Nonaqueous Systems (*continued*)

System	References
NITROMETHANE–Aromatics–Paraffins	473
Benzene, Toluene, or Xylenes–Cyclohexane	224, 743
Benzene–*n*-Heptane (iso-optics)	172, 224, 328, Fig. 42
Butyl cellulose–Carbon tetrachloride	128
Castor oil methyl esters–Hexane	380
Ethane–Ethylene	142
Ethylene glycol–Decyl alcohol (three separate curves)	174, Fig. 67
2-Ethylhexanol (three separate curves)	197
n-Heptane(iso-optics)	163, Fig. 9
Lauryl alcohol (three separate curves)	174, 415A, Figs. 74, 75
Methyl ricinoleate–Cyclohexane	381
Toluene–*n*-Heptane	328
Triptane–other Paraffins	185
Three Xylenes–Heptane	328
p-NITROPHENOL–Nitrobenzene–Hexane	683
o-NITROTOLUENE–Butane–Isobutane	167, 183
OLEIC ACID–Abietic acid–Propane	180 (p. 1087)
Acetic acid or Furfural–Peanut oil	725
Acetic acid–Vegetable oils	737
Carbon disulfide–Methanol–Olive oil	113, 114, 419
Cottonseed oil–Propane	180 (p. 1087), 563
Ethyl alcohol–Groundnut oil	726
Ethyl alcohol–Olive oil	180 (p. 1081), 555, 563
Furfural–Cyclohexane of Heptane	582
Methanol–Olive oil	180 (p. 1074), 555, 563
Methanol–Peanut oil	727
Olive oil (Triolein)–Propane	180 (p. 1087)
Palmitic acid–Acetone or Hexane	627
Propylene glycol–Cyclohexane, Xylene, or Heptane	582
Stearic acid–Acetone or Hexane	626
OLEUM–Ethyl or Methyl sulfate–Benzene– Pentane or Heptane	195
OLIVE OIL (Triolein)–Acetone–Ethyl alcohol	498
Acetone–Glycerol	419, 556
Carbon disulfide–Methanol–Oleic acid	113, 114, 419
Ethyl alcohol or Methanol–Oleic acid	555
Methanol–Acetone, Benzene, or 2-Butanone	556
Propane	180 (p. 1087)
2,2′-OXYDIPROPIONITRILE–Benzene– Cyclohexane	180 (p. 1095)
Benzene, Toluene, or Ethylbenzene–*n*-Heptane	224, 549, 629

(*continued*)

TABLE II: Nonaqueous Systems (*continued*)

System	References
2,2′-OXYDIPROPIONITRILE (*continued*)	
Fourteen other Dinitriles or Sulfides–Benzene and Heptane or Cyclohexane	180 (p. 1096)
n-Heptane (distribution coefficient)–14 Aromatic hydrocarbons, 10 Pyridine derivatives, and 20 Alkylated anilines	425
2-Methylnaphthalene–Tetralin or Dodecane	180 (p. 1109)
Toluene–*n*-Heptane	134
OXYGEN–Ozone–Fluorine	648B
PALMITIC ACID–Methanol–Palm oil	180 (p. 1074)
Oleic acid–Acetone or Hexane	627
Stearic acid–Propane	180 (p. 1086)
n-PENTANE–1-Pentene–33 Solvents	218
PEANUT OIL–Acetic acid or Furfural–Oleic acid	725
Methanol–Oleic acid	727
PERFLUOROCYCLO-OCTYL ETHER–Perfluoro-*n*-heptane–Heptane or Carbon tetrachloride	378
PERFLUOROHEPTANE–Acetone–C_7HF_{15}	133A
PERFLUOROKEROSINE–Benzene–Heptane or Cyclohexane	199
PERFLUOROMETHYLDECALIN–Acetonitrile or Triethylene glycol (three layers)	199
Propane (iso-optic)	171
PERFLUORONONYLDECALIN–Hydrogen sulfide, Sulfur dioxide, Ethylene oxide, Methyl chloride (iso-optics)	171
PERFLUOROTRIBUTYLAMINE–Cyclohexane	205C
Nitroethane–Iso-octane	738
PHENACETIN–Urea–Urethane	180 (p. 1074)
p-PHENETIDINE–Aromatic hydrocarbon–Cyclohexane or Decalin	11
Nine Aromatics–Cyclohexane, Methyl-cyclohexane, or Iso-octane	180 (pp. 1100–1103)
PHENOL–Aniline or Pyridine–Iso-octane	774
Aniline–Tridecane	648A
Antipyrine–Ligroin	363
Glycerol or Triethylene glycol–Nitrobenzene	120, 128
Hexane–Sulfur	435D
Pentene–*n*-Pentane	179 (p. 245), 180 (p. 1093)

(*continued*)

TABLE II: Nonaqueous Systems (*continued*)

System	References
PHENOL (*continued*)	
m-Phenylenediamine–Benzene	180 (p. 1095)
Phenylhydrazine–Iso-octane	775
Quinoline–Sulfur	361
PHENOXYETHANOL (Phenyl Cellosolve)–	
2-Methyl-2-butene–Pentane	250
Toluene, *n*-Heptane–Methylcyclohexane	148, 250
m-PHENYLENEDIAMINE–Phenol–Benzene	180 (p. 1095)
PHENYLHYDRAZINE–Aromatics–Paraffins	473
Phenol–Iso-octane	775
PHENYLISOTHIOCYANATE–Aniline–Sulfur	449
2-PICOLINE–Triethylene glycol–Benzene–Non-	
aromatics–Zinc chloride–seven Alcohols	603 (p. 420)
POLYMETHYLMETHACRYLATE–Benzene–	
Cyclohexane	180 (pp. 1073, 1095)
Propyl or Butyl alcohols–*p*-Cymene	303
65 Solvents	304
POLYOLEFINS–light Hydrocarbons	
(lower CST)	204
POLYSTYRENE–Acetone–Propyl laurate and	
11 other pairs	180 (p. 1113)
n-Butyl alcohol, Ethyl and Vinyl acetates, or	
Methyl malonate	305
Carbon tetrachloride–Cyclohexane	620
Cyclohexanol–Ethylcyclohexane	620
Methanol–2-Butanone	620
POLY(VINYLPYRROLIDINE)–Glycerol–	
Isoamyl alcohol	128
POTASSIUM–Potassium iodide–Ammonia	180 (p. 1066)
PROPANE–Abietic acid–Oleic acid, 9-Butyl-	
anthracene, or two other polycyclic	
hydrocarbons	180 (pp. 1087–1088), 200 (p. 236)
Methane–Stearic acid or Trimyristin	180 (p. 1088)
Mineral oil	730
Oleic acid–Cottonseed oil or Triolein	180 (p. 1087), 563
Palmitic acid–Stearic acid	180 (p. 1086)
Phenanthrene–Naphthalene	200 (p. 236)
Sulfur dioxide–Propylene	179 (p. 265), 180 (p. 1067)
PROPIONIC ACID–Aniline–Cyclohexane	180 (p. 1099)
Glycerol–Chloroform	603 (p. 193)
Hydrogen bromide–Heptane	
(triangular island)	175, Fig. 95

(*continued*)

TABLE II: Nonaqueous Systems (*continued*)

System	References
PROPIONITRILE–Silicon tetrachloride	3
n-PROPYL ALCOHOL–Methanol–	
Polymethylmethacrylate	303
PROPYLENE–Amides–	
Cuprous hydrogen chloride	203
PROPYLENE CARBONATE–Toluene–	
Heptane (iso-optic)	228
PROPYLENE GLYCOL–Benzene–six Soaps	180 (p. 1089)
Ethyl alcohol–Benzene, Hexane, or	
Cyclohexane	125
Oleic acid–Xylene–Heptane or Cyclohexane	582
Tributyrin–Di(methoxyethyl)phthalate	214
n-PROPYL SULFIDE–Hydrogen fluoride–	
n-Heptane	180 (p. 1064)
PYRIDINE–Acetic acid–*n*-Octane	
(island curve)	779
Ammonia–Heptane (isopycnic)	276
Calcium nitrate or Lithium chloride–	
Lubricating oil	181, 182
Ethanolamine–Ethyl ether	180 (p. 1085), 625
Hexane–Sulfur	435D
Methyl pyridonium iodide	27, 546, Fig. 12
Phenol–Iso-octane	774
PYROGALLOL–Nitrobenzene–Heptane	683
QUINOL–Nitrobenzene–Heptane	683
QUINOLINE–Diphenylamine–Sulfur	359
Phenol–Sulfur	361
RESINS–Toluene–Decane, Tetradecane,	
Octadecane	514
RESORCINOL–Diphenylamine–Urea	180 (p. 1075)
1-Naphthylamine–Sulfur	180 (p. 1067)
Nitrobenzene–Heptane	683
SALICYLIC ACID–Aminopyrine–Gasoline	366
Antipyrine–Gasoline	355
SILICA–Alumina–Fluorides of barium, calcium,	
magnesium, or strontium	144, 145
Fluorides of barium, calcium, potassium,	
magnesium, or strontium	146
Silicon tetrafluoride–Calcium oxide–	
Calcium fluoride	484
SILICON TETRACHLORIDE–Acetonitrile or	
Propionitrile	3

(*continued*)

TABLE II: Nonaqueous Systems (*continued*)

System	References
SILVER NITRATE–Acetonitrile–Olefins	190, 205, Fig. 48
1-Butene–Paraffins	168, 187, 190
Propylene–Carbon dioxide	186
Propylene–Propane	168, 180 (p. 1064), 187, Fig. 46
SOAPS–Propylene glycol–Benzene	180 (p. 1089)
SODIUM–Ammonia–Sodium iodide	180 (p. 1066)
SOYBEAN OIL–Ethyl alcohol–Trichloroethylene	424B
STEARIC ACID–Methane–Propane	180 (p. 1088)
Oleic acid–Acetone or Hexane	626
Palmitic acid–Propane	180 (p. 1086)
STRONTIUM FLUORIDE–Strontium oxide– Silicon fluoride–Silicon dioxide	484
SUCCINIC ACID–Methanol–Carbon disulfide	130A
SUCCINONITRILE–Ethyl alcohol–Ethyl ether	438
SULFOLANE–Toluene–Petroleum	180 (p. 1106)
SULFOLANE and 36 other solvents–Benzene– Hexane	124A, 224, 247
SULFONAL–Antipyrine–Urea	180 (p. 1075)
SULFUR–Allyl isothiocyanate–Methyl- or Dimethylaniline or *o*-Toluidine (island curve)	180 (pp. 1066–1067), 763, Fig. 93
Aniline–Phenyl isothiocyanate	449
Diphenylamine–2-Naphthylamine	351
Diphenylamine–Quinoline	359
Diphenylthiourea	449
Phenol–Quinoline	361
Resorcinol–Naphthylamine	180 (p. 1067)
SULFUR DIOXIDE–Aromatics–Nonaromatics	153, 180 (pp. 1067–1068), 544, 585
Benzene–*n*-Butane	61
Benzene–Cyclohexane	585
Benzene–Butane, Hexane, Heptane, or Decane	224, 585
Benzene–Nonaromatics	153
n-Butane–*n*- or Isopentane (iso-optics)	171, Fig. 2
sec-Butylbenzene–*n*-Decane or Kerosine	224, 585
Ethylene glycol–Benzene–Heptane	196
Formamide–Benzene–Heptane	196
n-Heptane–Methylcyclohexane	148
Isopropylbenzene–*n*-Hexane	671
2-Methyl-2-butene–*n*-Pentane	671

(*continued*)

TABLE II: Nonaqueous Systems (*continued*)

System	References
SULFUR DIOXIDE (*continued*)	
Methylcyclohexane–*n*-Heptane	671
Methylnaphthalene–Cetane	671
Naphthenes–Paraffins	180 (pp. 1067–1068)
Olefins–Saturated hydrocarbons	180 (pp. 1067–1068)
Propane–Propylene	179 (p. 265), 180 (p. 1067)
Toluene–*n*-Heptane	224, 585
Toluene–Methylcyclohexane	148, 671
Toluene–Petroleum	180 (p. 1106), 544
Toluene–Nonaromatics	153
Xylenes–*n*-Nonane	224, 585
Xylenes–*n*-Pentane	648
SULFURIC ACID–aromatic Sulfonic acids–	
Xylene	650
Ethyl alcohol–Ethyl ether	197, Fig. 108
Ethylbenzylaniline sulfate–Ethylbenzylaniline	447A
Ethyl ether–Tetrachloroethylene	163, 180 (p. 1065), 681, Fig. 111
Ethyl or Methyl sulfate–Olefins–Paraffins	194
Isopropyl acetate–Petroleum ether	179 (p. 266), 180 (p. 1065)
Isopropyl alcohol–Isopropyl ether	197, Fig. 109
Nicotine–Carbon tetrachloride	158
Nitrobenzene–Olefins–Paraffins	194
TETRABROMOETHANE–Diethylene glycol–	
Diethyl phthalate	214
TETRACHLOROETHANE–Cellulose	
triacetate–Petroleum ether	460
TETRACHLOROETHYLENE–Ether–	
Sulfuric acid (isopycnic)	163, 180 (p. 1065), 681, Fig. 111
TETRANITROMETHANE–Miscible with all	
liquid hydrocarbons	473
2,2′-THIODIPROPIONITRILE–Benzene–	
Cyclohexane	180 (p. 1095)
Benzene–*n*-Heptane	180 (p. 1096), 549
Ethylbenzene, Toluene, or Xylenes–Heptane	224, 629
Toluene–*n*-Heptane	134
THIOPHENE–Ammonia–Heptane	280
Diethylene glycol–Benzene	197, Fig. 32
TOLUENE–*n*-Heptane–nine Solvents	179 (p. 267), 180 (p. 1105), 227

(*continued*)

TABLE II: Nonaqueous Systems (*continued*)

System	References
o-TOLUIDINE–Acetic acid–*n*-Heptane	175, Fig. 96
Glycerol–Diethylaniline	353
Sulfur–Allyl isothiocyanate	763, Fig. 93
TRIBUTYRIN–Propylene glycol	214
TRICHLOROETHYLENE–Ethyl alcohol–	
Soybean oil	424B
TRIETHANOLAMINE–C_4 olefins	180 (p. 1072)
TRIETHYLENE GLYCOL–Benzene–	
Cyclohexane	199
Benzene–*n*-Heptane	199, 238, 307, 549
Ethylbenzene–Heptane	549
Perfluoromethyldecalin–Benzene–*n*-Heptane	
(three layers)	199
Phenols–Hydrocarbons	120
2-Picoline–four Hydrocarbons	98
Toluene–*n*-Heptane	179 (p. 267), 180 (p. 1105), 200 (p. 199), 549
TRIMYRISTIN–Propane–Methane	180 (p. 1088)
TRI-*n*-OCTYLAMINE–Mineral acids–	
Carbon tetrachloride or Xylene	53, 615
TRIOLEIN (see Olive oil)	
URANIUM HEXAFLUORIDE–	
Hydrogen fluoride–Chlorine trifluoride	577
URANYL NITRATE–Tributyl phosphate	151
UREA–Antipyrine–Sulfonal	180 (p. 1075)
Cuprous hydrogen chloride–Propylene	203
Methanol–Carbon disulfide	130A
Resorcinol–Diphenylamine	180 (p. 1075)
Salipyrine–Sulfonal	180 (p. 1075)
Urethane–Phenacetin	180 (p. 1074)
URETHANE–Aniline–Hexane	130A
VALERIC ACID–Nitrobenzene–*n*-Hexane	603 (pp. 359, 458)
VALEROLACTONE–Heptane–	
Methylcyclohexane	148, 226, 250, 399
Pentane–2-Methyl-2-butene	226, 399
Toluene–Cetane or Methylcyclohexane	226, 399
VEGETABLE OILS–Acetic acid–Oleic acid	737
VINYL ACETATE–Acetaldehyde–Acetone	68
Polystyrenes–Alcohols or Esters	305
XYLENE–Gasoline–nine Solvents	179 (p. 268), 180 (p. 1107)
ZINC CHLORIDE–2-Picoline–seven Alcohols	603 (p. 420)
ZINC SOAPS–Hydrocarbons	418

TABLE III
Critical Solution Temperatures
(supplementary to reference 178 in bibliography)

System	CST's in °C	References
ACETAMIDE–*o*-Bromotoluene	170	388, 684 (p. 799)
ACETONE–Ethane	−48.78	754
Propane	−50.37	754
n-Butane	−50.31	754
Isobutane	−55	197
n-Pentane	−42.71	754
Isopentane	−60	197
n-Hexane	−34.55	754
n-Heptane	−25	586, 754
n-Octane	−17.74	754
n-Nonane	−10.44	586, 754
sec-Butylcyclohexane	−7.1	567B
Carbon disulfide	−39 to −51.3	103, 684 (p. 928)
Hydroperfluoro-*n*-heptane (C_7HF_{15})	<0	133A
Perfluoro-*n*-heptane	93.5	133A
Glycerol	99.5	154
Glycerol with 37% Water	38.5	154
ACETONITRILE–Ethylene	>9.5	690A
Glycerol	90.0	154
Silicon tetrachloride	51.8	3
Triethylchlorobenzene	43.3	197
ACETONYLACETONE–Glycerol	68.0	154
ACETOPHENONE–Ethylene glycol	58	154
Glycerol	185.5	154
Water	221	154
ACETYLACETONE–Glycerol	133.5	154
ALKALI METALS–Alkali halides		71A, 71B, 72C, 137, 307A
ALLYL ALCOHOL–Paraffin oil	103.5	154
ALUMINUM–Zinc	351.6	461
AMINOPYRINE (Pyramidone)–	190	178
Water (LCST 69.5°C)	169	358, 765
AMMONIA–*n*-Hexane	56	279
n-Octane	ca 63	279
Iso-octane	60.15	279, 320A
Hexadecane (Cetane)	high	279
1-Octene	ca 40	279
Cyclohexane	59	279
Methylcyclohexane	63	279
Cyclohexene	ca 40	279

(continued)

TABLE III (*continued*)

System	CST's in °C	References
AMMONIA (*continued*)		
Decalin	ca 70	279
Mesitylene	33.9	279
n-Propylbenzene	23.9	279
Toluene	−7	277, 279
o-Xylene	11.9	279
m-Xylene	14.6	279
p-Xylene	12.8	279
Ethylbenzene	10.7	279
Cumene	20.0	279, 697
Cymene	<25	697
Styrene (Phenylethylene)	−15.5	279
1-Methylnaphthalene	28.8	279
Tetralin	ca 40	279
AMMONIUM CHLORIDE–		
Manganese chloride (dihydrate LCST 25°C)		102
ANETHOL–Ethylene glycol	199.5	154
ANILINE–Cyclohexane	29.53	301A, 570
n-Heptane	62.5	154
n-Octane	74.5	154
n-Nonane	77.5	154
n-Decane	79.8	154
n-Undecane	88.0	154
Cyclohexane	38.5	154
Paraffin oil	114.0	154
ANISOL–Ethylene glycol	201.5	154
AZACYCLO-OCTANE–Water (LCST <−13°C)	134.5	178, 459C, 687 (p. 91)
BENZYL CYANIDE (see Phenyl acetonitrile)		
BISMUTH–Bismuth chloride	780	757
Zinc	605	332
BROMAL HYDRATE–Water (LCST's 51 and 111°C) (three liquid phases)		773
BROMINE–Water (probably no CST, as with Ether–Water, Fig. 6)	>200	197
p-BROMOANISOL–Ethylene glycol	184.0	154
BROMOBENZENE–Succinonitrile	129.0	154
BROMOFORM–Formic acid	207.5	154

(*continued*)

TABLE III (*continued*)

System	CST's in °C	References
o-BROMOTOLUENE–Acetamide		
(m.p. 81°C)	170	388, 684 (p. 799)
Urethane (m.p. 50°C)	35	388, 684 (p. 799)
2-BUTANONE–Glycerol	166.0	154
n-BUTYL ALCOHOL–Polystyrene	181	305
Water (+ Hydrogen)	138	296
Water	128.5	154
23.55% Ammonia	41.8	154
30% Hydrogen peroxide	91.5	154
sec-BUTYL ALCOHOL–Water		
(LCST <2.6°C)	112	129, 687 (p. 233)
BUTYL CELLOSOLVE–Water		
(LCST 49.1°C)	130.3	96, 590
n-BUTYL CHLORAL HYDRATE–		
Water (LCST's 64 and 82.2°C)		
(three liquid phases)		773
n-BUTYRALDEHYDE–Glycerol	166.0	154
BUTYRONITRILE–Paraffin oil	68.5	154
CAPRONALDEHYDE–Glycerol	65	154
CAPRONITRILE–Ethylene	>19.5	690A
CARBON DIOXIDE–Ethylene	<0	571 (pp. 229, 230), 698
CARBON DISULFIDE–Acetone	−51.3	103, 684 (p. 928)
Methyl acetate	−52.6	104
CARBON TETRACHLORIDE–		
Nitromethane	3.5	128
Pentaerithritol perfluorotetrabutyrate	72.1	617
Perfluoromethylcyclohexane	28.23	235, 485, 684 (p. 319), 784
Resorcinol	135	685 (p. 345)
CARVONE–Ethylene glycol	100.5	154
CASTOR OIL–Kerosine	43.7	464
Diesel oil	39.6	464
CETYL ALCOHOL–Zinc chloride–		
4-Picoline	241	686 (p. 1199)
CHLORAL–Propyl acetate	5.5	388, 684 (p. 852)
CHLORAL HYDRATE–Diethylamine	113.5	367
Water (LCST 190)		745B
CHLORINE (crit. temp. 144°C)–		
Water (probably no CST,		
as with Ether–Water, Fig. 6)	>100	197

(*continued*)

TABLE III (*continued*)

System	CST's in °C	References
CHLOROBENZALDEHYDE–		
Ethylene glycol	100	154
CHLOROBENZENE–Succinonitrile	121.5	154
2-CHLOROETHANOL–15 Fatty oils		153A
CHLOROFORM–Formic acid	151.5	154
Pentaerithritol perfluorotetrabutyrate	43.5	617
o-CHLOROIODOBENZENE–		
Ethylene glycol	207.0	154
CHROMIUM–Yttrium	ca 2000	673
CINEOLE–Ethylene glycol	222.5	154
CITRAL–Ethylene glycol	133.5	154
CITRONELLAL–Ethylene glycol	258	154
CITRONELLAL (tech.)–Ethylene glycol	191	154
CUMENOL–Ethylene glycol	201.5	154
CYCLOHEXANOL–Water	182.5	154
CYCLOHEXANONE–Glycerol	129.5	154
Water	200	154
CYCLOPENTANONE–Water	105	52
DEUTERIUM OXIDE–		
Deuteriophenol	79.2	91, 525, 687 (p. 719)
Ethyl deuteroalcohol	131.1	525, 687 (p. 718)
Isobutyric deuterioacid	45.5	525, 687 (p. 719)
Methyl acetate	114	525, 687 (p. 718)
m-DIBROMOBENZENE–Ethylene glycol	118	154
Succinonitrile	199	154
p-DIBROMOBENZENE–Succinonitrile	201.5	154
cis-o-DIBROMOCYCLOHEXANE–		
Aniline	48.5	154
Succinonitrile	154.5	154
DICHLOROACETIC ACID–		
Paraffin oil	111.6	154
o-DICHLOROBENZENE–Ethylene	>11.4	690A
m-DICHLOROBENZENE–		
Succinonitrile	189.0	154
p-DICHLOROBENZENE–		
Succinonitrile	175.5	154
DIETHYLAMINE–Chloral hydrate	113.5	367
DIETHYLENE GLYCOL–		
o-Nitrobiphenyl (m.p. 37°C)	67	197
DIETHYLENE GLYCOL MONOAMYL ETHER–Water (LCST 36°C)		96

(*continued*)

TABLE III (*continued*)

System	CST's in °C	References
DIETHYLENE GLYCOL		
MONOHEXYL ETHER–Water		
(LCST <0°C)		96
N,*N*-DIMETHYLANILINE–		
Ethylene glycol	175	119
DIMETHYLFORMAMIDE–*n*-Octane	78.1	519A
n-Nonane	83.6	519A
4,6-DIMETHYL-1,2-PYRONE–Water		
(LCST 59.7°C)	86.3	687 (p. 60), 750
DIPHENYLAMINE–Sulfur	<105	359, 687 (p. 674)
ETHANE–Nitrogen	>−12.22	137A, 687 (p. 679)
ETHYL ACETATE–Polystyrene	−30.5	305
ETHYL ALCOHOL–Nitroglycerol	>40	603 (p. 134)
Zinc chloride–4-Picoline	33.4	686 (p. 1192)
ETHYL DEUTEROALCOHOL–		
Deuterium oxide	131.1	525, 687 (p. 718)
ETHYLENE–Acetonitrile	>9.6	690A
Carbon dioxide	<0	571 (pp. 229–230), 698
Capronitrile	>19.5	690A
Cetane	>10.5	690A
o-Dichlorobenzene	>11.4	690A
n-Hexyl alcohol	>19.5	690A
Nitrogen	<0	571 (pp. 229–230), 698
n-Propyl Alcohol	>10.5	690A
1,1,1,ω-Tetrachloro paraffins		
(C_3, C_5, C_7, C_9)	>9.5	137C
ETHYLENE BROMIDE–Formic acid	156.0	154
ETHYLENE CHLORIDE–Formic acid	92.0	154
ETHYLENE CYANIDE (see		
Succinonitrile)		
ETHYLENEDIAMINE–*n*-Hexane	98.5	75
Cyclohexane	91.5	75
ETHYLENE GLYCOL–Acetophenone	58.0	154
	114.5	178
Anethol	199.5	154
Anisol	201.5	154
	134.5	178
p-Bromoanisol	184.0	154
Carvone	100.5	154
Chlorobenzaldehyde	100	154

(*continued*)

TABLE III (*continued*)

System	CST's in °C	References
ETHYLENE GLYCOL (*continued*)		
o-Chloroiodobenzene	207.0	154
Cineole	222.5	154
Citral	133.5	154
Citronellal	258.0	154
	165	178
Citronellal (tech.)	191.0	154
Cumin oil	201.5	154
m-Dibromobenzene	118.0	154
N,*N*-Dimethylaniline	175	119
Eucalyptus oil	243	154
Fennel oil	174.5	154
d-Limonene	254	154
N-Methylaniline	60	119
Peppermint oil	234.5	154
Phenylacetonitrile	74.0	154
Sage oil	216.5	154
Steranisol	186.5	154
Templen oil	313	154
Thiophene	155.5	154
Thyme oil	246.0	154
Tricresyl phosphate	224	154
Turpentine oil	286	154
ETHYLENE GLYCOL		
MONOBUTYL ETHER–Water	130.3	590
ETHYL ETHER–Hydrogen peroxide		
(LCST $< -25°C$)	46	447, 687 (p. 719)
ETHYLIDINE ACETONE–Glycerol	147	154
EUCALYPTUS OIL–Ethylene glycol	243	154
EUGENOL METHYL ETHER–		
o-Phenylenediamine	87	388, 684 (p. 957)
FENNEL OIL–Ethylene glycol	174.5	154
FLUOROBENZENE–Succinonitrile	60	154
FORMIC ACID–Bromoform	207.5	154
Chloroform	151.5	154
Ethylene bromide	156.0	154
Ethylene chloride	92.0	154
Methylene chloride	87.0	154
Stannic chloride	>70	708
FREON 12 (CCl_2F_2)–Ozone	< -110	100A
FREON 22 ($CHCl_2F_2$)–Ozone	< -110	100A

(*continued*)

TABLE III (*continued*)

System	CST's in °C	References
FURFURAL–Benzene	−105(estd.)	547
n-Heptane	88	154
Paraffin oil	147.2	154
GLYCEROL–Acetone	99.5	154
Acetonitrile	90.0	154
Acetonyl acetone	68.0	154
Acetophenone	185.5	154
Acetylacetone	133.5	154
2-Butanone	166.0	154
n-Butyraldehyde	166.0	154
n-Capronaldehyde	65.0	154
Cyclohexanone	129.5	154
Ethylidine acetone	147.0	154
Isoamyl alcohol	68	128
Mesityl oxide	176.5	154
p-Methylacetophenone	215	154
Nitrobenzene	228	154
Phoron	276.0	154
o-Toluidine	154.5	154
m-Toluidine	119.5	154
Tricresyl phosphate	311.5	154
GLYCOL ETHERS (see Water)		
n-HEPTANE–Aniline	62.5	154
Furfural	88	154
Methane	−81.5	121A, 339
Methoxyacetic acid	171	154
Methoxypropionic acid	94.5	154
Nitromethane	108.3	411
HEXAMETHYLENEIMINE–Water		
(LCST 68.1°C)		344A
n-HEXYL ALCOHOL–Ethylene	>19.5	690A
HYDROGEN CHLORIDE–Methanol	<−65	275A (p. 212)
Sulfur monochloride	−56	676
HYDROGEN PEROXIDE–Ethyl		
ether (LCST <−25°C)	46	447, 687 (p. 719)
HYDROGEN SULFIDE		
Methyl ether	<−148.6	275A (p. 212)
HYDROPERFLUOROHEPTANE (C_7HF_{15})		
n-Heptane	31.1	339
n-Octane	48.0	339
n-Decane	78.2	339
n-Dodecane	102.0	339

(*continued*)

TABLE III (*continued*)

System	CST's in °C	References
HYDROPERFLUOROHEPTANE (*continued*)		
n-Tetradecane	127.0	339
Benzene	41.3	339
Toluene	34.0	339
n-Propylbenzene	67.1	339
Acetone	<0	133A
Acetonitrile	43.8	339
Methyl and Ethyl alcohols	25	339
Nitromethane	99.7	339
IODOBENZENE–Succinonitrile	149.0	154
o-IODOTOLUENE–Succinonitrile	198.0	154
p-IODOTOLUENE–Succinonitrile	188.2	154
ISOAMYL ALCOHOL–Glycerol	68	228
Water (+ Hydrogen)	204	296A
ISOBUTYRIC DEUTERIOACID–		
Deuterium oxide	45.5	525, 687 (p. 719)
LAURIC ACID–Zinc myristate	114	418, 686 (p. 1217)
Zinc stearate	113	418, 686 (p. 1217)
LEAD–Zinc	790	332
d-LIMONENE–Ethylene glycol	254	154
LITHIUM–Sodium	380	581
Lithium chloride	>1000	137
Lithium fluoride	1330	137
Lithium iodide	>950	137
MANGANESE CHLORIDE		
DIHYDRATE–Ammonium		
chloride (LCST 25°C)		102
MESITYL OXIDE–Glycerol	176.5	154
METHANE–Heptane	−81.5	121A, 339
Four Hexanes, two Dimethylpentanes,		
Isooctane, 1-Hexene	−102 to −77	121B
METHANOL–*n*-Butane	−4	30
n-Pentane	16.06	30
Isopentane	10.73	30
n-Hexane	33.2	30, 329, 622
3-Methylpentane	27.2	329
2,2-Dimethylbutane	14.2	329
2,3-Dimethylbutane	20.4	329
n-Heptane	51.2	329, 622
2,2,3-Trimethylbutane (Triptane)	28.2	622
	32	178
n-Octane	65.7, 66.7	329, 622

(*continued*)

TABLE III (*continued*)

System	CST's in °C	References
METHANOL (*continued*)		
3-Methylheptane	60.2	329
2,2,4-Trimethylpentane	43	329, 622
2,2,5-Trimethylhexane	57.5	329
Cyclopentane	16.6	329
	39.0	154
Methylcyclopentane	32.1	329
	47.2	154
Cyclohexane	45.75	329, 622
Methylcyclohexane	46.47	329, 622
METHANOL*–*n*-Pentane	38.0	154
n-Heptane	65.5	154
n-Octane	82.0	154
n-Nonane	94.0	154
n-Decane	101.5	154
n-Undecane	113.5	154
Cyclopentane	39.0	154
Methylcyclopentane	47.2	154
cis-o-Dibromocyclohexane	48.5	154
Hydrogen chloride	< -65	275A (p. 212)
METHOXYACETIC ACID–		
n-Heptane	171	154
METHOXYPROPIONIC ACID–		
n-Heptane	94.5	154
Paraffin oil	211	154
METHYL ACETATE–Carbon disulfide	-52.6	104
Deuterium oxide	114	525, 687 (p. 718)
p-METHYLACETOPHENONE–		
Glycerol	215	154
N-METHYLANILINE–Lubricating oils	3 to 53	217
Ethylene glycol	60	119
Sulfur	106.8	687 (p. 674)
METHYLENE CHLORIDE–		
Formic acid	87.0	154
Pentaerithritol perfluorotetrabutyrate	38.5	617
METHYL ETHER–Hydrogen sulfide	-148.6	275A (p. 212)
METHYLPELLETIERINE		
($C_{15}H_{17}NO$)–Water (LCST		
35.5°C)		669, 687 (p. 131)
METHYL TETRANITRODI-		
PHENATE–Mesitylene	48m	684 (p. 638)

*These CST are 10 to 20°C higher than those in reference 178.

(*continued*)

TABLE III (*continued*)

System	CST's in °C	References
2-NAPHTHYLAMINE–Sulfur	100.5	351, 687 (p. 675)
NICOTINE–Water (LCST 61.5°C)	233	88
NITROBENZENE–Diethylpentane	12.4	688
Glycerol	228	154
Zinc laurate	111	418, 686 (p. 1043)
Zinc myristate	113	418, 686 (p. 1145)
Zinc stearate	112	418, 686 (p. 1145)
o-NITROBIPHENYL–		
Diethylene glycol	67	197
NITROGEN–Ethane	>−12.22	137A, 687 (p. 679)
Ethylene	<0	571 (pp. 229–230), 698
Sulfur dioxide	>40	698
NITROGLYCEROL–Ethyl alcohol	>40	603 (p. 134)
NITROMETHANE–Isopentane	32.3	684 (p. 587)
n-Hexane	102.4	411
n-Heptane	108.3	411
n-Octane	114.5	411
2,2,4-Trimethylpentane	105	411
n-Nonane	120.3	411
n-Decane	125	411
n-Undecane	130.4	411
n-Dodecane	135.6	411
Carbon tetrachloride	3.5	128
n-OCTADECYL ALCOHOL–		
Zinc myristate	108	418, 686 (p. 1199)
Zinc stearate	104	418, 686 (p. 1199)
n-OCTYL ALCOHOL–Polystyrene	153	305
OZONE–Freons	<−110	100A
PARAFFIN OIL (n_D^{20} 1.4770)–		
Allyl alcohol	103.5	154
Aniline	114	154
Butyronitrile	68.5	154
Dichloroacetic acid	111.6	154
Furfural	147.2	154
Methoxypropionic acid	211.0	154
n-Propyl alcohol	44.5	154
Pyridine	33.4	154
o-Toluidine	60.5	154
m-Toluidine	68.5	154
Tricresyl phosphate	101.5	154

(*continued*)

TABLE III (*continued*)

System	CST's in °C	References
PARALDEHYDE–Water		
(LCST <8.5°C)		687 (p. 17)
PENTAERITHRITOL		
PERFLUOROTETRABUTY-		
RATE–*n*-Pentane	62.1	617
2,2,4-Trimethylpentane	78.8	617
n-Octane	119.4	617
Cyclopentane	80.8	617
Carbon tetrachloride	72.1	617
Chloroform	43.5	617
Methylene chloride	38.5	617
Octamethylcyclotetrasiloxane ($Me_8(SiO)_4$)	123.5	617
PENTAETHYLENE GLYCOL		
MONOOCTYL ETHER–Water		
(LCST 5.5°C)		96
PEPPERMINT OIL–Ethylene glycol	234.5	154
PERFLUORO-*n*-HEPTANE–Acetone	93.5	133A
Hydroperfluoroheptane (C_7HF_{15})	<0	133A
PERFLUOROMETHYLCYCLO-	28.23	
HEXANE–Carbon tetrachloride		235, 485, 684
PHENOL–Phosphoric acid		(p. 319), 784
(LCST 100°C)		350
Water	66	154
7N Hydrogen chloride	157	154
4.5N Hydrogen bromide	113.2	154
PHENYLACETONITRILE–		
Ethylene glycol	74.0	154
o-PHENYLENEDIAMINE–Eugenol		
methyl ether	87	388, 684 (p. 957)
PHORON–Glycerol	276	154
PHOSPHORIC ACID–Phenol		
(LCST 100°C)		350
POLYETHYLENE–Propane		
(high pressure)		138A
POLYISOBUTENE–Benzene (LCST		
150–170°C)	23	204
POLYSTYRENE–*n*-Butyl alcohol	181	305
Ethyl acetate	−30.5	305
Octyl alcohol	153	305
POTASSIUM–Potassium bromide	728	307A
Potassium chloride	790	307A

(*continued*)

TABLE III (*continued*)

System	CST's in °C	References
POTASSIUM (*continued*)		
Potassium fluoride	904	71B, 137, 307A
Potassium iodide	717	307A
POTASSIUM THIOCYANATE–		
Pyridine	>200	686 (p. 1131)
PROPANE–Polyethylene		
(high pressure)		138A
PROPIONITRILE–		
Silicon tetrachloride	−10	3
n-PROPYL ACETATE–Chloral	5.5	388, 684 (p. 852)
n-PROPYL ALCOHOL–Ethylene	>10.5	690A
Paraffin oil	44.5	154
Zinc chloride–4-picoline	52.5m	686 (p. 1195)
PYRAMIDONE (see Aminopyrine)		
PYRIDINE–Paraffin oil	33.5	154
Potassium thiocyanate	>200	686 (p. 1131)
RESORCINOL–Carbon tetrachloride	135	685 (p. 345)
RUBIDIUM–Rubidium bromide	<655	71C
Rubidium chloride	706	71C
Rubidium fluoride	790	71C, 137
Rubidium iodide	634	71C
RUBIDIUM BROMIDE–		
Rubidium chloride	−100	269
(solid solution)		
SAGE OIL–Ethylene glycol	216.5	154
SILICA–Zirconia	2430	692
SILICON TETRACHLORIDE–		
Acetonitrile	51.8	3
Propionitrile	−10	3
SODIUM–Lithium (m.p. 186°C)	380	581
Sodium bromide	1026	71B
Sodium chloride	1080	71B
Sodium fluoride	1180	71B, 137
Sodium iodide	1033	71B
SODIUM PALMITATE–Water	316	405
SODIUM STEARATE–Iso-octane	258	686 (p. 1033)
Cyclohexane	>310	686 (p. 1035)
Benzene	>238	686 (p. 1037)
Toluene	335	686 (p. 1042)
Ethylbenzene	>291	686 (p. 1045)
o-Xylene	>240	686 (p. 1047)
m-Xylene	>244	686 (p. 1047)

(*continued*)

TABLE III (*continued*)

System	CST's in °C	References
SODIUM STEARATE (*continued*)		
p-Xylene	>280	686 (p. 1048)
Cumene	>245	686 (p. 1046)
Cymene	>171	686 (p. 1050)
n-Butylbenzene	>239	686 (p. 1046)
STANNIC CHLORIDE–Formic acid	>70	708
STANNIC IODIDE–n-Heptane	136.2	326
2-Methylhexane	159.1	326
2,2-Dimethylpentane	195.9	326
2,3-Dimethylpentane	139.7	326
2,4-Dimethylpentane	189.8	326
2,2,3-Trimethylbutane	158.0	326
2,2,3-Trimethylpentane	145.5	326, 327
2,2,4-Trimethylpentane	195	326, 327
2,3,3-Trimethylpentane	125.0	326, 327
2,3,4-Trimethylpentane	135.2	326, 327
STERANISOL–Ethylene glycol	186.5	154
SUCCINONITRILE–Benzene	49.5	154
Toluene	134.5	154
o-Xylene	163.5	154
m-Xylene	174.2	154
p-Xylene	177.0	154
Crude Xylene	187.0	154
80% Benzene, 20% Thiophene	29.5	154
Bromobenzene	129.0	154
Chlorobenzene	121.5	154
m-Dibromobenzene	199	154
p-Dibromobenzene	201.5	154
o-Dichlorobenzene	154.5	154
m-Dichlorobenzene	189.0	154
p-Dichlorobenzene	175.5	154
Fluorobenzene	60	154
Iodobenzene	149.0	154
o-Iodotoluene	198.0	154
p-Iodotoluene	188.2	154
Water	59.0	154
SULFUR–Diphenylamine	<105	359, 687 (p. 674)
N-Methylaniline	106.8	687 (p. 674)
2-Naphthylamine	100.5	351, 687 (p. 675)
o-Toluidine	122.4	687 (p. 674)
SULFUR CHLORIDE–		
Hydrogen chloride	−56	676

(*continued*)

TABLE III (*continued*)

System	CST's in °C	References
SULFUR DIOXIDE–Tetralin	22.5	687 (p. 773)
Nitrogen	>40	698A
TEMPLEN OIL–Ethylene glycol	313	154
1,1,1-ω-TETRACHLOROPARAFFINS		
(C_3, C_5, C_7, C_9)–Ethylene	>9.5	137C
THIOPHENE–Ethylene glycol	155.5	154
THYME OIL–Ethylene glycol	246	154
o-TOLUIDINE–Glycerol	154.5	154
Paraffin oil	60.5	154
Sulfur	122.4	154
-TOLUIDINE–Glycerol	119.5	154
Paraffin oil	68.5	154
TRICRESYL PHOSPHATE–		
n-Octane	49.2	154
n-Nonane	52.0	154
n-Decane	56.5	154
n-Undecane	60.5	154
Paraffin oil	101.5	154
Ethylene glycol	223.5	154
Glycerol	311.5	154
TRIETHYLCHLOROBENZENE–		
Acetonitrile	43.3	197
TURPENTINE OIL–Ethylene glycol	286	154
URANYL SULFATE–Water		
(LCST 295°C)		601
URETHANE (m.p. 50°C)–		
o-Bromotoluene	<35	388, 684 (p. 799)
WATER–Acetophenone	221	154
Aminopyrine (Pyramidone)	169	358, 765
Aniline	167	154
Azacyclo-octane ($C_7H_{15}N$)		
(LCST < −13°C)		459C, 687 (p. 91)
Benzene (+ Hydrogen)	270	296A
Bromal hydrate		
(LCST's 51 and 111°C)		773
Bromine (probably no CST)	>200	197
n-Butyl alcohol (+ Hydrogen)	138	296
sec-Butyl alcohol (LCST < −2.6°C)	112	129, 687 (p. 233)
Butyl Cellosolve (LCST 49.1°C)	130.3	96, 590
Butyl chloral hydrate		
(LCST's 64 and 82.2°C)		773
Chloral hydrate	190	745B

(*continued*)

TABLE III (*continued*)

System	CST's in °C	References
WATER (*continued*)		
Chlorine (crit. temp. 144°C, probably no CST, as in Ether– Water, Fig. 6	>100	197
Cyclohexanol	182.5	154
Cyclohexanone	200	154
Cyclopentanone	105	52
Diethylene glycol monoamyl ether (LCST 36°C)		96
Diethylene glycol monohexyl ether (LCST <0°C)		96
4,6-Dimethyl-1,2-pyrone LCST 59.7°C)	86.3	687 (p. 60), 750
Ethylene glycol *n*-butyl ether	130.3	590
Hexamethyleneimine (LCST 68.1°C)		344A
Isoamyl alcohol (+ Hydrogen)	204	296A
Methylpellitierine ($C_{13}H_{17}NO$) (LCST 35.5°C)		669, 687 (p. 131)
Nicotine (LCST <61.5°C)	233	88
Paraldehyde (LCST <8.5°C)		687 (p. 17)
Pentaethylene glycol mono-octyl ether (LCST 5.5°C)		96
Sodium palmitate	316	405
Succinonitrile	59.0	154
Tetraethylene glycol monohexyl ether (LCST 60°C)		96
Tetraethylene glycol mono-octyl ether (LCST 35.5°C)		96
Triethylene glycol monohexyl ether (LCST 39.6°C)		96
Triethylene glycol mono-octyl ether (LCST 8°C)		96
Uranyl sulfate (LCST 295°C)		601
YTTRIUM–Chromium	ca 2000	673
ZINC–Aluminum	351.6	461
Bismuth (three phases at 415°C)	605	332
Lead	790	332
ZINC CHLORIDE–4-Picoline–		
Cetyl alcohol	241	155, 686 (p. 1199)
Ethyl alcohol	33.4	155, 686 (p. 1192)
Isoamyl alcohol	62.9	155, 686 (p. 1199)
Isobutyl alcohol	55	155, 686 (p. 1197)

(*continued*)

TABLE III (*continued*)

System	CST's in °C	References
ZINC CHLORIDE (*continued*)		
2-Octanol	97	155, 686 (p. 1199)
Propyl alcohol	52.5m	155, 686 (p. 1195)
ZINC DECANOATE–Toluene	86.0	418, 686 (p. 1043)
Xylene	89.0	418, 686 (p. 1049)
ZINC LAURATE–Toluene	90.8	418, 686 (p. 1043)
Xylene	93.7	418, 686 (p. 1045)
Nitrobenzene	111	418, 686 (p. 1145)
ZINC MYRISTATE–Toluene	93.0	418, 686 (p. 1043)
Xylene	96.0	418, 686 (p. 1049)
Lauric acid	114	418, 686 (p. 1217)
Nitrobenzene	113.0	418, 686 (p. 1145)
Octadecyl alcohol	108	418, 686 (p. 1199)
ZINC STEARATE–Lauric acid	113	418, 686 (p. 1217)
Nitrobenzene	112	418, 686 (p. 1145)
Octadecyl alcohol	104	418, 686 (p. 1199)
Toluene	97.0	418, 686 (p. 1043)
Xylene	98.5	418, 686 (p. 1049)
ZIRCONIA–Silica	2430	692

Bibliography

1. A. Aarna and L. Molder, *Eesti NSV Treaduste Akad. Toimetised Fuusikalis-Mat. Treaduste Seeria*, **11**, 254 (1962); *Chem. Abstr.*, **58**, 10788f (1963). Water–Phenols–Ethanolamine.

1A. L. Alders, *Liquid-Liquid Extraction*, 2nd ed., Elsevier, Houston, 1959, pp. 18, 56. Aniline–Toluene–n-Heptane; Water–Acetone–Chloroform.

1B. L. Alders and G. G. Baijle, U. S. Patent 3,041,373, June 26, 1962. Water–Acetic or Formic acid–Benzene.

2. G. F. Alfrey and W. G. Schneider, *Discussions Faraday Soc.*, **15**, 218 (1953); *Chem. Abstr.*, **48**, 6800g (1954). Water–Triethylamine; Nitrobenzene–n-Hexane. Ultrasonic absorption.

3. S. S. Alikberov *et al.*, *Russ. J. Phys. Chem. (English Transl.)*, **34**, 443 (1960); *Chem. Abstr.*, **57**, 2914f (1962). Silicon tetrachloride–Acetonitrile or Propionitrile.

4. C. B. Allen, *Dissertation Abstr.*, **22**, 1002 (1961); *Chem. Abstr.*, **56**, 5454i (1962). Water–Hydrogen chloride, Lithium chloride, Ferric chloride–Ether.

5. G. Allen, G. Gee, and J. P. Nicholson, *Polymer*, **1**, 56 (1960); *Chem. Abstr.*, **55**, 18275d (1961). Two polymers and a solvent.

6. K. A. Allen, *U. S. Atomic Energy Comm.*, *ORNL-2709*, 1959; *Nuclear Sci. Abstr.*, **13**, 14945 (1959); *Chem. Abstr.*, **53**, 20715i (1959). Water–Uranium salts–Trioctylamine sulfate in Benzene.

7. I. G. Almeida and J. Danon, *Anais assoc. brasil. quím.*, **19**, 133 (1960); *Chem. Abstr.*, **56**, 9501b (1962). Water, lithium nitrate–nitrates of cerium, praseodymium–Trioctylamine in Benzene.

8. A. R. Amell and T. Teates, *J. Phys. Chem.*, **59**, 285 (1955). Water–Acetic acid–Benzaldehyde.

9. K. I. Amirkhanov and I. G. Gurwich, *Doklady Akad. Nauk S. S. S. R.*, **91**, 221 (1953); *Chem. Abstr.*, **48**, 13363g (1954). Water–Phenol. Heat capacity and viscosity in critical region.

9A. D. L. Andersen *et al.*, *J. Phys. Chem.*, **66**, 621 (1962). Acetone–Hydroperfluoroheptane. CST 93.5 °C.

10. E. Angelescu, *Bul. soc. chim. România*, **7**, 79 (1925); *Chem. Abstr.*, **20**, 1348[9] (1926). Water–Acetic acid–o-Toluidine. "Closed curve."

11. E. Angelescu and L. Ciplea, *Rev. chim.*, *Acad. rép. populaire Roumaine*, **2**, 35 (1957); *Chem. Abstr.*, **52**, 11786c (1958). p-Phenetidine–Decalin–Nine aromatics.

12. E. Angelescu and L. Cristodulo, *Bul. chim.*, *Soc. chim. România* (2), **2**, 114, 123 (1940); *Chem. Abstr.*, **37**, 6186[9] (1943); *Chem. Abstr.*, **38**, 6166[9] (1944). Water–Butyric acid–Aniline or o-Toluidine. Isopycnics.

13. E. Angelescu and I. Ganea, *Rev. chim.*, *Acad. rép. populaire Roumaine*, **2**, 41 (1957); *Chem. Abstr.*, **52**, 11786e (1958). Acetic anhydride–Decalin–Nine aromatics.

14. E. Angelescu and C. Hölsky, *Acad. rep. populare Romîne*, *Bul. stiint. Sect. stiinte teh. si chim.*, **4**, No. 1–2, 129, 179 (1952); *Chem. Abstr.*, **50**, 13772b (1956). Water–Dimethyl or Diethyl aniline–Formic to Butyric acids.

15. E. Angelescu and D. Motoc, *Commun. acad. rép. populare Romîne*, **3**, 267 (1953); *Chem. Abstr.*, **50**, 9107g (1956). Water–Ethyl alcohol–Isoamyl alcohol–Salts.

16. E. Angelescu and A. Stratula-Angelescu, *Analele univ. "C. I. Parhon" Bucuresti, Ser. stiint. nat.*, **No. 19**, 55 (1958); *Chem. Abstr.*, **53**, 16674a (1959). Water–Phloroglucinol–Phenol.

16A. E. Angelescu and A. Stratula-Angelescu, *Analele Univ. "C. I. Parhon" Bucuresti Ser. Stiint. Nat.*, **10**, No. 30, 79 (1961); *Chem. Abstr.*, **58**, 7430b (1963). Water–1,2,4-Benzenetriol–Phenol.

17. G. Antonoff, M. Chanin, and M. Hecht, *J. Phys. Chem.*, **46**, 492 (1942). Water–Isobutyric acid or *sec*-Butyl or Isoamyl alcohols. Slow equilibrium.

18. G. Antonoff, M. Hecht, and M. Chanin, *J. Phys. Chem.*, **45**, 791 (1941). Water–Phenol. Slow equilibrium.

18A. I. A. Apraksin *et al.*, *Zhur. Neorg. Khim.*, **8**, 237 (1963); *Chem. Abstr.*, **58**, 10788h (1963). Water–Hydrogen chloride–Tributyl phosphate.

19. S. Arakawa and T. Kawaguchi, *Yakugaku Zasshi*, **78**, 148 (1958); *Chem. Abstr.*, **52**, 8690i (1958). Water–Alkylamines–Salts.

20. S. Arakawa, T. Kawaguchi, and H. Kato, *Yakugaku Zasshi*, **78**, 837 (1958); *Chem. Abstr.*, **52**, 17934b (1958). Water–Pyridine or Methylpyridine–Salts.

21. S. Arakawa, T. Kawaguchi, and H. Kato, *Yakugaku Zasshi*, **79**, 140 (1959); *Chem. Abstr.*, **53**, 10931h (1959). Water–Nicotine–Salts.

22. G. Arich, *Ann. chim. (Rome)*, **45**, 306 (1955); *Chem. Abstr.*, **50**, 6166g (1956). Prediction of ternary from binary systems.

23. G. Arich and G. Tagliavini, *Ricerca Sci.*, **28**, 1620 (1958); *Chem. Abstr.*, **53**, 6743d (1959). Water–Acetone–Benzene.

24. G. Arich, G. Tagliavini, and M. Biancani, *Chim. e ind. (Milan)*, **38**, 937 (1956); *Chem. Abstr.*, **51**, 4806c (1957). Aniline–Dichloroethylene–Heptane.

25. V. W. Arnold and E. R. Washburn, *J. Phys. Chem.*, **62**, 1088 (1958). Water–Isopropyl alcohol–Isoamyl alcohol.

26. T. Asahara and C. Kimura, *Kôgyô Kagaku Zasshi*, **56**, 702 (1953); *Chem. Abstr.*, **48**, 12011i (1954). Water–Phenol–Benzene–Heptane or Gasoline. Humps in binodal curve.

27. A. H. W. Aten, *Z. physik. Chem.*, **54**, 124 (1906). Methyl iodide–Pyridine.

28. M. Aubert and E. Aubrée, *Compt. rend.*, **182**, 577 (1926); *Chem. Abstr.*, **20**, 1712 (1926). Benzyl alcohol with two Hydrocarbons.

29. A. M. Avenarius and D. N. Tarasenkov, *Zhur. Obshcheĭ Khim.*, **16**, 1777 (1946); *Chem. Abstr.*, **41**, 5372g (1947). Formic acid–Bromoform–Benzene. Isopycnic. All tie lines isologous.

30. A. L. Babb and H. G. Drickamer, *J. Chem. Phys.*, **20**, 290 (1952); *Chem. Abstr.*, **46**, 7406d (1952). Methanol–Pentanes or Hexane. Effect of pressure on CST.

31. I. Backman, *Ind. Eng. Chem., Anal. Ed.*, **12**, 38 (1940). Equations for tie lines.

32. D. E. Badertscher, A. W. Francis, and G. C. Johnson, U. S. Patent 2,688,645, Sept. 7, 1954. Ethylene carbonate–Benzene–Heptane.

33. C. O. Badgett, *Ind. Eng. Chem.*, **43**, 2340 (1941). Water–Nicotine–Kerosine.

34. C. R. Bailey, *J. Chem. Soc.*, **123**, 2579 (1923). Water–Phenols or Cresols–Sodium oleate or 17 other substances.

35. *Idem*, **1925**, 1951. Water–Phenol–Salicylic acid. Two separate binodal curves.

36. E. Bak and C. J. Geankoplis, *Chem. Eng. Data Ser.*, **3**, 256 (1958). Water–Fatty acids–4-Methyl-2-pentanone.
37. E. M. Baker, *J. Phys. Chem.*, **59**, 1182 (1955). Water–*n*-Propyl alcohol–Toluene.
38. L. W. C. Baker and T. F. Anderson, *J. Am. Chem. Soc.*, **79**, 2071 (1957). Water–Ethyl alcohol–Carbon dioxide.
39. W. H. Baldwin, *Nuclear Sci. Abstr.*, **10**, 6168 (1956). Water–Uranium(VI)–Cyclohexanone. Cf. reference 261.
40. J. S. Ball, *U. S. Bur. Mines, Rept. Invest. 3721*, 1943. Aniline points of hydrocarbons.
41. W. D. Bancroft, *J. Phys. Chem.*, **1**, 403, 647 (1897). Triangular diagrams.
42. W. D. Bancroft and S. S. Hubard, *J. Am. Chem. Soc.*, **64**, 347 (1942). Water–Acetone–Chloroform; Water–Ethyl alcohol–Benzene. Graphical method for composition of layers.
43. A. Baouman, *Ind. chim.*, **35**, 63 (1948); *Chem. Abstr.*, **42**, 6142i (1948). Water–Phenol–Soap.
44. F. Barcánfalvi, *Nehézvegyipari Kutató Intézet Közleményei*, **2**, 143 (1960); *Chem. Abstr.*, **55**, 26627c (1961). Water–Hydrogen chloride–Germanium chloride.
45. A. S. Barkan and A. G. Beketova, *Uchenye Zapiski, Belorus. Gosudarst. Univ. im. V. I. Lenina, Ser. Khim.*, No. 29, 222 (1956); *Chem. Abstr.*, **54**, 6260g (1960). Water–Dioxane–Sodium chloride and Benzene.
45A. A. S. Barkan and S. V. Grin'ko, *Izv. Vysshikh Uchebn. Zavedenii, Khim. i Khim. Tekhnol.*, **5**, 394 (1962); *Chem. Abstr.*, **57**, 15882d (1962). Water, Potassium chloride–Isopropyl alcohol–Benzene.
46. A. S. Barkan and N. A. Kondrus, *Uchenye Zapiski, Belorus. Gosudarst. Univ. im. V. I. Lenina, Ser. Khim.*, No. 42, 221 (1958); *Chem. Abstr.*, **54**, 6261a (1960). Water–Methanol, Glycol, or Glycerol–Ammonium sulfate or Ethylene chloride.
47. A. S. Barkan and T. A. Serzhanina, *Uchenye Zapiski, Belorus. Gosudarst. Univ. im. V. I. Lenina, Ser. Khim.*, No. 42, 199 (1958); *Chem. Abstr.*, **54**, 6260h (1960). Water–Dioxane–Sodium nitrate–Aromatics, etc.
48. K. N. Baronov, *Russ. J. Phys. Chem. (English Transl.)*, **35**, 268 (1961); *Chem. Abstrs.*, **55**, 16111g (1961). Water–Ethyl alcohol–Sodium thiosulfate.
48A. C. J. Barton, G. M. Hebert, and W. L. Marshall, *J. Inorg. & Nuclear Chem.*, **21**, 141 (1961); *Chem. Abstr.*, **57**, 121b (1962). Water–Sulfuric acid–Uranium nitrate at 300°C.
49. A. Basiński and S. Poczopko, *Roczniki Chem.*, **33**, 1109 (1959); *Chem. Abstr.*, **54**, 7319f (1960). Water–Acetone–Cadmium sulfate.
50. A. Basiński and S. Poczopko, *Roczniki Chem.*, **34**, 1061 (1960); *Chem. Abstr.*, **55**, 10034h (1961). Water–Isopropyl alcohol–Cadmium or Lithium sulfates.
50A. I. N. Belyaev, *Russ. Chem. Rev. (English Transl.)*, **1960**, 428. Cf. *Chem. Abstr.*, **54**, 21966f (1960). Water–Hydrogen chloride or bromide.
51. C. Berg, M. Manders, and R. Switzer, *Chem. Eng. Progr.*, **47**, 11 (1951); *Chem. Abstr.*, **45**, 2186b (1951). Water–2-Butanone–Naphtha.
52. V. Bertini and P. Pino, *Chim. e ind. (Milan)*, **41**, 195 (1959); *Chem. Abstr.*, **53**, 19549c (1959). Water–Succinic acid–Cyclopentanone.

53. U. Bertocci and G. Rolandi, *Comit. Nazl. Energia Nucleare CNI-91*, 1961; *J. Inorg. & Nuclear Chem.*, **23**, 323 (1961); *Chem. Abstr.*, **56**, 2945i (1962). Tri-*n*-octylamine–Mineral acids–Xylene.

54. M. Biancani and D. DeFilippo, *Gazz. chim. ital.*, **88**, 1202 (1958); *Chem. Abstr.*, **53**, 21109d (1959). Water–Propionic acid–Benzene. Double solutrope. Plait point near top.

55. E. H. Binns, K. H. Squire, and L. J. Wood, *Trans. Faraday Soc.*, **56**, 1770 (1960); *Chem. Abstr.*, **55**, 12017a (1961). Water–Phenol–Toluene. Isopycnic.

56. C. A. Blake, Jr., C. F. Baes, Jr., and K. B. Brown, *Ind. Eng. Chem.*, **50**, 1763 (1958). Water–Uranium salts–Alkylphosphoric acid compounds.

57. C. A. Blake, Jr., K. B. Brown, and C. F. Coleman, *U. S. Atomic Energy Comm.*, *ORNL-1903-1964*, 1955; *Nuclear Sci. Abstr.*, **10**, 7573 (1956); **11**, 2357 (1957); *Chem. Abstr.*, **50**, 15320i (1956). Water–Salts of Uranium and Vanadium–Trialkylphosphine oxides.

58. C. A. Blake, Jr., J. G. Moore, and W. M. Whaley, *U. S. Atomic Energy Comm.*, *ORNL-1480*, 1956; *Nuclear Sci. Abstr.*, **11**, 2356 (1957). Water–Di(2-ethylhexyl)phosphoric acid–Uranium salts–Tributyl phosphate.

59. M. G. Blank and E. N. Vasenko, *Doklady L'vovsk. Politekhn. Inst.*, **4**, No. 1,2, 3,4,68 (1960); *Chem. Abstr.*, **55**, 25441d (1961); **56**, 5450b (1962). Form-amide–Acetone–Toluene or Chloroform.

59A. S. V. Bleshinskii, *Isv. Akad. Nauk Kirgiz. S.S.R.*, *Ser. Estestven. i Tekhn. Nauk*, **3**, No. 2, 125 (1961); *Chem. Abstr.*, **57**, 2917h (1962). Water–Perchloric acid–Isoamyl alcohol; Water–Hydrogen chloride–Benzyl alcohol; Water–Pyridine–Sodium mercuric iodide. Salting in.

60. T. C. Boberg, Presented at A. I. Ch. E. Meeting, Tulsa, Okla., Sept., 1960; *API (Am. Petrol. Inst.) Tech. Abstr.*, **7**, 7674 (1960). Water–Methanol–Paraffins.

61. T. C. Boberg and R. R. White, *Ind. Eng. Chem. Fundamentals*, **1**, 40 (1962). Calculations of plait points in eight systems of ethyl acetate and benzene.

62. A. A. Bobrova and V. I. Kuznetsov, *Izuch. i Kompleksn. Pererabotka Smol i Bitumov Burykh Uglei Dneprovsk. Basseina, Akad. Nauk Ukr. S. S. R.*, *Sbornik*, No. 2, 90 (1958); *Chem. Abstr.*, **54**, 20156f (1960). Water–Ethyl alcohol–Ethylene chloride or Benzene.

63. R. Bock and E. Bock, *Naturwissenschaften*, **36**, 344 (1949); *Chem. Abstr.*, **44**, 5749a (1950). Water, Nitric acid–Nitrates of rare earths–Ether.

64. G. S. Bogoslovskii, *Uchenye Zapiski Molotov Gosudarst. Univ.*, **3**, No. 4, 91 (1939); *Chem. Abstr.*, **37**, 4618[1] (1943). Aniline–Acetic acid–Benzene–Gasoline.

65. E. Bonauguri, *Chim. e ind. (Milan)*, **35**, 900 (1953); *Chem. Abstr.*, **48**, 9798a (1954). Water–Acetic acid–Ether.

66. M. G. Boobar et al., *Ind. Eng. Chem.*, **43**, 2922 (1951). Diethylene glycol–Styrene–Ethylbenzene.

67. S. T. Bowden and J. H. Purnell, *J. Chem. Soc.*, **1954**, 535. Water–Thorium or Uranium salts–Phenol.

68. A. V. Brancker, *Nature*, **166**, 960 (1950); *Ind. Chemist*, **27**, 243 (1951); *Petroleum (London)*, **14**, 123, 143 (1951); *Chem. Abstr.*, **45**, 2763h, 5504i (1951); **46**, 786f (1952). Water–Acetone–Acetaldehyde–Vinyl acetate.

69. A. V. Brancker, T. G. Hunter, and A. W. Nash, *Ind. Eng. Chem.*, **33**, 880 (1941). Water–Acetic acid–Acetone–Chloroform; Acetic acid–Lube oil–Chloroform.

70. *Idem, Anal. Ed.*, **12**, 35 (1940). Correlation of tie lines of 33 systems.

71. A. V. Brancker, T. G. Hunter, and A. W. Nash, *J. Phys. Chem.*, **44**, 683 (1940). Water–Acetic acid–Acetone–Chloroform.

71A. E. Brauer and E. Högfeldt, *J. Inorg. Nuclear Chem.*, **23**, 115 (1961). Water–Sulfuric acid–Tributyl phosphate–Benzene or Kerosine.

71B. M. A. Bredig and H. R. Bronstein, *J. Phys. Chem.*, **64**, 64 (1960). *Cf. J. Am. Chem. Soc.*, **77**, 307 (1955). CST of Sodium–Sodium halides.

71C. M. A. Bredig and J. W. Johnson, *Ibid.* **64**, 1899 (1960). CST of Rubidium–Rubidium halides.

71D. A. Brehm, *Z. physik. Chem.*, *(Leipzig)*, **221**, 1 (1962). Water–Adipic acid–Cyclohexanol; *Chem. Abstr.*, **58**, 60f.

72. W. S. Brey, Jr., *Anal. Chem.*, **26**, 838 (1954). Water–Isopropyl alcohol–Isopropyl ether.

73. S. W. Briggs and E. W. Comings, *Ind. Eng. Chem.*, **35**, 411 (1943). Furfural–Diphenylhexane–*n*-Docosane; Water–Acetone–Benzene.

74. R. R. Brooks and P. J. Lloyd, *Nature*, **189**, 375 (1961); *Chem. Abstr.*, **55**, 14039b (1961). Water, Hydrogen chloride–Chlorides of gallium and indium–Seven ethers.

75. A. S. Broun, *Zhur. Obshchei Khim.*, **3**, 973 (1933); *Chem. Abstr.*, **28**, 2983[8] (1934). Ethylene diamine–Cyclohexane–Hexane; 684, p. 521.

76. K. B. Brown *et al.*, *U. S. Atomic Energy Comm.*, *D-4142; Nuclear Sci. Abstr.*, **10**, 9740 (1956). Water–Uranyl sulfate–Amines.

77. S. H. Brown, H. H. Clark, *et al.*, *U. S. Atomic Energy Comm.*, *A-1069; Nuclear Sci. Abstr.*, **11**, 13362 (1957). Cf. reference 261. Water–Uranyl nitrate–Ether.

78. T. F. Brown, *Ind. Eng. Chem.*, **40**, 103 (1948). Aniline–Benzene or Heptane–Cetane–Cyclohexane.

78A. P. Brun, *Compt. rend.*, **182**, 1219 (1926); *Chem. Abstr.*, **20**, 2776[9] (1926). Water–Ethyl alcohol–Higher alcohols.

79. H. Brusset and D. Bono, *Compt. rend.*, **234**, 1688 (1952); *Chem. Abstr.*, **47**, 5198g (1953). Estimating whole binary binodal curve from the CST.

80. R. H. Buchanen, *Ind. Eng. Chem.*, **44**, 2449 (1952). Water–Acetone–Carbon tetrachloride.

81. H. Buchovski and J. Teperak, *Roczniki Chem.*, **33**, 1093 (1959); *Chem. Abstr.*, **54**, 7318g (1960). Water–Methanol–Iso-octane.

81A. J. E. Buckley and J. E. Caldwell, *J. Chem. Eng. Data*, **7**, 480 (1962). Water–*o*- and *p*-Toluenesulfonamide at 95 °C.

81B. E. J. Burcik, *Producers Monthly*, **26**, No. 3, 2 (1962); *Chem. Abstr.*, **57**, 123f (1962). Water–Isopropyl alcohol–Propane Solutrope.

82. L. L. Burger, *J. Phys. Chem.*, **62**, 590 (1958). Water–Nitrates of uranium and plutonium–Phosphorus compounds in Carbon tetrachloride.

83. C. A. Burkart *U. S. Atomic Energy Comm.*, *BMI-263; Nuclear Sci. Abstr.*, **11**, 12964 (1957). Water, Nitric acid–Thorium nitrate–Tributyl phosphate–Solvesso 100.

84. I. N. Bushmakin and N. V. Lutugina, *Vestnik Leningrad. Univ.*, **13**, No. 10, *Ser. Fiz. i Khim.*, No. 2, 75 (1958); *Chem. Abstr.*, **52**, 17927h (1958). Water–Acetic acid–Butyl acetate.

84A. K. L. Butcher and C. Hanson, *Chem. Process Eng.*, **43**, 540 (1962); *Chem. Abstr.*, **58**, 1951h (1963). Water–Sulfur dioxide.

85. S. Sh. Byk *et al.*, *J. Appl. Chem. U. S. S. R.* (*English Transl.*), **29**, 2023 (1956); *Chem. Abstr.*, **51**, 7824c (1957). Water–Phenol–Methylstyrene.

86. S. Sh. Byk *et al.*, *Zhur. Fiz. Khim.*, **30**, 305 (1956); *Chem. Abstr.*, **50**, 11092e (1956). Water–2-Butanone–Phenol.

87. Calvin, M., *Experientia*, **6**, 135 (1950); *Chem. Abstr.*, **45**, 940b (1951). Water–Metal chelates with $XOCH_2COCF_3$–Benzene.

88. A. N. Campbell, E. M. Kartzmark, and W. E. Falconer, *Can. J. Chem.*, **36**, 1475 (1958); *Chem. Abstr.*, **53**, 6743i (1959). Water–Nicotine–2-Butanone.

88A. A. N. Campbell, E. M. Kartzmark, and J. M. T. M. Gieskes, *Can. J. Chem.*, **41**, 407 (1963). Water–Acetic acid–Chloroform. Density and R. I.

89. D. E. Campbell, A. H. Laurene, and H. M. Clark, *J. Am. Chem. Soc.*, **74**, 6193 (1952). Water–Hydrogen chloride–Isopropyl ether.

90. J. A. Campbell, *Ind. Eng. Chem.*, **36**, 1158 (1944). Equation for distribution between phases. Sixteen aqueous systems.

91. R. Cardinaud, *Compt. rend.*, **246**, 415 (1958); *Chem. Abstr.*, **52**, 9697b (1958). Water or Deuterium oxide–Phenol or Deuteriophenol.

92. H. C. Carlson and A. P. Colburn, *Ind. Eng. Chem.*, **34**, 581 (1942). Prediction of phase equilibriums.

93. J. F. Carrière, *Chem. Weekblad.*, **41**, 58 (1945); *Chem. Abstr.*, **40**, 794 (1946). Five liquid phases.

94. N. H. Carrington, L. R. Hickson, and W. H. Patterson, *J. Chem. Soc.*, **127**, 2544 (1925). Water–Salts–Phenol.

95. A. Casarico, *Ann. chim.* (*Rome*), **41**, 199 (1951); *Chem. Abstr.*, **45**, 9354b (1951). Water–Acetic acid–Ether or Methylene chloride.

96. N. Chakhovsky, *Bull. soc. chim. Belges*, **65**, 474 (1956); *Chem. Abstr.*, **50**, 16230g (1956). Water–Glycol ethers–Sodium sulfonates.

96A. C. A. Chandy and M. R. Rao, *J. Chem. Eng. Data*, **7**, 473 (1962). Water–*n*-Hexyl alcohol–Propionic or Butyric acids.

97. Y. C. Chang and R. W. Moulton, *Ind. Eng. Chem.*, **45**, 2350 (1953). Water–Acetic acid or Ethyl alcohol–Benzene, Ethyl isovalerate, or Toluene.

98. E. J. Charles and F. Morton, *J. Applied Chem.* (*London*), **7**, 39 (1957); *Chem. Abstr.*, **51**, 14398i (1957). Water or Triethylene glycol-2-Picoline–Benzene–Nonaromatics.

99. G. Chavanne and L. J. Simon, *Compt. rend.*, **168**, 1111; **169**, 70, 185, 693 (1919); *Chem. Abstr.*, **13**, 2125 (1919); **14**, 117, 464 (1920). Aniline points.

99A. Y. M. Ch'en, P. J. Sun, and F. C. Chou, *J. Chinese Chem. Soc.* (*Taiwan*), (Ser. II), **8**, 56 (1961) (in English); *Chem. Abstr.*, **57**, 10584a (1962). Water, Thorium nitrate, Ammonium thiocyanate–Cyclohexanol, Isoamyl alcohol, or Ethyl acetate.

100. W. W. Chew and V. Orr, *J. Chem. Eng. Data*, **4**, 215 (1959); *Chem. Abstr.*, **46**, 5920e (1952). Water–*n*-Propyl alcohol–Hexamethyldisiloxane.

100A. A. Chretien *et al.*, *Bull. soc. chim. France*, **1960,** No. 1, 49 (1960); *Chem. Abstr.*, **54,** 12732a (1960). Ozone–Freons.

100B. R. M. Christenson and S. W. Gloyer, U. S. Patents 2,530,809 and 2,530,810, November 21, 1950; *Chem. Abstr.*, **45,** 2208b,d (1951). Water–Methanol or Isopropyl alcohol–Tall oil in Naphtha.

101. A. G. Chynoweth and W. G. Schneider, *J. Chem. Phys.*, **19,** 1536 (1951); *Chem. Abstr.*, **46,** 5920e (1952). Ultrasonic propagation near CST. Water–Aniline–Hexane, Triethylamine.

102. F. W. J. Clendinnen and A. C. D. Rivett, *J. Chem. Soc.*, **123,** 1344 (1923). Water–Manganese dichloride–Ammonium chloride.

103. K. Clusius and W. Ringer, *Z. physik. Chem. (Leipzig)*, **A187,** 186 (1940); *Chem. Abstr.*, **35,** 4665i (1941). Acetone–Carbon disulfide. CST −51.3°C.

104. K. Clusius and H. Ulmke, *Z. physik. Chem. (Leipzig)*, **A189,** 331 (1941); *Chem. Abstr.*, **36,** 6883⁶ (1942). Carbon disulfide–Methyl acetate. CST −52.6°C.

105. F. K. Cole and L. H. Brown, *Ind. Eng. Chem.*, **51,** 58 (1959). Water–Glycolic or Salicylic acid–Furfural–Metal nitrates.

106. R. Collander, *Acta Chem. Scand.*, **3,** 717 (1949); *Chem. Abstr.*, **44,** 2828d (1950). Water–Ether–224 other Organic compounds.

107. R. Collander, *Acta Chem. Scand.*, **4,** 1085 (1950); *Chem. Abstr.*, **45,** 3690d (1951). Water–Isobutyl alcohol–142 other Organic compounds.

108. R. Collander, *Acta Chem. Scand.*, **5,** 774 (1951); *Chem. Abstr.*, **46,** 7450f (1952). Water–Isoamyl, Octyl, or Oleyl alcohols–50 Organic compounds.

109. J. J. Conti, D. F. Othmer, and R. Gilmont, *J. Chem. Eng. Data*, **5,** 301 (1960). Water–Acetic or Formic acid–Chloroform at boiling point.

110. J. B. Conway and J. B. Philip, *Ind. Eng. Chem.*, **45,** 1083 (1953). Water–Furfural–4-Methyl-2-pentanone. Isopycnic.

111. H. W. Crandall, J. R. Thomas, and J. C. Reid, *U. S. Atomic Energy Comm.*, *CN-2657*, 1945; *Nuclear Sci. Abstr.*, **11,** 12369 (1957); *Chem. Abstr.*, **55,** 18268d (1961). Water–Plutonium nitrate–Benzene–Trifluoroacetylacetone.

112. A. G. Crawford, G. Edwards, and D. S. Lindsay, *J. Chem. Soc.*, **1949,** 1054 (1949). Water–Methanol–Methyl acetate.

113. M. A. Crespi, *Rev. cienc. apl. (Madrid)*, **6,** 331 (1952); *Chem. Abstr.*, **47,** 1988b (1953). Water–Acetic acid–Acetone–Chloroform; Methanol–Oleic acid–Olive oil–Carbon disulfide. Engineering. Four components.

114. M. A. Crespi, *Rev. cienc. apl. (Madrid)*, **6,** 438 (1952); *Chem. Abstr.*, **47,** 4181h (1953). Same components as in reference 113 and also Furfural–Methyl oleate–Methyl stearate–Naphtha.

115. M. A. Crespi, *Rev. cienc. apl. (Madrid)*, **6,** 517 (1952); *Chem. Abstr.*, **49,** 7952c (1955). List of 20 quaternary systems.

116. E. D. Crittenden, Jr., and A. N. Hixson, *Ind. Eng. Chem.*, **46,** 265 (1954). Water–Hydrogen chloride–32 Organic solvents.

117. L. F. Crooke, Jr., and M. Van Winkle, *Ibid.*, **46,** 1474 (1954). Water–Diacetone alcohol–Ethylbenzene or Styrene.

118. A. J. B. Cruikshank, N. Haertsch, and T. G. Hunter, *Ibid.*, **42,** 2154 (1950). Four-component systems. Theoretical. Deviations from straight-line profiles.

119. J. L. Crützen, W. Jost, and L. Sieg, *Z. Elektrochem.*, **61**, 229 (1957); *Chem. Abstr.*, **51**, 10214d (1957). Glycol–Aniline–Methyl or Dimethylaniline.

120. A. P. C. Cumming and F. Morton, *J. Appl. Chem. (London)*, **2**, 314 (1952); *Chem. Abstr.*, **47**, 292i (1953). Water–Glycerol or Triethylene glycol–Phenols. Solutropes.

121. A. P. C. Cumming and F. Morton, *J. Appl. Chem. (London)*, **3**, 358 (1953); *Chem. Abstr.*, **48**, 2461f (1954). Water–Ethylenediamine–Benzene–Hexane. Discussion of solutropes.

121A. A. J. Davenport, P. I. Freeman, and J. S. Rowlinson, *A. I. Ch. E. Journal*, **8**, 428 (1962). Methane–Hexanes and Heptanes. LCST.

121B. A. J. Davenport and J. S. Rowlinson, *Trans. Faraday Soc.*, **59**, 78 (1963); *Chem. Abstr.*, **59**, 74e (1963). Methane–C_6 to C_8 paraffins. LCST.

122. H. S. Davis, *J. Am. Chem. Soc.*, **38**, 1166 (1916). Supersaturation in liquid mixtures.

123. H. S. Davis and A. W. Francis, U. S. Patent 2,077,041, April 13, 1937. Water–Silver nitrate–Olefins–Paraffins.

124. J. R. Davis and L. R. Evans, *J. Chem. Eng. Data*, **5**, 401 (1960). Water–sec-Butyl alcohol–Benzene.

124A. C. H. Deal and E. L. Derr, Paper presented before the Petroleum Division of the American Chemical Society, Atlantic City, Sept., 1962. Selectivity of 38 solvents.

125. T. E. Degaleeson and G. S. Laddha, *J. Appl. Chem. (London)*, **12**, 111 (1962); *Chem. Abstr.*, **57**, 129g (1962). Propylene glycol–Ethyl alcohol–Benzene, Hexane, or Cyclohexane.

125A. T. E. Degaleeson and G. S. Laddha, *J. Madras Univ.*, **30B**, 133 (1960); *Chem. Abstr.*, **56**, 5450c (1962). Water–Propylene glycol–Alcohols, Esters, or 4-Methyl-2-pentanone.

126. D. G. Dervichian and C. Magnant, *Rec. trav. chim.*, **71**, 80 (1952); *Chem. Abstr.*, **46**, 5934b (1952). Cellulose diacetate–Ethyl alcohol–Chloroform.

126A. G. S. Deshmukh and A. L. J. Rao, *J. Sci. Ind. Research (India)*, **21B**, 141 (1962); *Chem. Abstr.*, **56**, 14993g (1962). Water–Sodium formate–Pyridine.

127. M. P. Dianov and N. A. Trifonov, *Doklady Akad. Nauk S. S. S. R.*, **123**, 1033 (1958); *Chem. Abstr.*, **53**, 7745h (1959). Water–Acetic anhydride at b.p.– Diphenylamine, Chloral, Piperidine, Allyl isothiocyanate, Ethylenediamine.

127A. G. A. M. Diepen and F. E. C. Scheffer, *J. Am. Chem. Soc.*, **70**, 4085 (1948); *J. Phys. Chem.*, **57**, 575 (1953). Ethylene–Naphthylene above crit. temp.

128. A. Dobry-Duclaux, *Makromol. Chem.*, **18/19**, 317 (1956); *Chem. Abstr.*, **50**, 15197g (1956). Water or Glycerol–Phenol–Carbon tetrachloride, Acetophenone, Chloroform–Polymers.

129. V. I. Dolgolenko, *Zhur. Russ. Fiz. Khim. Obshchestva*, **39**, 841 (1907); *Z. physik. Chem.*, **62**, 499 (1908); *Chem. Abstr.*, **2**, 1374 (1908). LCST due to hydrate. Water–sec-Butyl alcohol.

130. R. Domansky, *Chem. listy*, **46**, 765 (1952); *Chem. Abstr.*, **47**, 4181h (1953). Water–Ethyl alcohol–Furfural.

130A. C. Drucker, *Rec. trav. chim.*, **42**, 553 (1923); *Chem. Abstr.*, **17**, 3825[6] (1923). Aniline–Hexane–Six other compounds; Methanol–Carbon disulfide–Water, five Salts, Diphenylamine, Succinic acid, Urea.

131. C. E. Dryden, *Ind. Eng. Chem.*, **35**, 492 (1943). Ternary liquid equilibriums from binary vapor–liquid equilibriums.

132. M. J. Duhamel and P. A. Laurent, *Bull. soc. chim. France*, **1953**, 162 (1953); *Compt. rend.*, **234**, 2069 (1952); *Chem. Abstr.*, **46**, 8473f (1952); **47**, 7306e (1953). Water–Potassium hydroxide, Lithium hydroxide, Sodium hydroxide–Acetone, Dioxane, or Pyridine.

133. M. J. Duhamel and P. A. Laurent, *Bull. soc. chim. France*, **1954**, 862 (1954); *Chem. Abstr.*, **48**, 11899e (1954). Water–Potassium or Sodium carbonate–Acetone–Allyl alcohol, *n*- and Isopropyl alcohols.

133A. R. D. Dunlap and R. L. Scott, *J. Phys. Chem.*, **66**, 631 (1962). Acetone–Perfluoro-*n*-heptane–Hydroperfluoroheptane.

134. J. Durandet, *Rev. inst. franç. pétrole et Ann. combustibles liquides*, **12**, 1161 (1957); *Chem. Abstr.*, **52**, 9739b (1958). Oxydipropionitrile or Thiodipropionitrile–Toluene–Heptane.

135. J. Durandet and Y. L. Gladel, *Rev. inst. franç. pétrole et Ann. combustibles liquides*, **9**, 296 (1954); *Chem. Abstr.*, **48**, 12534f (1954). Aniline–Toluene–Heptane.

136. J. Durandet and Y. L. Gladel, *Rev. inst. franç. pétrole et Ann. combustibles liquides*, **11**, 811 (1956); *Chem. Abstr.*, **51**, 1050f (1957). Dimethylformamide–Toluene or Cyclohexane–Heptane.

136A. J. Durandet, Y. L. Gladel, and F. Graziani, *Rev. inst. franç. pétrole et Ann combustibles liquides*, **10**, 585 (1955); *Chem. Abstr.*, **50**, 8185d (1956). Benzyl alcohol–Toluene or Cyclohexane–Heptane.

137. A. S. Dworkin, H. R. Bronstein, and M. A. Bredig, *J. Phys. Chem.*, **66**, 572 (1962). CST of Alkali metals–alkali fluorides. Cf. reference 71B, 71C, 307A.

137A. B. E. Eakin, R. T. Ellington, and D. C. Gami, *Inst. Gas. Technol. Research Bull.*, No. 26 (1955); *Chem. Abstr.*, **50**, 3823e (1956). Ethane–Nitrogen.

137B. N. N. Efremov, *Zhur. Russ. Fiz. Khim. Obshchestva*, **50**, I 338 (1918); *Chem. Abstr.*, **17**, 3272[3] (1923). Water, Ethyl or *tert*-Amyl alcohol–Bromal or Chloral.

137C. G. D. Efremova and R. F. Kovpakova, *Zhur. Fiz. Khim.*, **32**, 1231 (1958); *Chem. Abstr.*, **53**, 841 g. (1959). Ethylene–1,1,1,2-tetrachloroethane through 1,1,1,5-tetrachloropentane. Two liquid phases even above crit. temp. of Ethylene.

138. G. D. Efremova and R. O. Pryankova, *Khim. Prom.*, **1961**, 564; *Chem. Abstr.*, **56**, 4151g (1962). Water–Acetic acid–Butane.

138A. P. Ehrlich and E. B. Graham, *J. Polymer Sci.*, **45**, 246 (1960); *Chem. Abstr.*, **55**, 5099c (1961). Propane–Polyethylene at 150°C and 500 atm. (crit. soln. pressure).

138B. P. Ekwall, I. Danielsson, and L. Mandell, *Vortraege Originalfassung Intern. Kongr., Grenzflaechenactive Stoffe, 3, Cologne, Germany*, **1**, 193 (1960) (in English); *Chem. Abstr.*, **57**, 5347i (1962). Water–Sodium caprylate–Decyl alcohol. Ten three-phase areas.

139. D. D. Eley and P. J. King, *J. Chem. Soc.*, **1952**, 2517; *Cationic Polymerization and Related Complexes*, **1952**, 10 (1953); *Chem. Abstr.*, **47**, 64a (1953); **48**, 5127e (1954). Aluminum bromide–Hydrogen bromide–Benzene.

140. J. C. Elgin, "Solvent Extraction," *Chemical Engineers' Handbook*, J. H. Perry, Ed., McGraw-Hill, New York, 1950, p. 726. List of ternary systems. Schematic graphs.

141. J. C. Elgin, U. S. Patent 2,436,209, Feb. 17, 1948; 2,479,041, Aug. 16, 1949. Aqueous Glycerol systems.

142. J. C. Elgin, U. S. Patent 2,736,756, Feb. 28, 1956. Acetonitrile–Ethylene–Ethane.

143. J. C. Elgin and J. J. Weinstock, *J. Chem. Eng. Data*, **4**, 3 (1959). Water–Ethylene–26 Liquids.

144. Z. P. Ershova, *Geokhimiya*, **1957**, 296 (1957) (English Abstr.); *Chem. Abstr.*, **52**, 13397i (1958). Silica–Alumina–Fluorides of magnesium, calcium, strontium, and barium. About 1400 °C.

145. Z. P. Ershova and Y. I. Ol'shanskii, *Geokhimiya*, **1957**, 214 (1957); *Chem. Abstr.*, **52**, 13396g (1958). Same components.

146. Z. P. Ershova and Y. I. Ol'shanskii, *Geokhimiya*, **1958**, 144 (1958); *Chem. Abstr.*, **52**, 15221c (1958). Silica–Fluorides of Sodium, potassium, magnesium, calcium, strontium, and barium. About 1200°C.

147. R. A. Ewing and J. B. Fishel, *U. S. Atomic Energy Comm.*, *BMI-262; Nuclear Sci. Abstr.*, **11**, 12986 (1957). Water–Tributyl phosphate–Thorium nitrate–Benzene.

148. M. R. Fenske *et al.*, *A. I. Ch. E. Journal*, **1**, 335 (1955); *Chem. Abstr.*, **50**, 2154b (1956). Twelve solvents including ammonia, aniline, sulfur dioxide with toluene and methylcyclohexane.

149. D. E. Ferguson and R. E. Lueze, *U. S. Atomic Energy Comm.*, *ORNL-372; Nuclear Sci. Abstr.*, **11**, 7553 (1957). Water–Uranyl nitrate-4-Methyl-2-pentanone.

150. D. E. Ferguson and T. C. Runion, *U. S. Atomic Energy Comm.*, *ORNL-260; Nuclear Sci. Abstr.*, **11**, 9655 (1957). Water–Uranyl nitrate–Tributyl phosphate–Hexane.

151. S. W. Ferris, E. R. Birkhimer, and L. M. Henderson, *Ind. Eng. Chem.*, **23**, 753 (1931). Lube oils with many solvents.

152. A. Findlay, *The Phase Rule*, 9th ed., A. N. Campbell and N. O. Smith, Eds., Longmans, Green, New York, 1951, pp. 291–293.

153. R. A. Findlay, U. S. Patent 2,758,141, Aug. 7, 1956. Sulfur dioxide–Benzene or Toluene–Nonaromatics.

153A. R. Fischer and J. Horner, *Mikrochim. Acta*, **1953**, 386 (1953); *Chem. Abstr.*, **48**, 2393a (1954). Water–2-Picoline–Sodium chloride (island curve) 2-Chloroethanol, Chloroform, Ethyl alcohol, Oleic acid–15 Vegetable oils. Water–Phenol–34 Salts.

154. R. Fischer and E. Neupauer, *Mikrochimie ver Mikrokhim. Acta*, **34**, 319 (1949); *Chem. Abstr.*, **43**, 8308h (1949). 116 micro CST of organic compounds.

154A. R. Fischer, E. Pinter, and H. Auer, *Pharm. Zentralhalle*, **99**, 299 (1960); *Chem. Abstr.*, **55**, 900e (1961). Microanalysis of binary systems by CST.

155. O. Flaschner, *Z. physik. Chem.*, **62**, 493 (1908); *J. Chem. Soc.*, **95**, 668 (1909); *Chem. Abstr.*, **2**, 1773 (1908). Water–Piperidines. Supersaturation.

156. P. J. Flory, *Principles of Polymer Chemistry*, Cornell Univ. Press, Ithaca, N. Y., 1953, pp. 541–594. Phase relations with polymers.

156A. E. Foa, N. Rosintal, and Y. Markus, *J. Inorg. Nuclear Chem.*, **23**, 109 (1961); *Chem. Abstr.*, **57**, 4093h (1962). Water–Hydrogen chloride–Tributyl phosphate–Hydrocarbons.

157. V. V. Fomin, *et al.*, *Zhur. Neorg. Khim.*, **5**, 1846 (1960); **6**, 481 (1961); *Russ. J. Inorg. Chem. (English Transl.)*, **5**, 896 (1960); **6**, 243 (1961); *Chem. Abstr.*, **56**, 5455d, 8074b (1962). Water–Nitric acid–Benzene, Butyl ether, Cyclohexanone, or 4-Methyl-2-pentanone.

158. R. T. Fowler and R. A. S. Noble, *J. Appl. Chem. (London)*, **4**, 546 (1954); *Chem. Abstr.*, **49**, 12941i (1955). Water–Nicotine–Carbon tetrachloride.

159. R. T. Fowler and R. A. S. Noble, *J. Appl. Chem. (London)*, **7**, 97 (1957); *Chem. Abstr.*, **51**, 11024c (1957). Water, Sulfuric acid–Nicotine–Carbon tetrachloride.

159A. A. W. Francis, *Chem. Eng. Sci.*, **10**, 37 (1959); *Chem. Abstr.*, **53**, 19502*b* (1959). Isopycnic of Water–Xenon.

159B. A. W. Francis, *Chem. Revs.*, **43**, 257 (1948). Effect of phase relations on reactions.

160. A. W. Francis, *Ind. Eng. Chem.*, **36**, 764 (1944). Selectivity by CST differences, nonaromatic.

161. *Idem*, **36**, 1096 (1944). CST of cyclic hydrocarbons.

162. *Idem*, **42**, 342 (1950). Aluminum chloride–Ethylbenzene–Benzene.

163. *Idem*, **45**, 2789 (1953). Isopycnics and iso-optics.

164. *Idem*, **46**, 205 (1954). Water–Methanol–Aniline–Benzene.

165. *Idem*, **47**, 230 (1955). Carbon dioxide extraction.

166. *Idem*, **49**, 1779 (1957). Pressure, temperature, density relations.

167. A. W. Francis, *Ind. Eng. Chem., Anal. Ed.*, **15**, 447 (1943); *Petrol. Refiner*, **25**, 109 (1944); *Natl. Petrol. News*, **35**, 35R, 418 (1943). *o*-Nitrotoluene–Butane–Isobutane.

168. A. W. Francis, *J. Am. Chem. Soc.*, **73**, 3709 (1951). Silver nitrate or Mercuric acetate–Other substances.

169. *Idem*, **76**, 393 (1954). Methanol–Nitrobenzene–Iso-octane. Merging of two separate binodal curves.

170. A. W. Francis, *J. Am. Pharm. Assoc.*, **30**, 229 (1941); *Chem. Abstr.*, **35**, 8207g (1941). Water–Phenol or Cresols–Camphor.

171. A. W. Francis, *J. Chem. Eng. Data*, **5**, 534 (1960). Refractive indices of liquefied gases.

172. A. W. Francis, *J. Phys. Chem.*, **56**, 510 (1952). Structural colors in emulsions. Nitromethane–Benzene–*n*-Heptane.

173. *Idem*, **58**, 1099 (1954). 464 ternary systems of carbon dioxide.

174. *Idem*, **60**, 20 (1956). Ternary systems with three separate binodal curves.

175. *Idem*, **62**, 579 (1958). Ternary systems of hydrogen halides. Island curves.

176. *Idem*, **63**, 753 (1959). Miscibility relations of hydrogen cyanide.

177. A. W. Francis, *"Liquid–Liquid Equilibria,"* Presented before the 44th Meeting Am. Inst. Chem. Engrs., New Orleans, La., Feb. 28, 1961.

178. A. W. Francis, *Critical Solution Temperatures*, Advances in Chemistry Series, No. 31, Am. Chem. Soc., 1961.

179. A. W. Francis, *"Solvent Extraction of Hydrocarbons," Physical Chemistry of Hydrocarbons*, Vol. I, A. Farkas, Ed., Academic Press, New York, 1950, pp. 241–313.

180. A. W. Francis, *"Ternary Systems Separating into Two Liquid Layers," Solubilities of Inorganic and Organic Compounds*, Supplement to the 3rd ed., A. Seidell and W. F. Linke, Eds., Van Nostrand, 1952, pp. 821–1122. Cf. reference 604.

181. A. W. Francis, U. S. Patent 2,133,691, Oct. 18, 1938. Pyridine–Lithium chloride–Lube oil.

182. A. W. Francis, U. S. Patent 2,142,939, Jan. 3, 1939. Pyridine–Calcium nitrate–Lube oil.

183. A. W. Francis, U. S. Patent 2,303,265, Nov. 24, 1942. *o*-Nitrotoluene–*n*-Butane–Isobutane.

184. A. W. Francis, U. S. Patent 2,368,653, Feb. 6, 1945. Aluminum chloride–Isoparaffins–Olefins–Organic oxygen compounds.

185. A. W. Francis, U. S. Patent 2,402,954, July 2, 1946. Methanol–Triptane–other Paraffins.

186. A. W. Francis, U. S. Patent 2,463,482, March 1, 1949. Carbon dioxide–Silver nitrate–Propylene.

187. A. W. Francis, U. S. Patent 2,498,204, Feb. 21, 1950. Anhydrous silver nitrate–Olefins–Paraffins.

188. A. W. Francis, U. S. Patents 2,631,966 and 2,632,030, March 17, 1953; U. S. Patent 2,646,387, July 21, 1953. Carbon dioxide–Lube oil–other solvents.

189. A. W. Francis, U. S. Patent 2,642,421, June 16, 1953. Water–Urea–Acetic acid–Hydrocarbons.

190. A. W. Francis, U. S. Patent 2,673,225, March 23, 1954. Water or Acetonitrile–Silver nitrate–Olefins.

191. A. W. Francis, U. S. Patent 2,691,048, Oct. 5, 1954. Glycol–Glycol ethers–Aromatic hydrocarbons.

192. A. W. Francis, U. S. Patents 2,698,276, 2,698,277, and 2,698,278, Dec. 28, 1954. Carbon dioxide–Acetic acid–Acetone, Furfural, etc.–Lube oils.

193. A. W. Francis, U. S. Patent 2,735,878, Feb. 21, 1956. Cuprous hydrogen chloride–Methanol–Olefins.

194. A. W. Francis, U. S. Patent 2,756,266, July 24, 1956. Sulfuric acid–Methyl sulfate or Nitrobenzene–Olefins.

195. A. W. Francis, U. S. Patent 2,776,327, Jan. 1, 1957. Oleum–Methyl sulfate–Aromatics.

196. A. W. Francis, U. S. Patent 3,003,006, Oct. 3, 1961. Sulfur dioxide–Glycol or Formamide–Benzene or Heptane.

196A. A. W. Francis, U. S. Patent 3,092,570, June 4, 1963. Methanol–Carbon disulfide and Jet fuel–Aromatics.

196B. A. W. Francis, U. S. Patent 3,092,571, June 4, 1963. Acetonitrile–Aromatics–Carbon disulfide and Lube oil.

197. A. W. Francis, Unpublished observations in Socony Mobil Laboratories.

198. A. W. Francis and W. H. James, U. S. Patent 2,389,250, Nov. 20, 1945. Aluminum chloride–Organic oxygen compound–*n*-Paraffin.

199. A. W. Francis and G. C. Johnson, U. S. Patent 2,663,670, Dec. 22, 1953. Fluorocarbons–Acetonitrile or Triethylene glycol–Benzene–Heptane.

200. A. W. Francis and W. H. King, "Principles of Solvent Extraction," *Chemistry of Petroleum Hydrocarbons*, Vol. I, B. T. Brooks and others, Eds., Reinhold, New York, 1954, Chap. 9.

201. A. W. Francis and W. H. King, "Solvent Refining," *Recent Advances in Petroleum Chemistry and Refining*, Vol. I, K. A. Kobe and J. J. McKetta, Eds., Interscience, New York, 1958, pp. 429–484.

201A. A. W. Francis and E. E. Reid, *Ind. Eng. Chem.*, **38**, 1194 (1946); U. S. Patent 2,397,542, April 2, 1946. Aluminum chloride–Ethylbenzene–Benzene.

202. A. W. Francis and E. E. Reid, U. S. Patent 2,377,221, May 29, 1945. Water–Silver nitrate–Styrene–Ethylbenzene.

203. A. W. Francis and E. E. Reid, U. S. Patent 2,445,520, July 20, 1948. Cuprous hydrogen chloride–Amides–Olefins.

203A. A. W. Francis and G. W. Robbins, *J. Am. Chem. Soc.*, **55**, 4339 (1933). Vapor pressures of propane and propylene. Manometer for pressure apparatus.

204. P. I. Freeman and J. S. Rowlinson, *Polymer*, **1**, 20 (1960); *Chem. Abstr.*, **54**, 16902c (1960). Polyolefins–Benzene–Other hydrocarbons.

204A. A. J. Frey and E. G. Scheibel, *Jubilee Volume, Emil Barell*, Basle, 1946; *Chem. Abstr.*, **41**, 1504b (1947). Developments in Liquid–liquid extraction.

205. B. S. Friedman and R. F. Stedman, U. S. Patent 2,458,067, Jan. 4, 1949. Acetonitrile–Silver nitrate–Olefins.

205A. H. L. Friedman, *J. Phys. Chem.*, **66**, 1595 (1962). Ferric ammonium chloride–Ether.

205B. R. H. Fritsche and D. L. Stockton, *Ind. Eng. Chem.*, **38**, 737 (1946). Water–Acetone–Isobutyl alcohol–Tetrachloroethane; Water–Isobutyl alcohol–Ether–Sodium chloride or Sodium hydroxide.

205C. R. Fujishiro and J. H. Hildebrand, *J. Phys. Chem.*, **66**, 573 (1962). Perfluorotributylamine–Cyclohexane, Binary, but no CST.

206. J. D. Garber and H. C. Reynolds, U. S. Patent 2,851,499, Sept. 9, 1958. 2,5-Dihydroxymethyltetrahydrofurane–Toluene–Nonaromatics.

207. A. W. Gardner, H. A. C. McKay, and D. T. Warren, *Trans. Faraday Soc.*, **48**, 997 (1952); *Chem. Abstr.*, **47**, 5220c (1953). Water–Uranyl nitrate–Butyl ethers.

208. F. H. Garner, S. R. M. Ellis, and D. W. Fosbury, *Trans. Inst. Chem. Engrs.* (*London*), **31**, 348 (1953); *Chem. Abstr.*, **48**, 10383b (1954). Water–Diethylamine–Toluene.

209. F. H. Garner, S. R. M. Ellis, and U. N. G. Roy, *Chem. Eng. Sci.*, **2**, 14 (1953); *Chem. Abstr.*, **47**, 6708a (1953). Water–Acetic acid–Benzene.

210. F. H. Garner and R. T. W. Hall, *J. Inst. Petroleum*, **41**, 15, 18, 24 (1955); *Chem. Abstr.*, **49**, 4390i (1955). Furfural–Toluene–Methylcyclohexane or Heptane.

211. L. Garwin and P. O. Haddad, *Anal. Chem.*, **25**, 435 (1953). Water–Acetic acid–Dimethylaniline.

212. L. Garwin and A. N. Hixson, *Ind. Eng. Chem.*, **41**, 2298 (1949). Water–Cobalt and Nickel chlorides–Capryl alcohol, etc.

213. L. Garwin and J. M. Winterbottom, *Ibid.*, **49**, 1355 (1957). Water–Furfural–Zinc salts.

214. J. H. Gary, J. S. Crichton, Jr., and R. Feild, Jr., *Chem. Eng. Data Ser.*, **3**, 111 (1958). Diethylene glycol or Propylene glycol–Alkyl phthalates–Tetrabromoethane or Tributyrin.

215. A. Gathman and R. W. Egberts, U. S. Patent 2,487,124, Nov. 8, 1949. Water–Ethyl alcohol–2-Butanone–Kerosine.

216. C. J. Geankoplis and A. N. Hixson, *Ind. Eng. Chem.*, **42**, 1141 (1950). Water, Hydrogen chloride–Ferric chloride–Ether.

217. B. W. Geddes, L. Z. Wilcox, and E. H. McArdle, *Ind. Eng. Chem., Anal. Ed.*, **15**, 487 (1943). Methylaniline points of hydrocarbons.

218. J. A. Gerster, J. A. Gorton, and R. B. Eklund, *J. Chem. Eng. Data*, **5**, 423 (1960). 33 solvents for separation of Pentane–Pentene by azeotropic distillation.

219. G. C. Gester, Jr., *Advances in Chemistry Series*, No. 5, Am. Chem. Soc., Washington, D. C., 1951, pp. 180–182. Triangular graph with property of oil on one side.

219A. D. D. Gilbert and E. B. Sandell, *J. Inorg. Nucl. Chem.*, **24**, 989 (1962); *Chem. Abstr.*, **58**, 5093c (1963). Water–Stannic iodide–Benzene.

220. E. C. Gilbert and L. L. Humphreys, *J. Chem. Eng. Data*, **6**, 342 (1961). Water–Ethyl alcohol–Hydrazine hydrochloride.

221. L. M. Gindin *et al.*, *Zhur. Neorg. Khim.*, **5**, 149, 1868 (1960); *Russ. J. Inorg. Chem. (English Transl.)*, **5**, 71, 906 (1960); *Chem. Abstr.*, **55**, 19435h (1961); **56**, 8074g (1962). Water–Chlorides of aluminum, cadmium, calcium, cobalt, copper, iron, lead, nickel, zinc–Isoamyl alcohol or Octanoic acid.

222. Y. L. Gladel and J. Durandet, *Rev. inst. franç. pétrole et Ann. combustibles liquides*, **9**, 221 (1954); *Chem. Abstr.*, **48**, 10416b (1954). Compilation of ternary systems with solvents, each with two hydrocarbons.

223. Y. L. Gladel and J. Durandet, *Rev. inst. franç. pétrole et Ann. combustibles liquides*, **10**, 258 (1955); *Chem. Abstr.*, **50**, 8183c (1956). Similar, with 25 solvents.

224. Y. L. Gladel and J. Durandet, *Rev. inst. franç. pétrole et Ann. combustibles liquides*, **11**, 488 (1956); *Chem. Abstr.*, **50**, 14337c (1956). Similar, with nine solvents.

225. Y. L. Gladel and J. Durandet, *Rev. inst. franç. pétrole et Ann. combustibles liquides*, **11**, 1075 (1956); *Chem. Abstr.*, **51**, 2331d (1957). Aniline–Toluene or Methylcyclopentane–*n*-Heptane.

226. Y. L. Gladel and J. Durandet, *Rev. inst. franç. pétrole et Ann. combustibles liquides*, **12**, 130 (1957). Systems of Ammonia with 16 pairs of hydrocarbons; Aniline and Dimethylformamide, each with two pairs; Dimethylsulfolane and Valerolactone, each with four pairs.

227. Y. L. Gladel, J. Durandet, and R. Roux, *Rev. inst. franç. pétrole et Ann. combustibles liquides*, **14**, 1147 (1959); *Chem. Abstr.*, **54**, 19069f (1960). Methoxyethanol–Toluene or Cumene–Heptane, and C_{12}, C_{14}, C_{16} paraffins.

228. Y. L. Gladel and P. LaBlaude, *Rev. inst. franç. pétrole et Ann. combustibles liquides*, **12**, 1236 (1957); *Chem. Abstr.*, **52**, 9739b (1958). Propylene carbonate–Toluene–*n*-Heptane. Iso-optic.

229. E. Glueckauf, H. A. C. McKay, and A. R. Mathieson, *Trans. Faraday Soc.*, **47**, 437 (1951); *Chem. Abstr.*, **45**, 10006b (1951). Water–Uranyl nitrate–Organic solvents.

230. M. M. Godneva and M. A. Klochko, *Izvest. Karel'sk. i Kol'sk. Filial. Akad. Nauk SSSR*, **1958**, No. 5, 122 (1958); *Chem. Abstr.*, **54**, 10487a (1960). Water–Acetone or Dioxane–Hydroxides of lithium, potassium, or sodium.

231. F. Gölles, *Monotsh. Chem.*, **91**, 669 (1960); *Chem. Abstr.*, **55**, 7017c (1961). Water–*n*-Butyl alcohol or *m*-Cresol–three Chloroacetic acids.

232. G. S. Golden and H. M. Clark, *J. Phys. Chem.*, **65**, 1932 (1961). Water–Hydrogen bromide, Ferric bromide–Ether.

233. A. Z. Golik and V. P. Solomko, *Ukrain. Khim. Zhur.*, **25**, 40 (1959); *Chem. Abstr.*, **53**, 17653a (1959). Water–Acetone–*n*-Butyl alcohol.

234. K. M. Golubkova, N. N. Petin, and K. P. Topchieva, *Zhur. Fiz. Khim.*, **15**, 198 (1941); *Chem. Abstr.*, **36**, 6403⁸ (1942). Water–Acetic or Formic acids–Phenol.

235. R. Gopal and O. K. Rice, *J. Chem. Phys.*, **23**, 2428 (1955); *Chem. Abstr.*, **50**, 4612c (1956). Carbon tetrachloride–Perfluoromethylcyclohexane, CST 28.6°C.

236. L. J. Gordon and R. L. Scott, *J. Am. Chem. Soc.*, **74**, 4138 (1952). Methylene iodide–Cyclohexane–Phenanthrene.

237. I. Y. Gorodetskii, and V. M. Olevskii, *Vestnik Leningrad. Univ.*, **15**, No. 16; *Ser. Fiz. i Khim.*, No. 3, 102 (1960); *Zavodskaya Lab.*, **26**, 547 (1960); *Chem. Abstrs.*, **55**, 1162b (1961); **56**, 5449f (1962). Water–Cyclohexanol–Cyclohexanone, 90°C.

238. H. L. Graham, *J. Chem. Eng. Data*, **7**, 214 (1962). Water, Di- or Triethylene glycol–Benzene–Heptane.

238A. W. F. Grimes and H. H. Rowley, *Proc. Okla. Acad. Sci.*, **32**, 79 (1951); *Chem. Abstr.*, **48**, 434i (1954). Water–Magnesium bromide–Ether–Benzene.

239. J. Griswold, R. V. West, and K. K. McMillan, *Chem. Eng. Progr.*, **48**, *Symposium Ser.*, No. 2, 62 (1952); *Chem. Abstr.*, **46**, 6454a (1952). Water–Furfural–C_3 and C_4 hydrocarbons.

239A. S. D. Gromakov, *Zhur. Fiz. Khim.*, **34**, 2431 (1960); *Russ. J. Phys. Chem. (English Transl.)*, **34**, 1149 (1960); *Chem. Abstr.*, **55**, 6115e (1961).

240. W. T. Grubb and R. C. Osthoff, *J. Am. Chem. Soc.*, **74**, 2108 (1952). Water–Hydrogen chloride or bromide–Dioxane.

241. L. Gutiérrez Jodra, J. L. Otero, and J. Solé, *Anales real soc. españ. fís. y quím. (Madrid)*, **51B**, 741 (1955); *Chem. Abstr.*, **50**, 6168i (1956). Water–Acetic acid–Sodium chloride–Benzene.

242. P. Hagenmuller, A. Lecerf, and J. C. Bovineau, *Compt. rend.*, **246**, 3459 (1958); *Chem. Abstr.*, **52**, 19416b (1958). Water–Phenol–Salts.

243. D. B. Hand, *J. Phys. Chem.*, **34**, 1961 (1930). Adjustment of units to make tie lines horizontal.

244. C. H. G. Hands and W. S. Norman, *Trans. Inst. Chem. Engrs. (London)*, **23**, 76 (1945); *Ind. Chemist*, **21**, 307 (1945); *Chem. Abstr.*, **39**, 4273 (1945). Water–Allyl alcohol–Carbon tetrachloride or Trichloroethylene.

244A. D. O. Hanson and M. Van Winkle, *J. Chem. Eng. Data*, **5**, 30 (1960). Water–Acetone or 2-Butanone–Chlorobenzene, *n*-Heptane, or 1,1,2-Trichloroethane.

245. R. D. Harris and C. J. Geankoplis, *J. Chem. Eng. Data*, **7**, 218 (1962). Water–Propionic and Sulfuric acids–4-Methyl-2-pentanone.

246. W. D. Harris and J. W. Haywood, *Bull. Agr. Mech. Coll. Texas*, **6**, No. 9 (1950); *Chem. Abstr.*, **46**, 1272h (1952). Water–Isopropyl alcohol–Oleic acid–Cottonseed oil or Hexane.

247. G. M. Hartwig, G. C. Hood, and R. L. Maycock, *J. Phys. Chem.*, **59**, 52 (1955). Water–Acetonitrile or Sulfolane–Benzene–Heptane. Three liquid phases.

247A. T. Hasegawa, *Kogyo Kagaku Zasshi*, **64**, 1239 (1961); *Chem. Abstr.*, **57**, 4104d (1962). Water–Furfural–Tributyl phosphate.

248. S. Havel and V. Andrle, *Chem. Prumysl*, **11**, 171 (1961); *Chem. Abstr.*, **55**, 26631d (1961). Water–Methanol–*p*-Xylene–Methyl *p*-toluate.

249. S. Havel and V. Andrle, *Sbornik věd. praci, Vysoka skola chem. technol. Pardubice*, **1960**, 73; *Chem. Abstr.*, **55**, 8022b (1961). Water–Methanol–Methyl *p*-toluate.

250. G. Herbolsheimer, Univ. Microfilms (Ann Arbor, Mich.) Publ. No. 552; *Penn. State Coll. Abstr.*, **5**, 308 (1943); *Chem. Abstr.*, **38**, 4782[3] (1944). Eight solvents with light hydrocarbons. *Cf.* references 148 and 223.

251. E. L. Heric, *Chemist Analyst*, **48**, 31 (1959); *Chem. Abstr.*, **53**, 18735h (1959). Water–Furfural–Ethyl acetate.

252. E. L. Heric and R. M. Rutledge, *Can. J. Chem. Eng.*, **38**, 46 (1960); *J. Chem. Eng. Data*, **5**, 272 (1960). Water–Acetic or Propionic acids–Furfural.

253. E. L. Heric and K. R. Williams, *Can. J. Chem. Eng.*, **39**, 165 (1961). Water–Acetic acid–Toluene.

254. G. D. Hiatt and J. Emerson, U. S. Patent 2,349,430, May 23, 1944. Water–Dioxane or Methoxyethanol–Cellulose acetate.

255. C. E. Higgins, W. H. Baldwin, and J. M. Ruth, *U. S. Atomic Energy Comm.*, *ORNL-1338* (1952); *Nuclear Sci. Abstr.*, **11**, 9663 (1957); *Chem. Abstr.*, **55**, 18267e (1961). Water–Uranium or Thorium salts–Phosphate esters in Carbon tetrachloride.

255A. J. H. Hildebrand, *J. Phys. & Colloid Chem.*, **53**, 944 (1949); *Science*, **80**, 125 (1934). Multiple liquid layers in equilibrium.

256. J. H. Hildebrand and R. L. Scott, *Regular Solutions*, Prentice-Hall, Englewood Cliffs, N. J., 1962. Ten liquid phases in equilibrium.

257. J. H. Hildebrand and R. L. Scott, "Polarity," *Solubility of Non-electrolytes*, 3rd ed., Reinhold, New York, 1950, pp. 155–169. CST and prediction of ternary equilibriums from binary ones.

258. A. E. Hill, *J. Am. Chem. Soc.*, **44**, 1163 (1922); *J. Am. Chem. Soc.*, **62**, 3524 (1940). Water–Silver perchlorate–Benzene.

259. A. E. Hill, "Heterogeneous Equilibria," *Treatise on Physical Chemistry*, Vol. I, H. S. Taylor, Ed., Van Nostrand, New York, 1931, pp. 574–575. Postulated typical graphs.

260. A. E. Hill and F. W. Miller, Jr., *J. Am. Chem. Soc.*, **47**, 2702 (1925). Water–Silver perchlorate–Toluene.

261. D. M. Himmelblau, B. L. Brady, and J. J. McKetta, Jr., *Texas, Univ., Bur. Eng. Research, Spec. Publ. 30* (1959). Compilation of ternary systems.

262. M. Hirata and S. Fujita, *Kagaku Kikai*, **21**, 201 (1957); *Chem. Abstr.*, **51**, 9281e (1957). Water–Phenol or Acetic acid–Benzene.

263. J. O. Hirschfelder, D. P. Stevenson, and H. Eyring, *J. Chem. Phys.*, **5**, 896 (1937); *Chem. Abstr.*, **32**, 15¹ (1938). Theory of liquid structure, CST, etc.

264. M. Hisamura, T. Okazaki, and I. Kato, *Kooru Taaru*, **4**, 282 (1952); *Chem. Abstr.*, **47**, 6120c (1953). Water–Pyridine–Ammonium sulfate.

264A. C. W. Hoerr *et al.* At least 15 papers in *J. Org. Chem.* and *J. Phys. Chem.* (1942–1955). Solubility of high molecular compounds in various solvents.

265. C. H. Holder and O. Maass, *Can. J. Research*, **18B**, 293 (1940); *Chem. Abstr.*, **35**, 19³ (1941). Ethane–Hexachloroethane in critical region.

266. J. Hollo and A. Wieg, *Yearbook Inst. Agr. Chem. Technol. Univ. Tech. Sci. (Budapest)*, **1952–1954**, 78 (1954). *Chem. Abstr.*, **49**, 13701i (1955). Water–Ethyl alcohol–Methylene chloride.

266A. J. Holmes, *J. Chem. Soc.*, **113**, 263 (1918). Glycerol–Kerosine–Nitrobenzene; Water–Nicotine–Kerosine.

267. G. Holst, *Acta chem. Scand.*, **12**, 1042 (1958); *Chem. Abstr.*, **53**, 21113d (1959). Water–Acetone, Ethyl alcohol, or Pyridine–Benzene, Carbon tetrachloride, Carbon disulfide, or Mustard gas.

268. L. H. Horsley, *Anal. Chem.*, **19**, 508 (1947); *Anal. Chem.*, **21**, 831 (1949); "Azeotropes" *Advances in Chem. Ser.*, No. 6, Am. Chem. Soc. (1952). Compilations of azeotropes.

268A. Y. Hoshino, *Japan Analyst*, **11**, 1050 (1962); *Chem. Abstr.*, **58**, 922g (1963). Water–Hydrogen chloride, Sulfuric acid, or Thiocyanic acid–Cyclohexanone.

269. V. Hovi, *Suomen Kemistilehti*, **27B**, No. 5/6, 33 (1954); *Chem. Abstr.*, **48**, 13393h (1954); **50**, 1404c (1956). Rubidium bromide–Rubidium chloride. CST −100 °C (solid solution).

270. E. Hudswell *et al.*, *U. S. Atomic Energy Comm., AERE-C/R-1520; Nuclear Sci. Abstr.*, **10**, 6588 (1956). Water–Nitric acid–Tributyl phosphate.

271. H. E. Hughes and J. O. Maloney, *Chem. Eng. Progr.*, **48**, 197 (1952); *Chem. Abstr.*, **46**, 4921d (1952). Water–Methanol–*n*-Butyl alcohol.

272. T. G. Hunter, *Ind. Eng. Chem.*, **34**, 963 (1942). Water–Acetic acid–Acetone–Chloroform. Projections of system of reference 69.

273. T. G. Hunter and T. F. Brown, *Ibid.*, **39**, 1343 (1947). Aniline–Cyclohexane–*n*-Heptane or Cetane.

273A. T. G. Hunter and A. W. Nash, *Ibid.*, **27**, 842 (1935). V. G. C. and aniline point diagrams.

274. T. G. Hunter and A. W. Nash, *J. Soc. Chem. Ind.*, **53**, 96T (1934); *Chem. Abstr.*, **28**, 4273⁵ (1934). Postulated phase diagrams.

275. *International Critical Tables*, Vol. III, McGraw-Hill, New York, 1928, pp. 356, 397, 403, 416. Effect of pressure on mutual solubility. Water–Hydrogen bromide–Sulfur dioxide.

275A. *Ibid.*, Vol. IV, p. 118.

276. K. Ishida, *Bull. Chem. Research Inst. Non-Aqueous Solutions, Tohoku Univ.*, **3**, 109 (1953); *Chem. Abstr.*, **48**, 11899c (1954). Ammonia–Pyridine–*n*-Heptane. Isopycnic.
277. K. Ishida, *Bull. Chem. Soc. Japan*, **29**, 956 (1956); *Chem. Abstr.*, **51**, 7823i (1957). Ammonia–Toluene–*n*-Heptane. Tie line correlation.
278. K. Ishida, *Bull. Chem. Soc. Japan*, **30**, 612 (1957); *Chem. Abstr.*, **52**, 5092b (1958). Ammonia–Benzene–Hexane or Cyclohexane; Ammonia–Styrene–Ethylbenzene.
279. K. Ishida, *Bull. Chem. Soc. Japan*, **31**, 143 (1958); *Chem. Abstr.*, **52**, 14309e (1958). Ammonia–21 Hydrocarbons.
280. K. Ishida, *Bull. Chem. Soc. Japan*, **33**, 693 (1960); *Chem. Abstr.*, **54**, 23687f (1960). Ammonia–Thiophene–*n*-Heptane. Tie line correlation for solutropic systems. Almost horizontal tie lines.
281. K. Ishida, *J. Chem. Eng. Data*, **6**, 489 (1961). Correlations for ternary liquid equilibriums. Water–Isopropyl alcohol–Benzene; Ammonia–Toluene–Heptane.
282. K. Ishida, *J. Chem. Soc. Japan, Ind. Chem. Sect.*, **56**, 469 (1953); *Chem. Abstr.*, **48**, 11899e (1954). Ammonia–Toluene–Heptane.
283. K. Ishida, *J. Chem. Soc. Japan, Ind. Chem. Sect.*, **57**, 479 (1954); *Chem. Abstr.*, **49**, 5096c (1955). Ammonia–Cyclohexane–Hexane; and Ammonia–1-Octene–Heptane.
284. K. Ishida, *J. Chem. Soc. Japan, Ind. Chem. Sect.*, **58**, 637 (1955); *Chem. Abstr.*, **50**, 8296b (1956). Ammonia, Aniline, and Furfural, each with a pair of Hydrocarbons; Water–Aniline–Nitrobenzene.
285. K. Ishida, *J. Chem. Soc. Japan, Ind. Chem. Sect.*, **60**, 864 (1957); *Chem. Abstr.*, **53**, 9801h (1959). Ammonia–Tetralin–Decalin; Ammonia–Toluene–Heptane.
286. K. Ishida, *Sci. Repts. Research Insts., Tohoku Univ.*, Ser. A, **5**, 377 (1953); *Chem. Abstr.*, **48**, 9045g (1954). Water–Ammonia–Phenols.
287. T. Ishiguro *et al.*, *Yakugaku Zasshi*, **74**, 1391 (1954); *Chem. Abstr.*, **49**, 4392b (1955). Water–Diethylamine–Sodium hydroxide.
288. T. Ishiguro *et al.*, *Yakugaku Zasshi*, **75**, 188 (1955); *Chem. Abstr.*, **49**, 7952a (1955). Water–Triethylamine–Sodium or Potassium hydroxides.
289. T. Ishiguro *et al.*, *Yakugaku Zasshi*, **75**, 434 (1955); *Chem. Abstr.*, **50**, 2587i (1956). Water–2-Picoline–Sodium hydroxide.
290. T. Ishiguro *et al.*, *Yakugaku Zasshi*, **75**, 540 (1955); *Chem. Abstr.*, **49**, 11380f (1955). Water–Nicotine–Sodium hydroxide.
291. T. Ishiguro *et al.*, *Yakugaku Zasshi*, **75**, 1191, 1196 (1955); *Chem. Abstr.*, **50**, 3054f, 3054h (1956). Water–Butylamine or Heptylamine–Sodium hydroxide. Gels in certain concentrations.
292. T. Ishiguro *et al.*, *Yakugaku Zasshi*, **75**, 1410 (1955); *Chem. Abstr.*, **50**, 3867a (1956). Water–Pyridine–Sodium hydroxide.
293. T. Ishiguro *et al.*, *Yakugaku Zasshi*, **76**, 757, 760, 762 (1956); *Chem. Abstr.*, **50**, 15197b–15197f (1956). Water–Alkylamines–Sodium hydroxide or chloride.
294. T. Ishiguro *et al.*, *Yakugaku Zasshi*, **80**, 311 (1960); *Chem. Abstrs.*, **54**, 16068e (1960). Water–Diethylamine–Potassium or Sodium chloride or Sodium sulfate.

295. T. Ishimori and K. Wantanabe, *Bull. Chem. Soc. Japan*, **33**, 1443 (1960); *Chem. Abstr.*, **56**, 4156e (1962). Water, Nitric acid–Tributyl phosphate–74 elements.

296. K. Ito, *Kagaku Kenkyusho Hokoku*, **32**, 207 (1956) (in English); *Chem. Abstr.*, **52**, 66h (1958). Water–Butyl alcohol–Hydrogen. CST 138°C.

296A. K. Ito, *Sci. Papers Inst. Phys. Chem. Research (Tokyo)*, **55**, 176, 189 (1961) (in English); *Chem. Abstr.*, **57**, 16186i (1962). Water–Hydrogen–Benzene or Isoamyl alcohol. CST 270 °C and 204 °C.

297. H. Ivekovic and B. Milic'evic', *Croat. Chem. Acta*, **31**, 83 (1959) (in English); *Chem. Abstr.*, **54**, 12761d (1960). Water–*p*-Dioxane or Acetone–DDT or Hexachlorocyclohexane.

298. E. Iwase and T. Isono, *Rikagaku Kenkyusho Hokoku*, **36**, 117 (1960); *Chem. Abstrs.*, **55**, 17178i (1961). Water, Hydrogen chloride–Uranium chloride–Tributyl phosphate in Kerosine. Three liquid phases.

299. N. A. Izmailov and A. K. Franke, *Zhur. Fiz. Khim.*, **29**, 120 (1955); *Chem. Abstr.*, **50**, 13586c (1956). Water–Isopropyl alcohol–Ethylene chloride. Solutrope.

300. N. A. Izmailov and A. K. Franke, *Zhur. Fiz. Khim.*, **29**, 263 (1955); *Chem. Abstr.*, **50**, 16323d (1956). Water–Isopropyl alcohol–Chloroform or Carbon tetrachloride.

301. N. A. Izmailov and A. K. Franke, *Zhur. Fiz. Khim.*, **29**, 620 (1955); *Chem. Abstr.*, **51**, 831g (1957). Water–Methanol–Ethylene chloride.

301A. M. E. Jacox, J. T. MacQueen, and O. K. Rice, *J. Phys. Chem.*, **64**, 972 (1960). Expansion coefficient near plait point.

302. G. V. Jeffreys, *J. Inst. Petrol.*, **46**, 26 (1960); *Chem. Abstr.*, **54**, 10486a (1960). Aniline–Cyclohexane–*n*-Heptane.

303. E. Jenckel and J. Delahaye, *Z. Naturforsch.*, **7A**, 682 (1952); *Chem. Abstr.*, **47**, 5766a (1953). Polymethylmethacrylate–*p*-Cymene, Propyl or Butyl alcohol–Acetone, Methanol, or Methyl acetate.

304. E. Jenckel and K. Gorke, *Z. Naturforsch.*, **5A**, 556 (1950); *Chem. Abstr.*, **45**, 2710g (1951). Solubility of polymethylmethacrylate esters in 65 solvents.

305. E. Jenckel and G. Keller, *Z. Naturforsch.*, **5A**, 317 (1950); *Chem. Abstr.*, **44**, 9724b (1950). Polystyrenes–Ethyl or Vinyl acetate or Methyl malonate; five Alcohols or ten Esters or Octene.

306. A. I. Johnson and T. W. Barry, *Can. J. Technol.*, **32**, 17 (1954); *Chem. Abstr.*, **48**, 6746i (1954). Water–Acetone or Propionic acid–Carbon tetrachloride.

307. G. C. Johnson and A. W. Francis, *Ind. Eng. Chem.*, **46**, 1662 (1954). Diethylene glycol–Benzene–Heptane.

307A. J. W. Johnson, and M. A. Bredig, *J. Phys. Chem.*, **62**, 604 (1958). CST of Potassium–Potassium halides.

308. O. Johnson and A. S. Newton, *U. S. Atomic Energy Comm.*, *CC-2954; Nuclear Sci. Abstr.*, **11**, 11652 (1957). Water, Nitric acid–Nitrates of calcium, thorium, or uranium–Tributyl phosphate.

309. D. C. Jones, *J. Chem. Soc.*, **123**, 1384 (1923). Water–Acetic acid–13 Solvents. Humps in curves.

309A. E. V. Jones and W. L. Marshall, *J. Inorg. Nuclear Chem.*, **23**, 287, 295 (1961); *Chem. Abstr.*, **57**, 5348c, 5348e (1962). Water or Deuterium oxide–Sulfuric acid–Uranium sulfate, Copper and Nickel oxides.

310. H. W. Jones and W. E. Grigsby, *Ind. Eng. Chem.*, **44,** 378 (1952). Water–Trimethylamine–Benzene.

311. J. H. Jones and J. F. McCants, *Ibid.*, **46,** 1956 (1954). Water–Butyl alcohol–2-Hexanone; Ethyl acetate–Butyraldehyde; 2-Butanone–Hexane.

312. D. Jordan et al., *Chem. Eng. Progr.*, **46,** 601 (1950); *Chem. Abstr.*, **45,** 939i (1951). Furfural–1-Butene–Isobutane.

313. G. Jura et al., *Proc. Natl. Acad. Sci. U. S.*, **39,** 19 (1953); *Chem. Abstr.*, **47,** 5750g (1953). Water–Triethylamine. Heat capacity near CST.

314. I. Kageyama and K. Tateyama, *Nippon Kagaku Zasshi*, **78,** 417 (1957); *Chem. Abstr.*, **52,** 8709g (1958). Glycerol–Three alcohols–Five Freons. Cf. reference 670.

315. A. G. Kasatkin, S. Z. Kagan, and V. G. Trukhanov, *Khim. Prom.*, **1961,** 190. *Chem. Abstr.*, **55,** 17179a (1961). Water, Ammonium sulfate–Caprolactam–Benzene, Carbon tetrachloride, Cyclohexane, or Trichloroethylene.

316. K. Kasturirangan and G. S. Laddha, *J. Madras Univ.*, **25B,** 213 (1955); *Chem. Abstr.*, **50,** 9763f (1956). Furfural–Castor oil methyl esters–Cyclohexane.

317. L. I. Katzin and J. R. Ferraro, *J. Am. Chem. Soc.*, **75,** 3825 (1953). Water–*tert*-Butyl alcohol–Cobaltous chloride.

318. L. I. Katzin and J. C. Sullivan, *J. Phys. & Colloid Chem.*, **55,** 346 (1951). Water–Uranyl nitrate–Ethers, Alcohols, and Ketones.

319. T. Kawai, *Bull. Soc. Chem. Japan*, **28,** 396 (1955); *Chem. Abstr.*, **52,** 5932a (1958). Water–Acetone or Methanol–Poly(vinyl acetate).

320. Y. Kawano and S. Kawabata, *Hakkô Kôgaku Zasshi*, **27,** 241 (1949); *Chem. Abstr.*, **47,** 9562a (1953). Water–Acetone or Ethyl alcohol–Butyl acetate.

320A. W. B. Kay and F. M. Warzel, *A. I. Ch. E. Journal*, **4,** 296 (1958). Ammonia–Iso-octane, CST 60.15°C.

321. H. Kehiaian, *Bull. Acad. Polon. Sci. Ser. Sci. Chim.*, **10,** 569 (1962); *Chem. Abstr.*, **58,** 13188g (1963). Binary island curves.

321A. H. B. Kendall, *Dissertation Abstr.*, **17,** 1476 (1957); *Chem. Abstr.*, **51,** 15237h (1957). Water–Phenol-o-Cresol.

322. J. Kendall, *Trans. Faraday Soc.*, **33,** 2 (1937); *Chem. Abstr.*, **31,** 2904[3] (1937). Water–Ethyl alcohol–Ether or Ethyl acetate. Undercut curves.

323. J. W. Kenny, *Chem. Eng. Sci.*, **6,** 116 (1957); *Chem. Abstr.*, **51,** 14398b (1957). Furfural–Benzene–Iso-octane.

324. A. S. Kertes and A. Beck, *J. Chem. Soc.*, **1961,** 1921, 1926. Water, Nitric acid–Potassium per-rhenate–Tributyl phosphate or Tri-isooctylamine.

325. A. S. Kertes and V. Kertes, *Can. J. Chem.*, **38,** 612 (1960); *J. Appl. Chem. (London)*, **10,** 287 (1960); *Chem. Abstr.*, **54,** 20425b, 23632c (1960). Water–Hydrogen bromide–Tributyl phosphate.

326. M. M. Ketslakh et al., *J. Appl. Chem. USSR (English Transl.)*, **32,** 2167 (1959); *Chem. Abstr.*, **54,** 8587i (1960). Stannic iodide–Trimethylpentanes.

327. M. M. Ketslakh et al., *Zhur. Anal. Khim.*, **5,** 151 (1950); *Chem. Abstr.*, **44,** 6331b (1950). Stannic iodide–Ten heptanes or octanes; CST.

328. G. Kimura et al., *Kôgyô Kagaku Zasshi*, **59,** 1126 (1956); *Chem. Abstr.*, **52,** 13396d (1958). Nitromethane–Benzene, Toluene, or three Xylenes–Heptane.

329. R. W. Kiser, G. D. Johnson, and M. D. Shetlar, *J. Chem. Eng. Data*, **6,** 339 (1961). Methanol–Hydrocarbons. (Binary.)

330. S. L. Kittsley and H. A. Goeden, *J. Am. Chem. Soc.*, **72,** 4841 (1950). Eight liquid phases in equilibrium.
331. M. Kiyama, S. Kosaki, and T. Kido, *Kooru Taaru*, **5,** 283 (1953); *Chem. Abstr.*, **48,** 2348a (1954). Aqueous methanol–Aromatics–Paraffins.
332. O. J. Kleppa, *J. Am. Chem. Soc.*, **74,** 6052 (1952). Zinc–Bismuth or Lead.
333. Y. B. Kletenik, *J. Gen. Chem. U.S.S.R. (English Transl.)*, **27,** 2079 (1957); *Chem. Abstr.*, **52,** 5108f (1958). Water, Hydrogen, Potassium, and Lithium chlorides, Sulfuric acid–Dioxane.
334. R. J. Kline and A. J. Ihde, *J. Colloid Sci.*, **13,** 163 (1958); *Chem. Abstr.*, **52,** 11524a (1958). Water–16 Salts–Triethylamine.
335. M. A. Klochko and O. P. Chanukvadze, *Bull. acad. sci. U. R. S. S., Classe sci. chim.*, **1948,** 40 (1948). *Chem. Abstr.*, **42,** 5325c (1948). Water–Acetic anhydride–Acetic acid–Aniline.
336. V. B. Kogan, *Zhur. Fiz. Khim.*, **29,** 1470(1955); *Chem. Abstr.*, **51,** 809h. Nine aqueous systems.
337. V. B. Kogan, *et al.*, *J. Appl. Chem. USSR (English Transl.)*, **29,** 1493 (1956); *Chem. Abstr.*, **51,** 2371g (1957). Water–Methanol–Paraffins.
338. V. B. Kogan et al., *J. Appl. Chem. USSR (English Transl.)*, **32,** 864 (1959); *Chem. Abstr.*, **53,** 13758e (1959). Ethylene glycol or Glycerol–Butyl alcohol–Heptane.
338A. J. P. Kohn, *A. I. Ch. E. Journal*, **7,** 514 (1961). Methane–*n*-Heptane. Two liquid phases from -103.5 to $-81.5°C$.
339. J. O. Konecny and C. H. Deal, *J. Phys. Chem.*, **67,** 504 (1963). Hydroperfluoroheptane, CST with ten substances.
339A. S. S. Korovin et al., *Isv. Vysshykh Uchebon. Zavedenii Khim. i Khim. Teknol.*, **5,** 553 (1962); *Chem. Abstracts*, **58,** 1943d (1963). Chlorides of H, Al, Fe, Ga, Hf, Zn–Water–Acetophenone or Dichloroethane.
340. S. S. Korovin et al., *J. Appl. Chem. USSR (English Transl.)*, **34,** 969 (1961); *Chem. Abstr.*, **55,** 19436a (1961). Water–Sulfuric acid–Gallium or Sodium chloride–Butyl acetate.
341. V. V. Kotel'nikov, and V. P. Skripov, *Nauch. Doklady Vysshei Shkoly, Khim. i Khim. Tekhnol.*, **1959,** No. 2, 248 (1959); *Chem. Abstr.*, **53,** 19525f (1959). Water–Deuterium oxide–Triethylamine.
342. K. N. Kovalenko, N. A. Trifonov, and D. S. Tisson, *J. Gen. Chem. U. S. S. R. (English Transl.)*, **26,** 2685 (1956); *Chem. Abstr.*, **51,** 4115b (1957); **52,** 6912d (1958). Water–Acetic anhydride–Dioxane. Synclinal edge at Acetic acid–Dioxane line.
343. P. P. Kozakevich and R. S. Yankelevich, *Zhur. Fiz. Khim.*, **10,** 113 (1936). *Chem. Abstr.*, **32,** 444[9] (1938). Water–Cobalt ions–Phenol.
344. V. N. Kozlov and G. A. Tokareva, *Gidrolizn. i Lesokhim. Prom.*, **15,** No. 1, 9 (1962); *Chem. Abstr.*, **56,** 14990f (1962). Water–Propionic or Butyric acids–Benzene, Ether, or Ethylacetate.
344A. I. R. Kriechevskii et al., *Doklady Acad. Nauk S. S. S. R.*, **94,** 509 (1954); **99,** 113 (1954); **100,** 737 (1955); *Russ. J. Phys. Chem.*, *(English Transl.)*, **33,** 17, 170 (1959); **34,** 598, 811, 911, 1027 (1960); *Chem. Abstr.*, **49,** 12089a, 13744c (1955); **50,** 1439f (1956); **54,** 9471c, e (1960); **55,** 5100d, 16108h (1961). Properties near plait point. Water–Hexamethyleneimine, Phenol, or Triethylamine.

344B. I. R. Kriechevskii and D. S. Tsiklis, *Acta Physicochim. U.R.S.S.*, **18,** 264 (1943)(in English); *Chem. Abstr.*, **38,** 5134⁶ (1944). Ammonia–Nitrogen; two liquids above critical temperature of ammonia.

344C. R. Krishnamurti, G. R. Rao, and C. V. Rao, *J. Sci. Ind. Research (India),* **21D,** 282 (1962); *Current Chem. Papers,* **1962,** 837 (1962). Water–Fatty acids–Pentyl acetate.

345. V. V. G. Krishnamurty, P. S. Murti, and C. V. Rao, *J. Sci. Ind. Research (India),* **12B,** 583 (1953); *Chem. Abstr.*, **49,** 7950a (1955). Water–Acetone–Gasoline, Solvent oil, or Ethyl ether; Acetic acid or Methanol systems.

346. V. V. G. Krishnamurty and C. V. Rao, *J. Sci. Ind. Research (India),* **14B,** 614 (1955); *Chem. Abstr.*, **50,** 9127a (1956). Water–Methanol–Hexyl alcohol or 2-Octanol.

347. V. V. G. Krishnamurty and C. V. Rao, *Trans. Indian Inst. Chem. Eng.*, **6,** 153 (1953–54); *Chem. Abstr.*, **49,** 15322i (1955). Water–Ethyl alcohol–Hexyl alcohol or 2-Octanol. Solutrope.

348. V. V. G. Krishnamurty and C. V. Rao, *Trans. Indian Inst. Chem. Eng.*, **8,** 52 (1955–56); *Chem. Abstr.*, **51,** 14399i (1957). Water–Butyric or Propionic acid–Benzene, Toluene, Xylenes, or Trichloroethylene. *Chem. Abstr.* erroneously lists alcohols instead of acids.

349. V. V. G. Krishnamurty, G. J. Rao, and C. V. Rao, *Trans. Indian Inst. Chem. Eng.*, **6,** 161 (1953–54); *Chem. Abstr.*, **50,** 3052a (1956). *Cf.* references 347 and 499. Water–Propionic acid–Benzene (double solutrope) or Chlorobenzene or Trichloroethylene.

350. I. L. Krupatkin, *J. Gen. Chem. U. S. S. R. (English Transl.),* **22,** 229 (1952); *Chem. Abstr.*, **47,** 9743i (1953). Water–Phosphoric acid–Phenol. Island curve between 68 and 100°C.

351. I. L. Krupatkin, *J. Gen. Chem. U. S. S. R. (English Transl.),* **23,** 1147 (1953); *Chem. Abstr.*, **50,** 3867i (1956). Sulfur–Diphenylamine–2-Naphthylamine.

352. I. L. Krupatkin, *J. Gen. Chem. U. S. S. R. (English Transl.),* **25,** 1599 (1955); *Chem. Abstr.*, **50,** 6164f (1956). Water–Picric acid–Salicylic acid.

353. I. L. Krupatkin, *J. Gen. Chem. U. S. S. R. (English Transl.),* **25,** 1815 (1955); *Chem. Abstr.*, **50,** 6168f (1956). Two aqueous systems and two glycerol systems.

354. I. L. Krupatkin, *J. Gen. Chem. U. S. S. R. (English Transl.),* **25,** 1971 (1955); *Chem. Abstr.*, **50,** 6166e (1956). Seven aqueous systems.

355. I. L. Krupatkin, *J. Gen. Chem. U. S. S. R. (English Transl.),* **25,** 2151 (1955); *Chem. Abstr.*, **50,** 6167h (1956). Water or Ligroin–Antipyrine–Salicylic acid.

356. I. L. Krupatkin, *J. Gen. Chem. U. S. S. R. (English Transl.),* **25,** 2301 (December 1955); *Chem. Abstr.*, **50,** 9126e (1956). Law of inverted similarity.

357. I. L. Krupatkin, *J. Gen. Chem. U. S. S. R. (English Transl.),* **26,** 393 (1956); *Chem. Abstr.*, **50,** 12623f (1956). Water–Antipyrine–Chloral hydrate.

358. I. L. Krupatkin, *J. Gen. Chem. U. S. S. R. (English Transl.),* **26,** 1197 (1956); *Chem. Abstr.*, **51,** 6305e (1957). Water–Salicylic acid–Aminopyrine. Island curve between 68 and 169°C.

359. I. L. Krupatkin, *J. Gen. Chem. U. S. S. R. (English Transl.),* **26,** 2043 (1956); *Chem. Abstr.*, **51,** 6303g (1957). Sulfur–Diphenylamine–Quinoline.

360. I. L. Krupatkin, *J. Gen. Chem. U. S. S. R.* (*English Transl.*), **26**, 3611 (1956); *Chem. Abstr.*, **51**, 8521c (1957). Water–Salicylic acid–Gasoline. Three liquid layers.

361. I. L. Krupatkin, *J. Gen. Chem. U. S. S. R.* (*English Transl.*), **27**, 627 (1957); *Chem. Abstr.*, **51**, 14396e (1957). Water or Sulfur–Phenol–Quinolin.

362. I. L. Krupatkin, *J. Gen. Chem. U. S. S. R.* (*English Transl.*), **27**, 633 (1957); *Chem. Abstr.*, **51**, 14398c (1957). Water or Ligroin–Antipyrine–Benzoic acid.

363. I. L. Krupatkin, *J. Gen. Chem. U. S. S. R.* (*English Transl.*), **27**, 1195 (1957); *Chem. Abstr.*, **52**, 5108h (1958). Water or Ligroin–Phenol–Antipyrine. Island curve in aqueous system.

364. I. L. Krupatkin, *J. Gen. Chem. U. S. S. R.* (*English Transl.*), **28**, 800 (1958); *Chem. Abstr.*, **53**, 10931d (1959). Water–Phenol–Anthranilic or Salicylic acid. Stable and metastable cols.

365. I. L. Krupatkin, *J. Gen. Chem. U. S. S. R.* (*English Transl.*), **28**, 1075 (1958); *Chem. Abstr.*, **52**, 19381b (1958). Water–Anthranilic acid–Gasoline. Three liquid phases (metastable) below 124°C.

366. I. L. Krupatkin, *J. Gen. Chem. U. S. S. R.* (*English Transl.*), **29**, 2452 (1959); *Chem. Abstr.*, **54**, 11963d (1960). Chloral hydrate–Antipyrine–Gasoline. Aminopyrine–Salicylic acid–Gasoline.

367. I. L. Krupatkin, *J. Gen. Chem. U. S. S. R.* (*English Transl.*), **29**, 3487 (1959); *Chem. Abstr.*, **54**, 17025i (1960). Water–Diethylamine–Chloral hydrate. Cf. references 368B and 769, and Figure 106.

368. I. L. Krupatkin, *J. Gen. Chem. U. S. S. R.* (*English Transl.*), **30**, 1095 (1960); *Chem. Abstr.*, **54**, 23687g (1960). Water–Ethyl alcohol–Anthranilic acid.

368A. I. L. Krupatkin, *J. Gen. Chem. U. S. S. R.* (*English Transl.*), **30**, 3517 (1960); *Chem. Abstr.*, **55**, 20592g (1961). Aqueous systems of *m*-Nitrobenzoic acid–Phenylacetic acid; Phenylhydrazine–Succinonitrile; Isobutyric acid–Phenol; and Aniline–Hexane–Heptane.

368B. I. L. Krupatkin, *J. Gen. Chem. U. S. S. R.* (*English Transl.*), **31**, 3248 (1961). Reply to Zhuravlev. Cf. reference 769.

369. I. L. Krupatkin, *Sbornik Stateĭ Obshcheĭ Khim. Akad. Nauk S. S. S. R.*, **1**, 151 (1953); *Chem. Abstr.*, **48**, 12532b (1954). Water–Ethyl alcohol–Salicylic acid.

370. I. L. Krupatkin, *Sbornik Stateĭ Obshcheĭ Khim. Akad. Nauk S. S. S. R.*, **2**, 771 (1953); *Chem. Abstr.*, **49**, 3636c (1955). Water–Quinoline–Ether or Aniline.

371. I. L. Krupatkin, *Sbornik Stateĭ Obshcheĭ Khim. Akad. Nauk S. S. S. R.*, **2**, 1221 (1953); *Chem. Abstr.*, **49**, 3636g (1955). Water–Salicylic acid–Anthranilic acid. All metastable. Col.

372. I. L. Krupatkin and E. F. Leschinskii, *Sbornik Stateĭ Obshcheĭ Khim. Akad. Nauk S. S. S. R.*, **1**, 144 (1953); *Chem. Abstr.*, **48**, 12532e (1954). Water–Benzoic acid–Salicylic acid.

373. I. L. Krupatkin and I. A. Todorov, *J. Gen. Chem. U. S. S. R.* (*English Transl.*), **27**, 2951 (1957); *Chem. Abstr.*, **52**, 8125g (1958). Water–Diethylamine–Aminopyrine.

374. K. T. Kuchynka, T. Boublik, and V. Fried, *Chem. listy*, **50**, 1848 (1956); *Chem. Abstr.*, **51**, 2372i (1957). Water–Ethoxyethanol–Ethylbenzene or Styrene.

375. G. I. Kudryavtseva and A. D. Krutikova, *J. Appl. Chem. U. S. S. R.* (*English Transl.*), **26**, 1129 (1953); *Chem. Abstr.*, **49**, 6693d (1955). Cf. references 457 and 677. Water–ε-Caprolactam–Chloroform, Ethylene chloride, or Methylene chloride. Solutrope.

376. C. W. Kuhlman, Jr., and W. Weber, *U. S. Atomic Energy Comm.*, *MCW-227* (1949); *Nuclear Sci. Abstr.*, **11**, 9688 (1957); *Chem. Abstr.*, **55**, 18267g (1961). Water–Boric acid–Uranium salts–Ether.

377. F. A. Kuznetsov, A. K. Lileeva, and N. I. Smirnov, *J. Appl. Chem. U. S. S. R.* (*English Transl.*), **34**, 1735 (1961); *Tr. Leningrad. Tekhnol. Inst. in Lensoveta*, **1960**, No. 60, 206; **57**, 6683b (1962). Water–Acetic, Propionic, or Butyric acids–Benzene, Hexane, or Kerosene.

378. B. G. Kyle and T. M. Reed, III, *J. Chem. Eng. Data*, **5**, 266 (1960). Fluorochemicals.

379. G. S. Laddha and J. M. Smith, *Ind. Eng. Chem.*, **40**, 494 (1948). Water–Glycol–Amyl alcohol.

380. C. M. Lakshmanan and G. S. Laddha, *J. Am. Oil Chemists' Soc.*, **37**, 466 (1960); *Chem. Abstr.*, **54**, 25898e (1960). Furfural or Nitromethane–Methyl esters of Castor oil–Hexane.

381. C. M. Lakshmanan and G. S. Laddha, *J. Madras Univ.*, **29B**, 97 (1959); *Chem. Abstr.*, **55**, 21624a (1961). Nitromethane–Methyl ricinoleate–Cyclohexane.

382. K. L. Lakshimarasimhan, S. Gopalan, and G. S. Laddha, *J. Madras Univ.*, **26B** (2) 281 (1956). Water–Glycol–*n*- or Isobutyl alcohol.

383. B. B. Lampert, J. V. Murray, Jr., and D. W. Peck, U. S. Patent 2,910,518, Oct. 27, 1959. Ketodioxane–Aromatic and Nonaromatic hydrocarbons.

384. Landolt-Börnstein-Roth-Scheel, *Tabellen*, Julius Springer, Berlin, 1923–35.

385. D. M. Langbridge, A. S. C. Lawrence, and R. Stenson, *J. Colloid Sci.*, **11**, 585 (1956); *Chem. Abstr.*, **51**, 4114b (1957). Water–Nicotine or Triethylamine–Soaps or other salts.

385A. B. N. Laskorin, G. N. Shivrin, and I. N. Plaksin, *Proc. Acad. Sci. U. S. S. R.*, *Chem. Tech. Section* (*English Transl.*), **139**, 123 (1961). Cf. *Chem. Abstr.*, **56**, 8362g (1962). Water–Gold or Silver cyanide–*n*-Trioctylamine in Kerosine.

386. P. A. Laurent and M. J. Duhamel, *Bull. soc. chim. France*, **1953**, 157 (1953); *Chem. Abstr.*, **47**, 7306d (1953). Water–Hydroxides of lithium, potassium, or sodium–Acetone, Dioxane, Pyridine.

387. G. Lazzari, *Ann. chim. appl.*, **38**, 287 (1948); *Chem. Abstr.*, **43**, 5273g (1949). Water–Butyl alcohol–Butyl ether.

388. M. Lecat, *Tables Azeotropiques*, Bruxelles, 1949. Various.

389. E. Leibnitz, *et al.*, *J. prakt. Chem.*, (4)**3**, 311 (1956); *Chem. Abstr.*, **51**, 6304g (1957). 75–80% Methanol–Benzene–Hexane; Heptane, Cyclohexane, Cyclohexene.

390. E. Leibnitz *et al.*, *J. prakt. Chem.*, (4)**4**, 105 (1956); *Chem. Abstr.*, **51**, 11024e (1957). Glycol or Diethylene glycol–Benzene–Hexane, Heptane, Cyclohexane, Cyclohexene.

391. E. Leibnitz *et al.*, *J. prakt. Chem.*, (4)**4**, 278 (1956); *Chem. Abstr.*, **52**, 27b (1958). Water–Methanol–Four hydrocarbons; Glycols–Hydrocarbon pairs.

392. E. Leibnitz *et al.*, *J. prakt. Chem.*, (4)**10**, 1, 239 (1960); *Chem. Abstr.*, **55**, 8021h (1961). Water–Sodium hydroxide–*o*-Cresol.

393. E. Leikola, *Suomen Kemistilehti*, **13B,** 13 (1940); *Chem. Abstr.*, **35,** 2772[8] (1941). Water–Nine water-miscible solvents, each with Carbon disulfide, Carbon tetrachloride, and Chloroform; Methanol with 14 other water-immiscible solvents; Butyric acid with Benzene, Toluene, Xylene.

394. P. Leone, *Atti II congresso nazl. chim. pura applicato*, **1926,** 1209 (1926); *Chem. Abstr.*, **22,** 2100[9] (1928). Water–Acetone–Nicotine.

395. R. T. Leslie, *J. Research Natl. Bur. Standards*, **13,** 95 (1934). Sulfur dioxide.

396. A. I. Levin *et al.*, *Trudy Vsesoyuz. Nauch.-Issledovatel. Inst. Neftekhim. Protsessov*, **1960,** No. 1, 89 (1960); *Chem. Abstr.*, **56,** 9492e (1962). Water–C_1 to C_4 acids. Benzene, 2-Butanone, Ethyl acetate.

397. H. F. Li and K. C. Wu, *Wu Han Ta Hsueh, Tzu Jan K'o Hsueh Hsueh Pao*, **1957,** No. 1, 64 (1957); *Chem. Abstr.*, **56,** 6710i (1962). Water–Ethyl alcohol–Furfural.

398. H. J. Lichtenstein *et al.*, *J. prakt. Chem.*, (4)**7,** 241 (1959); *Chem. Abstr.*, **54,** 4132f (1960). Water–Sodium hydroxide–Phenol.

398A. K. H. Lieser and C. E. Pfluger, *Chem. Ber.*, **93,** 176, 181 (1960); *Chem. Abstr.*, **54,** 8257g, 8257i (1960). Aluminum chloride–Hydrogen chloride–Toluene or Mesitylene.

398B. A. I. Likhacheva and G. P. Luchinski, *Zhur. Obshchei Khim.*, **8,** 916 (1938); *Chem. Abstr.*, **33,** 1202[4] (1939). Water, Potassium bromide–Bromine–Benzene.

399. R. B. Long, M. S. Thesis, Penn. State Univ., 1947. *Cf.* references 148 and 226. Valerolactone–Four pairs of hydrocarbons; Ammonia–13 pairs of hydrocarbons.

399A. M. R. Loran and E. P. Guth, *J. Am. Pharm. Assoc.*, **40,** 456 (1951); *Chem. Abstr.*, **45,** 10487e (1951). Water–Ethyl alcohol–Castor oil.

400. H. L. Lorentzen and B. B. Hansen, *Acta. Chem. Scand.*, **12,** 139 (1958); *Chem. Abstr.*, **53,** 3813a (1959). Water–Triethylamine; Ethyl alcohol–Succino-nitrile. Curves are cubics.

401. N. V. Lutugina and V. M. Kaluzhnyi, *J. Appl. Chem. USSR (English Transl.)*, **32,** 2599 (1959); **33,** 248 (1960); *Zhur. Priklad. Khim.*, **33,** 248 (1960); *Chem. Abstr.*, **54,** 8256g, 10485i (1960). Water–Methyl acetate–Chloroform.

402. E. H. McArdle, *Chem. & Met. Eng.*, **44,** 601 (1937); *Chem. Abstr.*, **32,** 5610[7] (1938). Mixed aniline points.

403. P. J. McAteer, R. W. Cox, and C. J. Geankoplis, *A. I. Ch. E. Journal*, **7,** 456 (1961). Water–Acetic and Sulfuric acids or Formic and Hydrochloric acids–4-Methyl-2-pentanone.

404. J. W. McBain and A. J. Burnett, *J. Chem. Soc. (London)*, **121,** 1320 (1922). Water–Sodium chloride–Sodium laurate.

405. J. W. McBain and G. M. Langdon, *J. Chem. Soc. (London)*, **127,** 852 (1925). Water–Sodium chloride–Sodium palmitate.

406. J. W. McBain and J. J. O'Connor, *J. Am. Chem. Soc.*, **62,** 2855 (1940). Water–Soap–Hexane, etc.

407. J. F. McCants, J. H. Jones, and W. H. Hopson, *Ind. Eng. Chem.*, **45,** 454 (1953). Water–*n*-Propyl or *n*-Butyl alcohol–Benzene–Hexane or Heptane.

408. W. J. McManamay, *J. Appl. Chem. (London)*, **11,** 44 (1961); *Chem. Abstr.*, **55,** 14038i (1961). Water–Nitrates of cobalt, copper, nickel, zinc–Butyl, or Amyl alcohols.

409. K. K. McMillan *et al.*, *Chem. Eng. Data Ser.*, **3**, 96 (1958). Water–Furfural–C_4 hydrocarbons.

410. J. T. McQueen, F. R. Meeks, and O. K. Rice, *J. Phys. Chem.*, **65**, 1925 (1961). Water–Aniline–Cyclohexane.

411. B. Malesińska and W. Malesiński, *Bull. acad. polon. sci.*, *Ser. sci. chim.*, **8**, 53, 61, 67 (1960); *Chem. Abstr.*, **55**, 6117g, 6117i, 6118a (1961). Nitromethane–Eight Paraffins, CST. Equations for binodal curves.

412. A. Maman, *Compt. rend.*, **198**, 1324 (1934); **205**, 320 (1937); **207**, 1401 (1938). Aniline, Benzyl alcohol, Nitrobenzene–Paraffins. CST. *Cf.* reference 178.

413. V. N. Mamuna, *et al. Trudy Vsesoyuz. Neftegaz. Nauch.-Isseldovatel. Inst.*, **1956**, No. 8, 392 (1956); *Chem. Abstr.*, **52**, 19095i (1958). Carbon dioxide–Petroleum oil.

414. J. Marek, *Chem. listy*, **49**, 1756 (1955); *Collection Czech. Chem. Communs.*, **21**, 269 (1956); *Chem. Abstr.*, **50**, 3825a, 16295g (1956). Water–Acetic acid–Acetic anhydride.

415. N. P. Markuzin, *Vestnik Leningrad. Univ.*, **16**, No. 4, *Ser. Fiz. i Khim.*, No. 1, 148 (1961); *Chem. Abstr.*, **55**, 16112c (1961). Water–Isobutyric acid–*sec*-Butyl alcohol. Highly convex band.

415A. N. P. Markuzin and L. A. Nikonorova, *Zhur. Obshchei Khim.*, **32**, 3469 (1962); *Chem. Abstr.*, **58**, 7415g (1963). *Cf.* reference 174. Ethylene glycol–Nitromethane–Lauryl alcohol. Three liquid phases. Three separate binodal curves.

415B. N. P. Markuzin and V. P. Plekhotkin, *Zhur. Fiz. Khim.*, **35**, 1973 (1962); *Chem. Abstr.*, **58**, 67a (1963). Ethylenediamine–Benzene–Heptane.

416. N. P. Markuzin and A. V. Storonkin, *Vestnik Leningrad. Univ.*, **12**, No. 10, *Ser. Fiz. i Khim.*, No. 2, 123 (1957); *Chem. Abstr.*, **52**, 5108i (1958). Water–Triethylamine–Phenol.

417. J. S. Marsh, *Principles of Phase Diagrams*, McGraw-Hill, New York, 1935, pp. 122–170. Schreinemakers' rule.

417A. W. L. Marshall and J. S. Gill, *J. Inorg. & Nuclear Chem.*, **22**, 115 (1961); *Chem. Abstrs.*, **57**, 121e (1962). Water–Uranium trioxide–Sulfuric acid.

417B. W. L. Marshall *et al.*, *J. Inorg. Nucl. Chem.*, **24**, 995 (1962); *Chem. Abstr.*, **58**, 6251g (1963). Water or Deuterium oxide–Sulfur trioxide–Cupric or Uranium oxide.

418. E. P. Martin and R. C. Pink, *J. Chem. Soc.*, **1948**, 1750. Zinc soaps–Hydrocarbons (binary only).

419. J. M. Martinez-Moreno and M. A. Crespi-Gonzales, *Anales real soc. españ. fiz. y quim.*, *Ser. B*, **44**, 391 (1948); *Chem. Abstr.*, **42**, 8602c (1948). Methanol–Carbon disulfide–Oleic acid–Olive oil.

419A. R. N. Maslova and V. V. Fomin, *Russ. J. Inorg. Chem.* (*English Transl.*), **6**, 375 (1961); *Chem. Abstr.*, **56**, 15124g (1962). Water–Nitric acid–Ethyl propyl ether or Dipropyl ether.

420. K. Matsumoto and S. Sone, *Yakugaku Zasshi*, **76**, 475, 478 (1956); *Chem. Abstr.*, **50**, 12622ef (1956). Water–Glycols–Butyl alcohol.

421. K. Matsumoto and S. Sone, *Yakugaku Zasshi*, **77**, 1149 (1957); *Chem. Abstr.*, **52**, 2516f (1958). Water–Pyridine or Ethyl alcohol–Carbon tetrachloride. Solutropes.

422. K. Matsumoto and S. Sone, *Yakugaku Zasshi*, **77**, 1151 (1957); *Chem. Abstr.*, **52**, 2516i (1958). Water–Glycerol–Butyl alcohol.

422A. K. Matsumoto and S. Sone, *Yakugaku Zasshi*, **77**, 1153 (1957); *Chem. Abstr.*, **52**, 2516h (1958). Water–Ethyl alcohol–Carbon tetrachloride; Water–*n*- or Isopropyl alcohols–Carbon tetrachloride. Solutropes.

423. K. Matsumoto and S. Sone, *Yakugaku Zasshi*, **80**, 264 (1960); *Chem. Abstr.*, **54**, 11649e (1960). Water–Alcohols or Glycols–Chlorine compounds.

424. E. R. Matyba, P. E. Connell, and J. R. Murray, *Can. Pharm. J.*, *Sci. Sect.*, **90**, 438 (1957); *Chem. Abstr.*, **52**, 17931e (1958). Water–Glycerol–Phenol.

424A. S. G. Measamer and O. R. Sweeney, *Proc. Iowa Acad. Sci.*, **47**, 207 (1940); *Chem. Abstr.*, **35**, 7254[4] (1941). Water–Ethyl alcohol–Trichloroethylene.

424B. S. G. Measamer (name misspelled in *Chem. Abstr.*), O. R. Sweeney, and L. K. Arnold, *Proc. Iowa Acad. Sci.*, **54**, 189 (1947); *Chem. Abstr.*, **43**, 1999c (1949). Trichloroethylene–Ethyl alcohol–Soybean oil.

425. E. C. Medcalf, A. G. Hill, and G. N. Vriens, *Petrol. Refiner*, **30**, No. 7, 97 (1951); *Chem. Abstr.*, **45**, 9251a (1951). Oxydipropionitrile–Aromatics–Paraffins.

426. F. R. Meeks, R. Gopal, and O. K. Rice, *J. Phys. Chem.*, **63**, 992 (1959). Water–Aniline–Cyclohexane.

427. H. P. Meissner, C. A. Stokes, *et al.*, *Ind. Eng. Chem.*, **36**, 816, 917 (1944). Water–Calcium chloride–2-Butanone.

428. M. A. Menkovskii *et al.*, *Zhur. Neorg. Khim.*, **1**, 1658 (1956); *Chem. Abstr.*, **51**, 1714f (1957). Water–Hydrogen bromide–Bromine.

429. F. S. Men'shchikov, *J. Gen. Chem. U. S. S. R.* (*English Transl.*), **23**, 965 (1953); *Chem. Abstr.*, **48**, 3128d (1954). Aqueous systems of Epichlorohydrin–Toluene or Phenol–Naphthalene or Benzoic acid.

430. R. V. Mertslin, *Zhur. Obshcheĭ Khim.*, **7**, 2490 (1937); *Chem. Abstr.*, **32**, 2012[8] (1938). Water–Piperidine–Phenol.

431. R. V. Mertslin, *Zhur. Obshcheĭ Chim.*, **10**, 1865 (1940); *Chem. Abstr.*, **35**, 4274[2] (1941); *Cf.* **34**, 932[9] (1940). Water–Ammonium sulfocyanate–Phenol.

432. R. V. Mertslin, *Uchenye Zapiski Molotov Gosudarst. Univ.*, **3**, No. 4, 37 (1939); *Chem. Abstr.*, **37**, 6532[9] (1943). Water–Acetone–Barium nitrate.

433. R. V. Mertslin and K. I. Mochalov, *J. Gen. Chem. U. S. S. R.* (*English Transl*)., **29**, 3138 (1959); *Chem. Abstr.*, **54**, 11679d (1960). Predicts three liquid phases in four components, but no example. Schematic curves similar to Figs. 21 and 62.

434. R. V. Mertslin and N. I. Nikurashina, *J. Gen. Chem. U. S. S. R.* (*English Transl.*), **29**, 2437 (1959); *Chem. Abstr.*, **54**, 9477i (1960). Four liquid phases in a quaternary system. Water–Phenol–Hexane–Sulfur (about 96°C).

435. R. V. Mertslin and N. I. Nikurashina, *J. Gen. Chem. U. S. S. R.* (*English Transl.*), **30**, 25 (1960); *Chem. Abstr.*, **54**, 19139a (1960). Three liquid phases in a quaternary system. Cf. reference 433.

435A. R. V. Mertslin and N. I. Nikurashina, *Russ. J. Phys. Chem.* (*English Transl.*), **35**, 1299 (1961); *Chem. Abstr.*, **58**, 8458a (1963). Water–Ethyl alcohol–Benzene or Toluene.

435B. R. V. Mertslin and N. I. Nikurashina, *Russ. J. Phys. Chem.* (*English Transl.*), **36**, 199 (1962). Properties of heterogeneous ternary systems near plait point.

435C. R. V. Mertslin and N. I. Nikurashina, *Zhur. Obshcheĭ Khim.*, **32**, 3122 (1962); *Chem. Abstr.*, **58**, 10777h (1963). Water–Piperidine–Benzene.

435D. R. V. Mertslin, N. I. Nikurashina, and P. I. Naumova, *J. Gen. Chem. U.S.S.R. (English Transl.)*, **32**, 1351 (1962); *Chem. Abstr.*, **58**, 3947d (1963). Water–Phenol or Pyridine–Hexane–Sulfur.

435E. R. V. Mertslin, N. I. Nikurashina, and V. A. Petrov, *Russ. J. Phys. Chem. (English Transl.)*, **35**, 1369 (1961); *Chem. Abstr.*, **56**, 13603c (1962). Water–Ethyl alcohol–*n*-Hexane.

436. R. V. Mertslin and V. V. Parkacheva, *J. Gen. Chem. U. S. S. R. (English Transl.)*, **20**, 1997 (1950); *Chem. Abstr.*, **45**, 8339a (1951). Water–Ether–Succinonitrile. Three phases.

437. R. V. Mertslin and V. F. Ust-Kachintsev, *Zhur. Obshcheĭ Khim.*, **5**, 904 (1935); *Chem. Abstr.*, **30**, 943[2] (1936). Water–Aniline–Benzylamine, Phenylhydrazine, Pyridine.

438. R. V. Mertslin and V. D. Vasev, *J. Gen. Chem. U. S. S. R. (English Transl.)*, **21**, 463 (1951); *Chem. Abstr.*, **46**, 8500h (1952). Succinonitrile–Ethyl alcohol–Ether.

439. R. V. Mertslin *et al.*, *Uchenye Zapiski Saratov. Univ.*, **71**, 99, 105 (1959); *Chem. Abstr.*, **56**, 2033h, 2033i (1962). Water–Sulfur–Phenol or Aniline–Hexane. Four liquid phases.

440. Z. Mervart and J. Křen, *Collection Czech. Chem. Communs.*, **24**, 3688 (1959); *Chem. Abstr.*, **54**, 10486b (1960). Water–Acetone–1,3-Butadiene.

441. E. A. Mezhov, A. A. Pushkov, and V. S. Schmidt, *Russ. J. Inorg. Chem. (English Transl.)*, **7**, 481 (1962). Water–Nitric acid–Di-*n*-octylamine in *o*-Xylene.

442. A. W. F. Middelberg *et al.*, *S. African Ind. Chemist*, **15**, 85 (1961); *Chem. Abstr.*, **55**, 24206h (1961). Water–Methanol–Butyl alcohol–Hydrocarbons.

443. V. A. Miller, *Ind. Eng. Chem.*, *Anal. Ed.*, **17**, 5, 566 (1945). Ethyl phthalate or Nitrobenzene with mixed Hexanes or Heptanes.

444. A. L. Mills and F. Hughes, *Chem. Eng. Data Ser.*, **2**, 35 (1957). Water–Sodium hydroxide–Isopropyl alcohol.

445. A. L. Mills and F. A. Smith, *Chem. Eng. Data Ser.*, **2**, 30 (1957). Water–Sodium sulfate–Isopropyl alcohol.

446. P. Mion, *Compt. rend.*, **193**, 1330 (1931); *Chem. Abstr.*, **26**, 1503 (1932). Water–Acetic acid or Ethyl alcohol–Ethyl acetate.

447. K. E. Mironov, *Doklady Akad. Nauk S. S. S. R.*, **104**, 91 (1955); *Chem. Abstr.*, **50**, 5384b (1956). Hydrogen peroxide–Ether. CST 46°C.

447A. K. I. Mochalov, *Izvest. Vysshikh Ucheb. Zavedenii, Khim i Khim. Tekhnol.*, **3**, 434 (1960); *Chem. Abstr.*, **54**, 21968h (1960). Water–Ethylbenzylaniline sulfate–Sulfuric acid or Ethylbenzylaniline. Two systems adjacent.

448. K. I. Mochalov, *Zhur. Obshcheĭ Khim.*, **8**, 529 (1938); *Chem. Abstr.*, **32**, 7333[6] (1938). Water–Acetic anhydride–Carbon disulfide.

449. K. I. Mochalov, *Uchenye Zapiski Molotov Gosudarst. Univ.*, **3**, No. 4, 81 (1939); *Chem. Abstr.*, **37**, 6532[7] (1943). Aniline–Phenyl isothiocyanate or Diphenylthiourea–sulfur.

450. P. Mondain-Monval and J. Quiquarez, *Bull. soc. chim. France*, (5)**7**, 240 (1940); *Chem. Abstr.*, **34**, 4651[7] (1940). Isopycnics.

451. P. Mondain-Monval and J. Quiquarez, *Bull. soc. chim. France*, **11**, 26 (1944); *Chem. Abstr.*, **39**, 8⁵ (1945). Thirty ternary systems; critical opalescence.

452. P. Mondain-Monval and J. Quiquarez, *Bull. soc. chim. France*, **12**, 380 (1945); *Chem. Abstr.*, **40**, 270⁴ (1946). Twelve systems, some with high viscosity near plait point.

453. P. Mondain-Monval and J. Quiquarez, *Compt. rend.*, **210**, 246 (1940); *Chem. Abstr.*, **34**, 2665⁴ (1940). Cf. *Chem. Abstr.*, **33**, 7636⁹ (1939). Opalescence near plait point.

454. M. Monet, *U. S. Atomic Energy Comm.*, *CN-2491; Nuclear Sci. Abstr.*, **10**, 9756 (1956). Water–Uranyl nitrate–Ether.

455. R. J. Moore, J. C. Morrell, and G. Egloft, *Met. Chem. Eng.*, **18**, 396 (1918); *Chem. Abstr.*, **12**, 1923 (1918). Sulfur dioxide–Pairs of hydrocarbons.

456. A. G. Morachevskii and V. P. Belousov, *Vestnik Leningrad. Univ.*, **13**, No. 4, *Ser. Fiz. i Khim.*, No. 1, 117 (1958); *Chem. Abstr.*, **52**, 12535f (1958). Water–Ethyl alcohol–Benzene.

457. A. G. Morachevskii and V. E. Sabinin, *J. Appl. Chem. U. S. S. R. (English Transl.)*, **33**, 1755 (1960); *Chem. Abstr.*, **54**, 23677b (1960). Water–Caprolactam–Benzene, Carbon tetrachloride, or Ethylene chloride. Cf. references 375 and 677.

458. J. L. R. Morgan and W. V. Evans, *J. Am. Chem. Soc.*, **39**, 2151 (1917). Surface tensions of liquids in equilibrium.

458A. A. F. Morgunov and V. V. Fomin, *Russ. J. Inorg. Chem. (English Transl.)*, **7**, 490 (1962); *Chem. Abstr.*, **57**, 5561i (1962). Hydrogen chloride–Chlorides of antimony, indium, iron, and tin–Ether.

458B. D. F. C. Morris and E. L. Short, *J. Inorg. Nucl. Chem.*, **25**, 291 (1963); *Chem. Abstr.*, **58**, 10788g (1963). Water–Lithium chloride–Tributylphosphate.

459. L. I. Moseev and A. G. Karabash, *Zhur. Neorg. Khim.*, **6**, 1944 (1961); *Russ. J. Inorg. Chem. (English Transl.)*, **6**, 992 (1961); *Chem. Abstr.*, **56**, 5454e (1962). Water–Radio isotypes of antimony, iron, indium, or zinc–Ethers.

459A. M. Mrnka and Z. Malek, *Chem. Prumysl*, **12**, 297 (1962); *Chem. Abstr.*, **57**, 13228b (1962). Water, Sulfuric acid–Uranium salts–Tri-*n*-octylamine–Benzene, Carbon tetrachloride, and other solvents.

459B. G. Mueh, *Makromol. Chem.*, **54**, 222 (1962); *Chem. Abstr.*, **57**, 13958c (1962). Water–Ethers–Dimethylformamide–Poly(*p*-iodostyrene).

459C. A. Müller et al., *Monatsh. Chem.*, **83**, 386(1952); *Chem Abstr.*, **47**, 7511d. Aza- and Diazacyclo-octanes.

460. A. Munster, *J. Polymer Sci.*, **5**, S8, 333 (1950); *Chem. Abstr.*, **44**, 10458f (1950). Cellulose triacetate–Tetrachloroethane–Petroleum ether.

461. A. Munster and K. Sagel, *Z. Elektrochem.*, **59**, 946 (1955); *Chem. Abstr.*, **50**, 4612f (1956). Aluminum–Zinc.

462. S. P. Mulliken and R. L. Wakeman, *Ind. Eng. Chem.*, *Anal. Ed.*, **7**, 276 (1935); *Rec. trav. chim.*, **54**, 367 (1935); *Chem. Abstr.*, **29**, 3975⁷ (1935). Miscibilities of Hydrocarbons with Aniline, Benzyl alcohol, Ethyl sulfate, or Nitromethane.

463. N. N. Murach, *et al.*, *J. Appl. Chem. U. S. S. R. (English Transl.)*, **34**, 2080 (1961); *Chem. Abstr.*, **56**, 8075a (1962). Water, Hydrogen chloride–Germanium chloride–Tributyl phosphate in Benzene, Carbon tetrachloride, or Chloroform.

464. M. Murari and B. P. Gyani, *J. Indian Chem. Soc.*, *Ind. & News Ed.*, **17**, 193 (1954); *Chem. Abstr.*, **49**, 12900i (1955). Castor oil–Diesel oil or Kerosine (CST).

465. N. F. Murphy and S. P. McConnell, *J. Chem. Eng. Data*, **5**, 143 (1960). Water–Triethylene glycol dimethyl ether–Benzene.

466. J. N. Murrell, L. I. Katzin, and B. L. Davies, *Nature*, **183**, 459; *Chem. Abstr.*, **53**, 12813h (1959). Water–Acetone–Cobalt chloride. Island curve.

467. P. S. Murti, A. Venkataratnam, and C. V. Rao, *J. Sci. Ind. Research (India)*, **13B**, 392 (1954); *Chem. Abstr.*, **49**, 4391h (1955). Water–Acetic acid or Acetone–Esters.

468. G. Nakagawa, *Nippon Kagaku Zasshi*, **81**, 747, 750 (1960); *Chem. Abstr.*, **55**, 19436c, 19436e (1961). Water–Salts of aluminum, arsenic, bismuth, iron, antimony, or titanium–Dodecenyl (trialkylmethyl) amine.

469. A. Nakajima, A. Ogawa, and I. Sakurada, *Kobunshi Kakaku*, **14**, 596 (1957); *Chem. Abstr.*, **53**, 5850f (1959). Water–Acetone–Poly(vinyl acetate).

469A. K. S. Narasimham, C. C. Reddy, and K. S. Chari, *J. Chem. Eng. Data*, **7**, 340 (1962). Water–Phenol–*n*-Butyl acetate. Isopycnic. Cf. reference 597.

469B. *Ibid.*, **7**, 457 (1962). Water–Phenol–Isoamyl acetate or 4-Methyl-1-pentanone.

470. I. P. Naumova, N. I. Nikurashina, and R. V. Mertslin, *J. Gen. Chem. U. S. S. R. (English Transl.)*, **30**, 3129 (1960); *Chem. Abstr.*, **55**, 21774e (1961). Water–Pyridine–Phenol–Sulfur. Island curves.

471. O. Navratil and Z. Kolarik, *Collection Czech. Chem. Communs.*, **26**, 3009 (1961); *Chem. Abstr.*, **56**, 9490i (1962). Water–Strontium and Yttrium complexes–Picrolonic acid in Methylcyclohexane.

472. J. Néel and B. Sébille, *Compt. rend.*, **252**, 3045 (1961); *Chem. Abstr.*, **55**, 24206i (1961). Water–Acrylic acid–Poly(vinylpyrrolidinone). Island curve.

473. Nguyen Quang Trinh., *Compt. rend.*, **218**, 718 (1944); *Chem. Abstr.*, **40**, 3873[6] (1946). Nitromethane or four other organic compounds–Aromatics–Paraffins; Tetranitromethane miscible with all liquid hydrocarbons.

474. S. Niese, *J. prakt. Chem.*, **7**, 251 (1959); *Chem. Abstr.*, **54**, 1034g (1960). Water–Nitrates–Ether or 4-Methyl-2-pentanone; Water–Cobalt compounds–Isoamyl Alcohol.

475. S. Niese and E. Liebnitz, *J. prakt. Chem.*, **10**, 311 (1960); *Chem. Abstr.*, **55**, 10029h (1961). Water, Nitric acid, Nitrates–Thorium nitrate–Six organic liquids.

476. A. V. Nikolaev and M. P. Mikhailova, *Izvest. Sibirsk. Otdel. Akad. Nauk SSSR*, **1961**, No. 3, 46; *Doklady Akad. Nauk S. S. S. R.*, **136**, 364 (1961); *Chem. Abstr.*, **55**, 19445c (1961); **56**, 5455a (1962). Water–Hydrogen and Ferric chlorides–Ether.

476A. A. V. Nikolaev and I. I. Yakovlev, *Doklady Akad. Nauk S. S. S. R.*, **145**, 1064 (1962); **146**, 102 (1962); *Chem. Abstr.*, **58**, 2901g, 5091f (1963). Water–Nitric acid–Uranyl and Ceric nitrate–Tributyl phosphate.

477. N. I. Nikurashina *et al.*, *J. Gen. Chem. U. S. S. R. (English Transl.)*, **29**, 349 (1959); *Chem. Abstr.*, **53**, 19547a (1959). Aniline–Nitrobenzene–Hexane.

478. N. I. Nikurashina *et al.*, *J. Gen. Chem. U. S. S. R. (English Transl.)*, **29**, 354 (1959); *Chem. Abstr.*, **53**, 19550c (1959). Water–Aniline–Nitrobenzene–Hexane. Three liquid phases.

479. N. I. Nikurashina *et al.*, *J. Gen. Chem. U. S. S. R. (English Transl.)*, **29**, 3127 (1959); *Chem. Abstr.*, **54**, 12760g (1960). Water–Phenol–Hexane or Sulfur.

480. N. I. Nikurashina *et al.*, *J. Gen. Chem. U. S. S. R. (English Transl.)*, **29**, 3133 (1959); *Chem. Abstr.*, **54**, 12760h (1960). Water–Phenol–Heptane; Water–Aniline–Sulfur.

480A. N. I. Nikurashina *et al.*, *J. Gen. Chem. U. S. S. R. (English Transl.)*, **32**, 997 (1962); *Chem. Abstr.*, **58**, 2893a (1963). Water–Pyridine–Toluene.

481. N. I. Nikurashina, *et al.*, *Uchenye Zapiski Saratov. Univ.*, **71**, 89 (1959); *Chem. Abstr.*, **56**, 988i (1962). Water–Aniline–*n*-Hexane. Three phases.

482. J. Nowakowska, C. B. Kretschmer, and R. Wiebe, *Chem. Eng. Data Ser.*, **1**, 42 (1956); *Chem. Abstr.*, **51**, 15237i (1957). Water–Ethyl alcohol–Iso-octane–1-Octene.

483. S. Oksne, *Acta Chem. Scand.*, **13**, 1814 (1959); *Chem. Abstr.*, **56**, 8074h (1962). Water–Dialkylfluorophosphate–Carbon tetrachloride or Whale oil.

484. Y. I. Ol'shanskii, *Doklady Akad. Nauk S. S. S. R.*, **114**, 1246 (1957); *Chem. Abstr.*, **52**, 3499b (1958). Oxides and fluorides of calcium and silicon.

485. R. A. Oriani, *J. Chem. Phys.*, **25**, 186 (1956). Subcooling of liquid equilibriums, 0.1 to 0.5°C. Carbon tetrachloride–Perfluoromethylcyclohexane, CST 26.8°C.

486. D. F. Othmer, M. M. Chudgar, and S. L. Levy, *Ind. Eng. Chem.*, **44**, 1872 (1952). Water–Acetone–2-Butanone.

487. D. F. Othmer and P. L. Ku, *J. Chem. Eng. Data*, **5**, 42 (1960). Water–Acetic or Formic acids–Chloroform.

488. D. F. Othmer and J. Serrano, Jr., *Ind. Eng. Chem.*, **41**, 1031 (1949). Water–Acetic acid–Caproic acid, 2-Ethylbutyric or 2-Ethylhexoic acids. Hump and plait point on concavity.

489. D. F. Othmer and P. E. Tobias, *Ibid.*, **34**, 690 (1942). Water–Acetaldehyde–Amyl alcohol, Furfural, Benzene, Toluene. Acetic acid (+ water)–Toluene–Heptane.

490. *Idem*, **34**, 693, 696 (1942). Tie line correlation.

491. D. F. Othmer, R. E. White, and E. Trueger, *Ibid.*, **33**, 1240 (1941). Many ternary systems and methods for their determination.

492. C. M. Oualline, Jr., and M. Van Winkle, *Ibid.*, **44**, 1668 (1952). Water–Acetic acid or Ethyl alcohol–3-Heptanol.

492A. L. S. Palatnik and N. D. Gorban, *Russ. J. Phys. Chem. (English Transl.)*, **36**, 674 (1962); *Chem. Abstr.*, **57**, 9284a (1962). Aniline–Dioxane or Toluene–Heptane or Iso-octave. Aniline–Heptane–Iso-octane.

492B. L. S. Palatnik and V. B. Kuropyatnik, *Russ. J. Phys. Chem. (English Transl.)*, **35**, 1037 (1961); *Chem. Abstr.*, **56**, 12335d (1962). Aniline–Chlorobenzene or Chloroform–*n*-Heptane; Aniline–Cyclohexane–2-Heptene.

493. L. S. Palatnik *et al.*, *Russ. J. Phys. Chem. (English Transl.)*, **33**, 230 (1959); *Chem. Abstr.*, **54**, 12759i (1960). Aniline–Carbon tetrachloride or Chloroform–Heptane; Water–Methanol or Isopropyl alcohol–Ethylene chloride. Solutrope.

493A. L. S. Palatnik *et al.*, *Russ. J. Phys. Chem. (English Transl.)*, **34**, 1134 (1960); *Chem. Abstr.*, **55**, 6120a (1961). Aniline–Carbon tetrachloride or Chloroform or Ethylene chloride–Heptane or Iso-octane.

494. E. Papafil, M. A. Papafil, and C. Beldie, *Analele stiint univ. "A. I. Cuza" Iasi Sect. I* (N.S.)**4**, 153 (1958); *Chem. Abstr.*, **53**, 14666e (1959). Water–Salts–Phenol.

495. S. P. Papkov, *Vysokomolekulyarnye Soedineniya*, **1**, No. 1, 84 (1959); *Chem. Abstr.*, **55**, 25445c (1961). Water–Acetone–Cellulose nitrate; Cellulose di-acetate–Ethyl alcohol–Chloroform.

496. D. A. Pascale, *Dissertation Abstr.*, **19**, 968 (1958); *Chem. Abstr.*, **53**, 5850c (1959). Water–Dioxane–Ferric chloride.

497. E. A. Pasquinelli, *Trans. Faraday Soc.*, **53**, 935 (1952); *Chem. Abstr.*, **52**, 7819e (1958). Correlations of solubilities with other properties.

498. K. C. Patel, R. D. Patel, and S. A. Patel, *Indian J. Appl. Chem.*, **21**, 77 (1958); *Chem. Abstr.*, **55**, 14039c (1961). Ethyl alcohol–Acetone–Triolein.

499. J. S. Peake and K. E. Thompson, Jr., *Ind. Eng. Chem.*, **44**, 2439 (1952). Water–Acetic acid, *n*-Butylamine, Dichloroacetic acid, Pyridine–Chloro-benzene.

500. M. Pegoraro and G. Guglielmi, *Chim. e ind.* (*Milan*), **37**, 1035 (1955); *Chem. Abstr.*, **50**, 6895i (1956). Water–Acetic acid–Furfural.

500A. A. L. Peiker and C. C. Coffin, *Can. J. Research*, **9**, 114 (1933); *Chem. Abstr.*, **27**, 2086[3] (1933). Hydrogen chloride–Hydrogen cyanide.

501. E. N. Pennington and S. J. Marwil, *Ind. Eng. Chem.*, **45**, 1371 (1953). Aniline, Furfural, or Methyl carbitol, each with two Hydrocarbons. Prediction of ternary systems from binary ones.

502. D. F. Peppard, G. W. Mason, and J. L. Maier, *J. Inorg. Nuclear Chem.*, **3**, 215 (1956); *Chem. Abstr.*, **51**, 2364c (1957). Water–Hydrogen chloride or Nitric acid–Salts of scandium, thorium, or zirconium–Tributyl phosphate.

503. F. Perel'man, *Bull. acad. sci. U. R. S. S., Classe sci. math. nat.*, Ser. chim., **1936**, 379 (1936). *Chem. Abstr.*, **31**, 3369[1] (1937). Multicomponents by using in-clined prisms for components beyond three.

504. N. N. Petin and K. V. Topchieva, *Zhur. Fiz. Khim.*, **15**, 507 (1941); *Chem. Abstr.*, **36**, 6403[9] (1942). Water–Sodium oleate–Phenol. Solutrope.

505. S. Petralia and M. Cevolani, *Atti. Accad. nazl. Lincei. Rend. Classe sci. fis. mat. e nat.*, **12**, 674 (1952); *Chem. Abstr.*, **49**, 8648i (1955). Effect of ultrasonic waves in Water–Phenol, or Aniline–Cyclohexane systems.

506. V. E. Petritis and C. J. Geankoplis, *J. Chem. Eng. Data*, **4**, 197 (1959). Water–Lactic acid–Butyl alcohol.

507. P. Piha, R. J. Peltonen, and M. Kitunen, *J. Appl. Chem.* (*London*), **8**, 576 (1958); *Chem. Abstr.*, **54**, 6283a (1960). Water–Acetic acid–Isoamyl alcohol. Horizontal tie lines.

508. R. L. Pilloton, *Am. Soc. Testing Materials, Spec. Tech. Publ.*, **No. 238**, 5 (1958); *Chem. Abstr.*, **53**, 14604g (1959). Water–Hydrogen chloride–Five ketones; Water–Hydrogen chloride or fluoride-4-Methyl-2-pentanone.

509. Poczopko and K. Prószyńska, *Roczniki Chem.*, **34**, 1071 (1960); *Chem. Abstr.*, **55**, 10035a (1961). Water–Cadmium or Lithium sulfates–Isopropyl alcohol.

510. J. W. Poole et al., *Ind. Eng. Chem.*, **21**, 1099 (1929); **23**, 170 (1931). Lube oil with many solvents.

511. K. K. Ponomarev, *Zhur. Obshchei Khim.*, **8**, 544 (1938); *Chem. Abstr.*, **32**, 7334[1] (1938). Water–Acetone–Glycerol–Acetic anhydride.

512. K. K. Ponomarev, *Uchenye Zapiski Molotov Gosudarst. Univ.*, **3**, No. 4, 65 (1939); *Chem. Abstr.*, **37**, 5903[7] (1943). Acetic acid–Methyl or Dimethylani-line–Benzene–Gasoline.

513. J. Popelka and L. Rychta, *Collection Czech. Chem. Communs.*, **24**, 3553 (1959); *Chem. Abstr.*, **54**, 4132a (1960). Water–Ammoniacal cuprous acetate–Butadiene–Butenes.

514. P. O. Powers, *Ind. Eng. Chem.*, **41**, 126 (1949). Aniline or Resins–Toluene–Decane, Tetradecane, or Octadecane.

515. M. Prasad, G. S. Hattiangdi, and B. K. Wagle, *J. Colloid Sci.*, **2**, 467 (1947); *Chem. Abstr.*, **42**, 1107c (1948). Water–three Soaps–40 Solvents.

516. H. R. C. Pratt and S. T. Glover, *Trans. Inst. Chem. Engrs. (London)*, **24**, 54 (1946); *Ind. Chemist*, **22**, 317 (1946); *Chem. Abstr.*, **43**, 2042e (1949). Water–Acetaldehyde or Acetone–Vinyl acetate.

517. R. G. H. Prince, *Chem. Eng. Sci.*, **3**, 175 (1954); *Chem. Abstr.*, **49**, 672g (1955). Water–Acetic acid–Benzene–Carbon tetrachloride.

518. R. G. H. Prince and T. G. Hunter, *Chem. Eng. Sci.*, **6**, 245 (1957); *Chem. Abstr.*, **52**, 4302e (1958). Same reagents.

519. A. Prins, *Rec. trav. chim.*, **79**, 1311 (1960). Water–Cetyltrimethylammonium bromide–Phenol. Island curve and separate binodal curve.

519A. M. M. Prokopets and A. M. Zeliznyi, *Izvest. Vysshikh Ucheb. Zavedenii Neft. i Gaz.*, **5**, No. 7, 51 (1962); *Chem. Abstr.*, **57**, 14484h (1962). Dimethylformamide–Aromatics–Paraffines (C_6 to C_9).

520. C. F. Prutton, T. J. Walsh, and A. M. Desai, *Ind. Eng. Chem.*, **42**, 1210 (1950). Water–Phenols–Hydrocarbons.

521. W. A. Pryor and R. E. Jentoff, *J. Chem. Eng. Data*, **6**, 36 (1961). Water–Ammonia–Xylenes.

522. S. M. Przhevlotskaya and E. N. Vasenko, *Ukrain. Khim. Zhur.*, **20**, 631 (1954); *Chem. Abstr.*, **49**, 15423b (1955). Formamide–Diethylformamide–Benzene.

523. J. H. Purnell and S. T. Bowden, *J. Chem. Soc.*, **1954**, 539. Water–Alcohols or Aliphatic acids–Phenyl ether.

524. C. Quantie, *Proc. Roy. Soc. (London)*, **A224**, 90 (1954). Nine CST. Opalescence near CST.

525. I. B. Rabinovich et al., *Doklady Akad. Nauk. S. S. S. R.*, **105**, 108 (1955); *Chem. Abstr.*, **50**, 9845e (1956). Deuterium oxide. Effect of Deuterium on solubility in organic compounds.

525A. G. S. Radyshevskaya, N. I. Nikurashina, and R. V. Mertslin, *J. Gen. Chem. U. S. S. R. (English Transl.)*, **32**, 673 (1962); *Chem. Abstr.*, **58**, 2893b (1963). Three liquid phases in a quaternary system. Water–Ammonium sulfate–Ethyl alcohol–Benzene.

526. H. K. Rae, Dissertation, Princeton, 1950, Publ. No. 10977; *Dissertation Abstr.*, **15**, 542 (1955); *Chem. Abstr.*, **49**, 10031e (1955). Furfural–Aromatics–Paraffins.

527. K. R. Rakhimov and L. G. Fatkulina, *Doklady Akad. Nauk Uzbek. S. S. R.*, **1955**, No. 9, 21; *Chem. Abstr.*, **53**, 9802f (1959). Water–Pyridine–Carbon tetrachloride.

528. K. R. Rakhimov et al., *Doklady Akad. Nauk Uzbek. S. S. R.*, **1953**, No. 6, 52; No. 7, 19; *Chem. Abstr.*, **49**, 2155f, 9360g (1955). Water–Anabasine or Aphilidine–Benzene.

529. K. R. Rakhimov et al., *Trudy Sredneaziat. Politekh. Inst.*, **1957**, No. 4, 326; *Chem. Abstr.*, **54**, 23685g (1960). Water–Pyridine–Benzene. Solutrope.

530. M. Ramamurty, M. R. Rao, and C. V. Rao, *J. Sci. Ind. Research (India)*, **17B,** 103 (1958); *Chem. Abstr.*, **52,** 16852g (1958). Water–Adipic acid–Amyl acetate or alcohol, Butyl acetate, 4-Methyl-2-pentanol, or 4-Methyl-2-pentanone.

530A. C. N. Rao, C. C. Reddy, and K. S. Chari, *Indian J. Technol.*, **1,** No. 1, 54 (1963); *Chem. Abstr.*, **58,** 10788d (1963). Water–Levulinic acid–4-Methyl-2-pentanone.

531. G. J. Rao, V. V. G. Krishnamurty, and C. V. Rao, *Trans. Indian Inst. Chem. Engrs.*, **8,** 46 (1955–56); *Chem. Abstr.*, **51,** 14397i (1957). Water–Acetic or Propionic acid–Ether or Butyl acetate; Water–Butyric acid–Butyl acetate. *Chem. Abstr.* erroneously lists alcohols instead of Acetic, Propionic, and Butyric acids.

532. G. J. Rao and C. V. Rao, *J. Sci. Ind. Research (India)*, **14B,** 444 (1955); *Chem. Abstr.*, **50,** 6166a (1956). Water–Acetic or Propionic acid–Ethyl acetate, propionate, or butyrate.

533. G. J. Rao and C. V. Rao, *J. Sci. Ind. Research (India)*, **16B,** 102 (1957); *Chem. Abstr.*, **51,** 14398e (1957). Water–Formic to Butyric acids–Ethyl benzoate.

534. K. S. Rao, M. V. R. Rao, and C. V. Rao, *J. Sci. Ind. Research (India)*, **20B,** 283 (1961); *Chem. Abstr.*, **56,** 990f (1962). Water–Acetone–Heptyl or Octyl alcohols. Both solutropic.

535. M. R. Rao, M. Ramamurty, and C. V. Rao, *Chem. Eng. Sci.*, **8,** 265 (1958); *Chem. Abstr.*, **52,** 16023b (1958). Water–Formic to Butyric acids–4-Methyl-2-pentanol.

536. M. R. Rao and C. V. Rao, *J. Appl. Chem. (London)*, **6,** 269 (1956); *Chem. Abstr.*, **51,** 1715a (1957). Water–Propionic acid–Tetrachloroethylene or Hydrocarbons.

537. M. R. Rao and C. V. Rao, *J. Appl. Chem. (London)*, **7,** 659 (1957); *Chem. Abstr.*, **52,** 7835b (1958). Water–Acetic acid–Hexane; Water–Glycol-2-Butanone or *n*-Butyl alcohol; Water–2-Butanone–Cyclohexane.

538. M. R. Rao and C. V. Rao, *J. Sci. Ind. Research (India)*, **14B,** 204 (1955); *Chem. Abstr.*, **50,** 3054b (1956). Glycol–Acetone–Cyclohexane or four Esters.

539. M. R. Rao and C. V. Rao, *Trans. Indian Inst. Chem. Engrs.*, **7,** 78 (1954–55); *Chem. Abstr.*, **50,** 13586a (1956). Water–Acetone–Tetrachloroethylene.

540. M. V. R. Rao, K. S. Rao, and C. V. Rao, *J. Sci. Ind. Research (India)*, **20B,** 379 (1961); *Chem. Abstr.*, **57,** 1619a (1962). Water–Formic acid. Ethyl, Propyl, or Butyl acetates.

541. R. J. Rao and C. V. Rao, *J. Appl. Chem. (London)*, **7,** 435 (1957); *Chem. Abstr.*, **52,** 2517b (1958). Water–Methanol–Butyl or Amyl acetates; Ethyl propionate or butyrate.

542. R. J. Rao and C. V. Rao, *J. Appl. Chem. (London)*, **9,** 69 (1959); *Chem. Abstr.*, **53,** 10930h (1959). Water–Propyl alcohol–Propyl, Butyl, or Amyl acetates; Ethyl propionate or butyrate.

543. R. K. Rao and L. K. Arnold, *J. Am. Oil Chemists' Soc.*, **33,** 389 (1956); *Chem. Abstr.*, **50,** 17483i (1956). Water–Ethyl alcohol–Six vegetable oils.

544. R. A. Ratliff and W. B. Strobel, *Oil Gas J.*, **53,** No. 4, 87 (1955); *Petrol. Eng.*, **26,** 12, C26 (1954); *Petrol. Refiner*, **33,** No. 5, 151 (1954); *Chem. Abstr.*, **49,** 597e (1955). Sulfur dioxide–Aromatics–Nonaromatics.

545. J. A. Renard, *J. Chem. Eng. Data*, **7**, 203 (1962). Water–Potassium carbonate or Ammonium or Magnesium sulfates–2-Chloroethanol or Tetrahydrofurfuryl alcohol.

546. J. E. Ricci, *The Phase Rule and Heterogeneous Equilibrium*, Van Nostrand, New York, 1951, pp. 150, 179, 208, 214–217, 244.

547. H. T. Rice and E. Lieber, *Ind. Eng. Chem., Anal. Ed.*, **16**, 107 (1944). Furfural points of Hydrocarbons.

548. O. K. Rice, *J. Chem. Phys.*, **23**, 164, 169 (1955); *Chem. Abstr.*, **49**, 5944f, 5944h (1955). Aniline–Cyclohexane. Shape of binodal curve near CST.

549. M. E. Rifai, *Riv. combustibili*, **11**, 810, 829 (1957); *Chem. Abstr.*, **52**, 11530f (1958). Triethylene glycol or Dipropylene glycol–Hydrocarbon pairs.

550. R. Rigamonti and G. Botto, *Oleagineux*, **13**, 199 (1958); *Chem. Abstr.*, **52**, 12425b (1958). Water–Acetone–Cottonseed oil.

551. R. Rigamonti and G. Schiavani, *Chim. e ind.* (*Milan*), **36**, 611 (1954); *Chem. Abstr.*, **49**, 3510b (1955). 95% Methanol–*m*- or *p*-Cresol–Ligroin.

552. R. Rigamonti and E. Spaccamela-Marchetti, *Chim. e ind.* (*Milan*), **35**, 787 (1953); *Chem. Abstr.*, **48**, 4727c (1954). Water–Furfural–Tetralin.

553. R. Rigamonti and E. Spaccamela-Marchetti, *Chim. e ind.* (*Milan*), **36**, 91 (1954); *Chem. Abstr.*, **48**, 7485h (1954). Water–Cobalt or Nickel thiocyanates–Amyl alcohol.

554. R. Rigamonti and E. Spaccamela-Marchetti, *Chim. e ind.* (*Milan*), **37**, 1039 (1955); *Chem. Abstr.*, **50**, 6877e (1956). Water–Furfural or Acetic acid–22 Organic solvents.

555. R. Rigamonti, C. Vaccarino, and A. Duzzi, *Chim. e ind.* (*Milan*), **33**, 619 (1951); *Chem. Abstr.*, **46**, 3775c (1952). Methyl or Ethyl alcohol–Oleic acid–Triolein.

556. R. Rigamonti and A. Vacirca, *Ann. chim.* (*Rome*), **48**, 478 (1958); *Chem. Abstr.*, **52**, 19184b (1958). Methanol–Olive oil–2-Butanone or Acetone or Benzene; Glycerol–Acetone–Olive oil.

557. D. Ripa, A. DeAngelis, and V. Berti, *Riv. combustibili*, **10**, 803 (1956); *Chem. Abstr.*, **51**, 8415b (1957). 1,2-Bis(2-cyanoethoxy)ethane or Diethylene glycol or 12 Nitriles–Benzene–Heptane. *Cf.* reference 180 (p. 1096).

557A. B. D. Ripley and R. McIntosh, *Can. J. Chem.*, **39**, 526 (1961); *Chem. Abstr.*, **55**, 12978b (1961). Nitrobenzene–Isooctane. Dielectric constant near CST.

558. A. Rius and C. Alfonso, *Anales real soc. españ. fís. y quím.* (*Madrid*), **51B**, 571 (1955); *Chem. Abstr.*, **50**, 14335f (1956). Water–Acetic acid–Toluene at boiling point.

559. A. Rius and C. Alfonso, *Anales real soc. españ. fís. y quím.* (*Madrid*), **51B**, 649 (1955); *Chem. Abstr.*, **50**, 6895f (1956). Water–Formic acid–Propyl formate.

560. A. Rius and M. A. Crespi, *Anales real soc. españ. fís. y quím.* (*Madrid*), **47B**, 243 (1951); *Chem. Abstr.*, **45**, 10617f (1951). Methanol–Fatty acids–Grapeseed, Linseed, or Walnut oil.

561. A. Rius and M. A. Crespi, *Anales real soc. españ. fís. y quím.* (*Madrid*), **49B**, 63 (1953); *Chem. Abstr.*, **47**, 11900c (1953). Furfural–Methyl oleate or Methyl stearate–Naphtha.

562. A. Rius, L. Gutierez Jodra, and J. Solé, *Anales real soc. españ. fis. y quím.* (*Madrid*), **51B**, 731 (1955); *Chem. Abstr.*, **50**, 6169b (1956). Water and Salt–Acetic acid, Ephedrin, or Pseudoephedrin–Benzene.

563. A. Rius and J. M. Martinez-Moreno, *Chem. Prods.*, **11**, 63 (1958); *Chem. Abstr.*, **42**, 7999b (1948). Cf. reference 180, pp. 1074, 1081, 1087. Methanol or Ethyl alcohol–Oleic acid–Olive oil; Propane–Oleic acid–Cottonseed oil.

564. A. Rius and J. L. Otera de la Gándaro, *Anales real soc. españ. fis. y quím.* (*Madrid*), **48B**, 569 (1952); *Chem. Abstr.*, **47**, 3678b (1953). Water–Acetic acid–Toluene.

565. R. A. Robinson, *J. Am. Chem. Soc.*, **74**, 6125 (1952). Water–Hydrogen chloride–Dioxane.

566. H. Röck and R. Rothe, *Z. physik. Chem.* (*Frankfurt*), **12**, 47 (1957); *Chem. Abstr.*, **51**, 14398d (1957). Water–Phenol–Butyl acetate.

567. S. Röthlin, J. L. Crützen, and G. R. Schultze, *Chem.-Ingr.-Tech.*, **29**, 211 (1957); *Chem. Abstr.*, **51**, 8522a (1957). Water–Dimethylformamide–Benzene; Water–Methanol–Trichloroethylene.

567A. M. Roland, *Bull. soc. chim. Belges*, **37**, 117 (1928); *Chem. Abstr.*, **22**, 2305 (1928). Acetone–*sec*-Butylcyclohexane, 2,7-Dimethyloctane.

567B. J. Rose, *Dynamic Physical Chemistry*, Wiley, New York, 1961, p. 450. Water–Succinonitrile–Ether.

568. J. R. Ross, J. B. Rosenbaum, and J. B. Klemner, *U. S. Atomic Energy Comm.*, *AECU-3181* (1956); *Nuclear Sci. Abstr.*, **11**, 176 (1957); *Chem. Abstr.*, **51**, 3098a (1957). Water–Uranium salts–Dodecylphosphoric acid in Kerosene.

569. L. A. Rotinyants, *Izvest. Sektora Fiz.-Khim. Anal. Inst. Obshchei i Neorg. Khim. Akad. Nauk S. S. S. R.*, **17**, 64 (1949); *Chem. Abstr.*, **45**, 3232h (1951). No solutropes.

570. R. W. Rowden and O. K. Rice, *J. Chem. Phys.*, **19**, 1423 (1951); *Chem. Abstr.*, **46**, 5418b (1952). Aniline–Cyclohexane.

570A. H. H. Rowley and W. R. Reed, *Proc. Oklahoma Acad. Sci.*, **31**, 129 (1950); *Chem. Abstr.*, **46**, 5946c (1952). Water–Magnesium bromide–Ether. Magnesium bromide is all in the aqueous layer.

571. J. S. Rowlinson, *Liquids and Liquid Mixtures*, Academic Press, New York, and Butterworth, London, 1959, pp. 229–230. Ammonia–Nitrogen and many other systems.

572. J. S. Rowlinson and P. I. Freeman, *Pure Appl. Chem.*, **2**, 329 (1961). Ethane; CST with seven higher Hydrocarbons. Cf. reference 178.

573. B. Rubin and T. E. Hicks, *U. S. Atomic Energy Comm.*, *UCRL-126; Nuclear Sci. Abstr.*, **10**, 2332 (1956); Cf. reference 261. Water–Nitric acid–Thenoyltrifluoroacetone–Plutonium salts–Benzene.

574. T. C. Runion, *U. S. Atomic Energy Comm.*, *CF51-2-144-5; Nuclear Sci. Abstr.*, **11**, 11602 (1957). Cf. reference 261. Water, Nitric acid–Uranyl nitrate–Tributyl phosphate.

575. A. I. Rusanov, *Vestnik Leningrad. Univ.*, **13**, No. 16, *Ser. Fiz. i Khim.*, No. 3, 99 (1958); *Chem. Abstr.*, **53**, 4879b (1959). Water–Isopropyl alcohol–Phenol.

576. A. I. Rusanov, *Vestnik Leningrad. Univ.*, **14**, No. 4, *Ser. Fiz. i Khim.* No. 1, 132 (1959); *Chem. Abstr.*, **53**, 14666g (1953). Same reagents.

577. G. P. Rutledge and W. Davis, Jr., *J. Phys. Chem.*, **63**, 166 (1959). Hydrogen fluoride–Chlorine trifluoride–Uranium hexafluoride.

578. B. H. Sage and W. N. Lacey, *Volumetric and Phase Behavior of Hydrocarbons*, Stanford Univ. Press, California, 1939, pp. 118, 138, 170.

579. H. Saisho, *Bull. Chem. Soc. Japan*, **34**, 859, 1254 (1961); *Chem. Abstr.*, **56**, 2944f, 9502c (1962). Water, Nitric acid–Nitrates of Ce, Eu, Pm, Th, U, Y, Zr–Tetrabutylethylene diphosphate in Kerosine.

580. S. A. Saletore, P. S. Mene, and U. R. Warhadpande, *Trans. Indian Inst. Chem. Engrs.*, **2**, 16 (1948–49); *Chem. Abstr.*, **45**, 7862h (1951). Water–Acetic acid–Carbon tetrachloride–Trichloroethylene or Creosote.

581. O. N. Salmon and D. H. Ahmann, *J. Phys. Chem.*, **60**, 13 (1956). Lithium–Sodium. CST 380°C.

582. N. L. Sample, C. O. Bennett, and D. E. Holcomb, *Chem. Eng. Data Ser.*, **1**, 17 (1956). Furfural or Propylene glycol–Oleic acid–Hydrocarbons. Mutual solubilities of many pairs of liquids.

583. T. Samuel and G. S. Laddha, *J. Appl. Chem. (London)*, **9**, 246 (1959). Water–Glycol–Cyclohexanol, Isobutyraldehyde, or Triethylamine.

584. T. Samuel and G. S. Laddha, *J. Madras Univ.*, **28B**, 147 (1958); *Chem. Abstr.*, **53**, 16674d (1959). Water–Glycol–Cyclohexanone–Ethyl formate, Methyl acetate, or 4-methyl-2-pentanone.

585. C. N. Satterfield *et al.*, *Ind. Eng. Chem.*, **47**, 1458 (1955). Sulfur dioxide–Aromatic hydrocarbon–Nonaromatic hydrocarbon.

586. K. Schäfer, W. Rall, and F. C. Wirth-Lindemann, *Z. physik. Chem. (Frankfurt)*, **14**, 197 (1958); *Chem. Abstr.*, **52**, 8661b (1958). Acetone–Heptane or Nonane. CST.

587. E. J. Scharf and C. J. Geankoplis, *A. I. Ch. E. Journal*, **5**, 76 (1959). Water, Nitric acid–Nitrates of nickel or cobalt–n-Butyl alcohol.

588. R. W. Schiessler *et al.*, *Ind. Eng. Chem.*, **47**, 1660 (1955). Aniline or Furfural points of 264 higher Hydrocarbons. Cf. reference 178, Table II.

589. C. S. Schlea and C. J. Geankoplis, *Ibid.*, **49**, 1056 (1957). Water, Sulfuric acid–Metal sulfates–Butyl alcohol or 22 other organic compounds.

590. G. Schneider and G. Wilhelm, *Z. physik. Chem. (Frankfurt)*, **20**, 219 (1959); *Chem. Abstr.*, **54**, 1998i (1960). Water–Butyl Cellosolve. CST 130.3°C.

591. W. Schneider, *Arch. Pharm.*, **290**, 32 (1957); *Chem. Abstr.*, **51**, 8359i (1957). Water–Pyridine–Sulfur–Sodium hydroxide.

592. P. G. Scholefield, S. T. Bowden, and W. J. Jones, *J. Soc. Chem. Ind.*, **65**, 354 (1946); *Chem. Abstr.*, **41**, 1922c (1947). Water–Phenol–DDT.

593. H. Schott, *Dissertation Abstr.*, **19**, 969 (1958); *Chem. Abstr.*, **53**, 5850c (1959). Water–Dioxane–Chlorides of cobalt or nickel.

594. F. A. H. Schreinmakers, *Z. physik. Chem.*, **25**, 543 (1898). Water–Ether–Succinonitrile. Three liquid phases.

595. *Idem*, **27**, 95 (1898). Water–Ethyl alcohol–Succinonitrile. Two binodal curves.

596. F. A. H. Schreinemakers, *Die heterogenen Gleichgewichte*, Drittes Heft, Zweiter Teil, H. W. B. Roozeboom, Ed., Friedr. Vieweg u Sohn, Braunschweig, 1911, pp. 6–17. Schreinmakers' rule.

597. H. Schuberth and E. Leibnitz, *J. prakt. Chem.*, **6,** 31, 332 (1958); *Chem. Abstr.*, **52,** 14309h (1958); **53,** 5846h (1959). *Cf.* reference 469A. Water–Phenol–Butyl acetate. Isopycnic. Calculation of curves.

598. W. W. Schulz and E. E. Voiland, *U. S. Atomic Energy Comm., HW-32417* (1954); *Nuclear Sci. Abstr.*, **11,** 12967 (1957); *Chem. Abstr.*, **55,** 18268a (1961). Water, Nitric acid–Thorium nitrate–Tributyl phosphate–Amsco.

599. J. L. Schweppe and J. R. Lorah, *Ind. Eng. Chem.*, **46,** 2391 (1954). Water–Ethyl alcohol–Heptane.

600. W. H. Seaton and C. J. Geankoplis, *A. I. Ch. E. Journal*, **5,** 379 (1959). Water–Hydrogen chloride or Phosphoric acid–27 solvents.

601. C. H. Secoy, *J. Am. Chem. Soc.*, **72,** 3343 (1950). Water–Uranyl sulfate. LCST 295°C.

602. A. Seidell, *Solubilities of Inorganic and Metal-Organic Compounds*, 3rd ed., Van Nostrand, Princeton, N. J., 1940.

603. A. Seidell, *Solubilities of Organic Compounds*, 3rd ed., Van Nostrand, Princeton, N. J., 1941.

604. A. Seidell and W. F. Linke, *Solubilities of Inorganic and Organic Compounds*, Supplement to Third ed., Van Nostrand, Princeton, N. J., 1952. Cf. reference 180.

605. V. K. Semenchenko and M. Azimov, *Zhur. Fiz. Khim.*, **29,** 1342 (1955); **30,** 1821 (1956); *Chem. Abstr.*, **50,** 8272a, 13589e (1956); **51,** 7786h (1957).

606. V. K. Semenchenko and V. P. Skripov, *Doklady Akad. Nauk S. S. S. R.*, **85,** 1325 (1952); *Zhur. Fiz. Khim.*, **25,** 362 (1951); *Chem. Abstr.*, **45,** 7862f (1951); **47,** 1448i (1953). Heat capacity near plait point for Water–Triethylamine and for Nitrobenzene–Hexane.

607. V. K. Semenchenko and V. P. Skripov, *Zhur. Fiz. Khim.*, **29,** 194 (1955); *Chem. Abstr.*, **50,** 13589e (1956). Water–Triethylamine–Tetramethyl ammonium iodide or Isoamyl alcohol.

608. V. K. Semenchenko and E. L. Zorina, *Doklady Akad. Nauk S. S. S. R.*, **73,** 331 (1950); **80,** 903 (1951); **84,** 1191 (1952); *Zhur. Fiz. Khim.*, **26,** 520 (1952); *Chem. Abstr.*, **44,** 10419c (1950); **46,** 1320a, 9365g (1952); **47,** 3643a (1953). Hysteresis of viscosity in critical region for same components.

609. V. K. Semenchenko and E. L. Zorina, *Zhur. Fiz. Khim.*, **33,** 1176 (1959); *Chem. Abstr.*, **55,** 7010g (1961). Water–Triethylamine–Nonyl alcohol. Cf. reference 786.

610. W. F. Seyer and E. Todd, *Ind. Eng. Chem.*, **23,** 325 (1931). Sulfur dioxide-Paraffins. Binary systems. Cf. reference 178.

611. W. F. Seyer et al., *Ind. Eng. Chem.* (1922–37). Eight other papers on Sulfur dioxide–Hydrocarbons. Binary systems. Cf. reference 178.

612. B. M. Sharp and M. Smutz, *U. S. Atomic Energy Comm., IS-335* (1960); *Nuclear Sci. Abstr.*, **16,** 87 (1962); *Chem. Abstr.*, **56,** 5454a (1962). Water–Nitric acid–Tributyl phosphate–Nitrates of lanthanum or praseodymium.

613. L. I. Shcherbak, S. S. Byk, and M. E. Aerov, *J. Appl. Chem. U. S. S. R. (English Transl.)*, **28,** 1075 (1955); **29,** 391 (1956); *Chem. Abstr.*, **50,** 639b, 14337c (1956). Water–Phenol–Methylstyrene. Hollow in curve.

614. T. K. Sherwood and R. L. Pigford, *Absorption and Extraction*, 2nd ed., McGraw-Hill, New York, 1952, pp. 414–420. Conjugate lines.

615. V. B. Shevchenko *et al.*, *Russ. J. Inorg. Chem.* (*English Transl.*), **5**, 898 (1960); *Chem. Abstr.*, **56**, 8074d (1962). Trioctylamine–Nitric acid–Water–Carbon tetrachloride or *o*-Xylene.

616. A. D. Sheveleva, *Izvest. Vysshikh Ucheb. Zavedeniǐ, Khim. i Khim. Tekhnol.*, **2**, 881 (1959); *Chem. Abstr.*, **54**, 10486d (1960). Water–Aniline–Isooctane.

617. K. Shinoda and J. H. Hildebrand, *J. Phys. Chem.*, **62**, 481 (1958); **65**, 1885 (1961). CST of Fluorine compounds with eight other compounds.

618. B. H. Shoemaker and J. A. Bolt, *Ind. Eng. Chem., Anal. Ed.*, **14**, 200 (1942). Mixed Aniline points.

619. A. Shükarev, *Z. physik. Chem.*, **71**, 90 (1910); *Chem. Abstr.*, **4**, 981 (1910). Properties near plait point. Methanol–*n*-Hexane; Water–Nicotine.

620. A. R. Shultz and P. J. Flory, *J. Am. Chem. Soc.*, **75**, 5681 (1953). Polystyrene with pairs of solvents.

621. K. B. Shvetsova, *Zhur. Obshchei Khim.*, **8**, 690 (1938); *Chem. Abstr.*, **33**, 460[8] (1939). Water–Sulfuric acid–Phenol.

622. L. Sieg, *Chem.-Ingr.-Tech.*, **23**, 112 (1951); *Chem. Abstr.*, **45**, 7513a (1951). *Cf.* reference 330. Water–Methanol or Benzyl alcohol–Hydrocarbons.

623. M. Siekierska, *Roczniki Chem.*, **32**, 1369 (1958); *Chem. Abstr.*, **53**, 7726d (1959). Tributyl phosphate–Uranyl nitrate–Other solvents.

624. S. Siekierski and R. Gwóźdź, *Nukleonika*, **5**, 205 (1960) (in English); *Chem. Abstr.*, **55**, 8022e (1961). Water–Tributyl phosphate or Perchloric acid–Benzene.

624A. S. Siekierski and M. Taube, *Nukleonika*, **6**, 489 (1961); *Chem. Abstr.*, **57**, 13227a (1963). Synergic effects in extraction of uranium or plutonium compounds.

625. S. Siggia and J. G. Hanna, *Anal. Chem.*, **21**, 1086 (1949). Analysis of ternary systems by titration to binodal curves.

626. W. S. Singleton, *J. Am. Oil Chemists' Soc.*, **25**, 15 (1948); *Chem. Abstr.*, **42**, 1747f (1948). Stearic acid–Oleic acid–Hexane or Acetone.

627. W. S. Singleton, *J. Am. Oil Chemists' Soc.*, **26**, 332 (1949); *Chem. Abstr.*, **43**, 6839a (1949). Palmitic acid–Oleic acid–Acetone or Hexane.

628. T. Sitarimayya and G. S. Laddha, *J. Madras Univ.*, **29B**, 187, 193 (1959); *Chem. Abstr.*, **55**, 6119h (1961). Water–Acetone–Kerosine.

628A. M. Sivokova and A. Matejicek, *Chem. Prumysl*, **12**, 544 (1962); *Chem. Abstr.*, **58**, 3947c (1963). Water–Methanol–Ethylene chloride.

629. D. A. Skinner, *Ind. Eng. Chem.*, **47**, 225 (1955). Diethylene glycol, Oxydipropionitrile, and Thiodipropionitrile with Aromatic hydrocarbons.

630. V. P. Skripov and N. Y. Rusinov, *Nauch Doklady Vysshei Shkoly, Khim. i Khim. Tekhnol.*, **1959**, No. 2, 250 (1959). *Chem. Abstr.*, **53**, 19525i (1959). Water–Deuterium oxide–Triethylamine.

631. V. P. Skripov and V. K. Semenchenko, *Zhur. Fiz. Khim.*, **29**, 174 (1955); *Chem. Abstr.*, **50**, 13589c (1956). Heat capacity near plait point. Water–Triethylamine or Nitrobenzene–Heptane.

632. B. Skrivan, I. Sedláček, and J. Pinkava, *Collection Czechoslov. Chem. Communs.*, **24**, 3693 (1959); *Chem. Abstr.*, **54**, 10486h (1960). Water–Cyclohexanol–Cyclohexanone, Glycerol, or Sodium benzoate, Sodium salicylate, or Sodium xylene sulfonate. Two separate binodal curves, or concave bands.

633. A. E. Skrzek and N. F. Murphy, *Ind. Eng. Chem.*, **46**, 2245 (1954). Water–Acetic acid–2-Butanone, *n*-Butyl alcohol, Cyclohexanol, Furfural, or Nitromethane.

634. N. A. Smirnova, A. G. Morachevskiĭ, and A. V. Storonkin, *Vestnik Leningrad. Univ.*, **14**, No. 22, *Ser. Fiz. i Khim.*, No. 4, 70 (1959); *Zhur. Fiz. Khim.*, **34**, 2546 (1960); *Chem. Abstr.*, **54**, 9475a (1960); **55**, 6117f (1961). Water–Propyl alcohol–Propyl acetate.

635. A. Smith, W. B. Holmes, and E. S. Hall, *J. Am. Chem. Soc.*, **27**, 806 (1905); *Z. physik. Chem.*, **52**, 613 (1905). Sulfur–Aromatic hydrocarbons.

636. A. S. Smith, *Ind. Eng. Chem.*, **42**, 1206 (1950). Solutropes.

637. D. M. Smith, *Ibid.*, **26**, 392 (1934). Water–Methanol–Isobutyl alcohol.

638. E. L. Smith, *J. Phys. Chem.*, **36**, 1401, 1672, 2455 (1932). Increased solubility in soap solutions.

639. E. L. Smith, *Nature*, **127**, 91 (1931); **131**, 167 (1933); *Chem. Abstr.*, **25**, 2034[9] (1931); **27**, 1810[6] (1933). Four liquid phases. Water–Sodium hydroxide–Ethyl alcohol–Oleic acid, Aniline, Hexane. (Five layers with mercury.)

640. J. C. Smith, *Ind. Eng. Chem.*, **36**, 68 (1944). Tie lines in quaternary systems.

641. *Idem*, **41**, 2932 (1949); **42**, 1438 (1950). Lists of ternary systems.

642. J. C. Smith, N. J. Foecking, and W. B. Barber, *Ibid.*, **41**, 2289 (1949). Water–Aniline–Nitrobenzene.

643. J. C. Smith, V. D. Stibolt, and R. W. Day, *Ibid.*, **43**, 190 (1951). Distinction between solutropes and azeotropes. Water–Pyridine–Benzene.

644. R. P. Smith, *U. S. Atomic Energy Comm.*, MCW 21 Rev. (1946); *Nuclear Sci. Abstr.*, **11**, 11645 (1957); *Chem. Abstr.*, **55**, 18267h (1961). Water, Nitric acid–Phosphomolybdic acid, Silicomolybdic acid, or Uranyl nitrate–Ether.

645. A. Smits *et al.*, *Z. physik. Chem. (Leipzig)*, **B46**, 43 (1940); *Chem. Abstr.*, **35**, 965[1] (1941). Phosphorous pentoxide. "Unary system." Two liquid phases and two solid phases, only one of each stable.

646. V. R. Sohoni and U. R. Warhadpande, *Ind. Eng. Chem.*, **44**, 1428 (1952). Water–Acetic acid–Ethyl acetate.

646A. V. P. Solomko, V. D. Panasyuk, and A. M. Zelenskaya, *J. Appl. Chem. U. S. S. R. (English Transl.)*, **35**, 602 (1962); *Chem. Abstr.*, **57**, 1624g (1962). Water–Acetone–Ethyl alcohol–Butyl alcohol. Quaternary system with developable surface.

647. A. S. Solovkin, *Zhur. Neorg. Khim.*, **5**, 1857 (1960); *Russ. J. Inorg. Chem. (English Transl.)*, **5**, 903 (1960); *Chem. Abstr.*, **56**, 8074e (1962). Water–Sulfuric acid–Di-isoamyl methylphosphonate.

648. M. Souders, U. S. Patent 2,562,068, July 24, 1951. Sulfur dioxide–Xylenes–Pentane at −68°C.

648A. J. S. Stadnicki, *Bull. acad. polon. sci., Ser. sci. chim.*, **10**, 345 (1962); *Current Chem. Papers*, **1962**, 926. Aniline–Phenol–*n*-Tridecane.

648B. C. S. Stokes and A. G. Streng, *J. Chem. Phys.*, **37**, 920 (1962). Oxygen–Ozone–Fluorine at 77.4°K.

649. A. V. Storonkin and N. P. Markuzin, *Zhur. Fiz. Khim.*, **33**, 279, 581 (1959); *Vestnik Leningrad. Univ.*, **16**, No. 4, *Ser. Fiz. i Khim.*, No. 1, 75 (1961); *Chem. Abstr.*, **53**, 21114h (1959); **54**, 23694d (1960); **55**, 16112a (1961). Water–Triethylamine–Phenol.

649A. A. V. Storonkin and A. I. Rusanov, *Russ. J. Phys. Chem. (English Transl.,)* **34,** 251, 354, 464, 579, 674, 800 (1960); *Chem. Abstr.,* **54,** 23694d (1960); **55,** 7008b, 10025b, 18278a (1961); **56,** 13612c (1962). Critical mixing in ternary systems.

650. A. P. Stuart, U. S. Patent 2,802,888, Aug. 13, 1957. Water–Sulfuric acid–Aromatic sulfonic acid–*m*- and *p*-Xylene.

651. J. E. Such and R. H. Tomlinson, *J. Soc. Chem. Ind.,* **67,** 110 (1948); *Chem. Abstr.,* **42,** 7135d (1948). Water–Hydrogen chloride–Benzene.

652. R. Suhrmann and R. Walter, *Abhandl. braunschweig. wiss. Ges.,* **3,** 135 (1951); *Chem. Abstr.,* **46,** 4468h (1952). Methanol–*n*-Hexane; small amounts of eight other substances.

653. V. P. Sumarokov and E. V. Klinskikh, *Zhur. Priklad. Khim.,* **22,** 1087 (1949); *Chem. Abstr.,* **46,** 4342i (1952). Water–Methanol–Ether or Ethyl or Butyl acetate.

654. V. P. Sumarokov and E. V. Klinskikh, *J. Appl. Chem. U. S. S. R. (English Transl.),* **23,** 675 (1950); *Chem. Abstr.,* **44,** 8742a (1950). Water–Acetic acid–Ethyl acetate, propionate, or butyrate, or Butyl acetate.

655. V. P. Sumarokov and A. M. Volodutskaya, *J. Appl. Chem. U. S. S. R. (English Transl.),* **32,** 2594 (1959); *Chem. Abstr.,* **54,** 8225i (1960). Water–Formic, Acetic, or Propionic acid–Isopropyl ether.

656. V. P. Sumarokov and A. M. Volodutskaya, *J. Appl. Chem. U. S. S. R. (English Transl.),* **33,** 907 (1960); *Chem. Abstr.,* **54,** 14877e (1960). Water–Furfural–Ethyl acetate, Ethyl or Isopropyl ether, or Benzene.

657. C. V. Suryanarayana and K. M. Somasundaram, *Acta Chim. Acad. Sci. Hung.,* **20,** 231 (1959); *Chem. Abstr.,* **54,** 5194d (1960). Water–Isopropyl alcohol–Toluene.

658. C. V. Suryanarayana and K. M. Somasundaram, *Bull. Chem. Soc. Japan,* **32,** 666 (1959); *Chem. Abstr.,* **54,** 12760e (1960). Water–Isopropyl alcohol–Carbon tetrachloride.

659. C. V. Suryanarayana and K. M. Somasundaram, *Monatsh. Chem.,* **90,** 375 (1959); *Chem. Abstr.,* **54,** 13785a (1960). Water–Isopropyl alcohol–Benzene.

660. M. P. Susarev and N. A. Smirnova, *Vestnik Leningrad. Univ.,* **11,** No. 16, *Ser. Fiz. i Khim.,* No. 3, 85 (1956); *Chem. Abstr.,* **51,** 832c (1957). Water–Aniline–Aniline hydrochloride.

661. L. E. Swabb and E. L. Mongan, *Chem. Eng. Progr., Symposium Ser. No. 48,* No. 3, 40 (1952); *Chem. Abstr.,* **46,** 10797a (1952). Water–Sodium sulfate–Acetic acid–Isopropyl ether.

661A. W. Swietoslawski, A. Bylicki, and J. Jankan, *Bull. acad. polon. sci., Ser. sci. chim.,* **9,** 7 (1961); *Chem. Abstr.,* **57,** 4100b (1962). Water–Pyridine or 2,6-Lutidine–Sodium hydroxide.

662. G. Tagliavini and G. Arich, *Ricerca Sci.,* **28,** 1902 (1958); *Chem. Abstr.,* **53,** 6743b (1959). Methanol–Morpholin–*n*-Heptane.

663. G. Tagliavini and G. Arich, *Ricerca Sci.,* **28,** 2557 (1958); *Chem. Abstr.,* **53,** 14666b (1959). Water–Phenol–Benzene.

664. G. Tagliavini, G. Arich, and M. Biancani, *Ann. chim. (Rome),* **45,** 292 (1955); *Chem. Abstr.,* **49,** 13753b (1955). Water–Acetic acid–Benzene at 60 to 120°C.

665. G. Tagliavini, G. Arich, and M. Biancani, *Chim. e ind.* (*Milan*), **37**, 882 (1955); *Chem. Abstr.*, **50**, 3054e (1956). Water–Morpholin–Benzene. Solutrope at 100°C.

666. T. Takahashi and T. Yamamoto, *Kogyo Kagaku Zasshi*, **59**, 517 (1956); *Chem. Abstr.*, **52**, 4520f (1958). Water–Dimethylformamide–Hydrocarbon.

667. T. Takahashi and T. Yamamoto, *Kogyo Kagaku Zasshi*, **59**, 634, 639 (1956). *Chem. Abstr.*, **52**, 4966e, 4966g (1958). Water–Phenol–Benzene or Toluene–Hexane, Cyclohexane, Decalin, White oil.

668. M. F. Talina and I. A. Malafeev, *Zhur. Fiz. Khim.*, **11**, 270 (1938); *Chem. Abstr.*, **33**, 4500⁹ (1939). Water–Phenol–Isobutyl alcohol.

669. G. Tanret, *Bull. soc. chim. France*, **27**, 621 (1920); *Compt. rend.*, **170**, 1118 (1920); *Chem. Abstr.*, **14**, 2336⁵ (1920); **15**, 60⁶ (1921). Water–Methylpelletierine. LCST 35.5 °C.

670. K. Tateyama and I. Kageyama, *Nippon Kagaku Zasshi*, **77**, 1312 (1956); *Chem. Abstr.*, **52**, 6912c (1958). Alcohols–Freons–Paraffins.

671. B. R. Tegge, M. S. thesis, Penn. State Univ., 1940; *Cf.* reference 148. Sulfur dioxide–Five pairs of Hydrocarbons.

672. C. C. Templeton and L. K. Daly, *J. Am. Chem. Soc.*, **73**, 3989 (1951). Water–Nitrates of calcium, cobalt, lanthanum, magnesium, or zinc–*n*-Hexyl alcohol.

673. V. F. Terekhova, I. A. Markova, and E. M. Savitskiĭ, *Russ. J. Inorg. Chem.* (*English Transl.*), **6**, 641 (1961); *Chem. Abstr.*, **55**, 24474a (1961). Chromium–Yttrium. CST about 2000 °C.

674. E. Terres *et al.*, *Brennstoff-Chem.*, **36**, 289 (1955); *Chem. Abstr.*, **50**, 8175h (1956). Water–Cyclohexane with 33 phenols.

675. E. Terres *et al.*, *Bremstoff-Chem.*, **36**, 359 (1955); *Chem. Abstr.*, **50**, 8176b (1956). Water–Methanol–27 Phenols.

676. H. Terrey and H. Spong, *J. Chem. Soc.* (*London*), **1932**, 219 (1932). Hydrogen chloride–Sulfur monochloride. CST −56°C.

677. K. Tettamanti, M. Nógrádi, and J. Sawinsky, *Periodica Polytech.*, **4**, 201 (1960); *Chem. Abstr.*, **55**, 16112h (1961). Cf. references 375 and 457. Water–ε-Caprolactam–Benzene, Carbon tetrachloride–Chloroform, Cyclohexanol, Trichloroethylene, or Nitrobenzene.

678. B. J. Thamer, *J. Am. Chem. Soc.*, **79**, 4298 (1957). Water–Uranyl phosphates–Dibutyl phosphate in Kerosine.

679. F. E. A. Thompson, *Science of Petroleum*, Vol. 3, A. E. Dunstan, Ed., Oxford Univ. Press, London, 1938, p. 1829. Triangular graphs with specific gravity or V.G.C. plotted on base line.

680. J. D. Thornton and F. H. Garner, *J. Appl. Chem.* (*London*), **1**, Suppl. No. 1, S61, S68, S74 (1951); *Chem. Abstr.*, **46**, 4345h (1952). Furfural or Methoxyethanol–Benzene–Cyclohexane; Furfural–Toluene–Iso-octane.

681. A. Tian, *Bull. soc. chim. France*, **13**, 583 (1946); *Chem. Abstr.*, **41**, 3358d (1947). Water–Sulfuric acid–Ether or Tetrachloroethylene.

682. J. Timmermans, *Arch. Neerland Sci.*, **6**, 147 (1922); *J. chim. phys.*, **20**, 502 (1923); Cf. reference 275. *Chem. Abstr.*, **16**, 4110⁴ (1922). Effect of pressure on mutual solubility.

683. J. Timmermans, *Z. physik. Chem.*, **58**, 145, 159, 186, 196 (1907). Numerous ternary systems.

684. J. Timmermans, *The Physico-Chemical Constants of Binary Systems in Concentrated Solutions*, Vol. I, Interscience, New York, 1959.
685. *Idem*, Vol II, 1959.
686. *Idem*, Vol. III, 1960.
687. *Idem*, Vol. IV, 1960.
688. J. Timmermans and Mme. Hennaut-Roland, *J. chim. phys.*, **52**, 223 (1955); *Chem. Abstr.*, **49**, 11333i (1955). Nitrobenzene–Diethylpentane; CST 12.4°C.
689. J. Timmermans and J. Lewin, *Discussions Faraday Soc.*, **15**, 195 (1953); *Chem. Abstr.*, **48**, 6801e (1954). About 40 systems, seven of them new. Water–Salts–Alcohols or Acetone. Negative saturation curve.
690. H. T. Tizard and A. G. Marshall, *J. Soc. Chem. Ind.*, **40**, 20T (1921). Aniline points. Aniline–Aromatic or Nonaromatic hydrocarbons.
690A. D. B. Todd and J. C. Elgin, *A. I. Ch. E. Journal*, **1**, 20 (1955). Ethylene–Other organic compounds; two liquid phases above its critical temperature.
691. G. A. Tokareva and V. N. Kozlov, *Trudy Inst. Khim. Akad. Nauk S. S. S. R., Ural. Filial, Sbornik Rabot*, **2**, No. 1, 19 (1958); *Chem. Abstr.*, **53**, 7727a (1959)- Water–Acetic acid–Organic solvent.
692. N. A. Toropov and F. Y. A. Galakhov, *Isvest. Akad. Nauk S. S. S. R., Otdel. Khim. Nauk*, **1956**, 158; *Chem. Abstr.*, **50**, 12621g (1956). Silica–Zirconia; CST 2430°C.
693. R. E. Treybal, *Ind. Eng. Chem.*, **36**, 875 (1944). Prediction of ternary equilibriums from binary ones.
694. R. E. Treybal, *Liquid Extraction*, McGraw-Hill, New York, 1951.
694A. S. Tribalat, *Compt. rend.*, **251**, 2687 (1960); *Chem. Abstr.*, **56**, 9490g (1962). Water, Acids–Pertechnetic acid–Isoamyl alcohol or 4-Methyl-2-pentanone.
695. N. A. Trifonov, *Trudy Saratov. Avtodo Rozhnogo Inst.*, **1939**, No. 5, 167; *Chem. Abstr.*, **35**, 7812² (1941). Water–Acetic acid–Acetic anhydride.
696. N. A. Trifonov and K. N. Kovalenko, *Bull. acad. sci. U. R. S. S., Classe sci. chim.*, **1947**; *Chem. Abstr.*, **42**, 4039c (1948). Water–Acetone–Acetic anhydride (Acetic acid).
697. H. Tropsch and B. G. Simek, *Mitt. Kohlenforsch.-Insts. Prag.*, **1931**, 62 (1931); *Chem. Abstr.*, **26**, 2636² (1932). Ammonia or Aniline–Aromatics–Gasoline.
698. D. S. Tsiklis, *Doklady Akad. Nauk S. S. S. R.*, **76**, 97 (1951); **86**, 993 (1952); **91**, 1361 (1953); **101**, 129 (1955); *Zhur. Fiz. Khim.*, **21**, 349, 355 (1947); *Chem. Abstr.*, **41**, 6124b (1947); **46**, 8496c (1952); **47**, 5747g, 6204c (1953); **50**, 3824a (1956). Immiscible gases.
698A. D. S. Tsiklis and Y. N. Vasillev, *Proc. Acad. Sci. U. S. S. R. (English Transl.)*, **136**, 69 (1961); *Chem. Abstr.*, **56**, 9447b (1962). Helium–Ammonia, Carbon dioxide, Ethylene, Propane. Immiscible gases.
699. D. G. Tuck, *Anal. Chim. Acta*, **20**, 159 (1959); *Chem. Abstr.*, **54**, 1033i (1960). Water–Hydrogen chloride–Isopropyl ether.
700. O. F. Tuttle and I. I. Friedman, *J. Am. Chem. Soc.*, **70**, 919 (1948). Water–Sodium hydroxide–Silica at 250 to 350°C.
701. V. V. Udovenko and L. P. Aleksandrova, *Zhur. Fiz. Khim.*, **32**, 1889 (1958); *Russ. J. Phys. Chem. (English Transl.)*, **34**, 655 (1960); *Chem. Abstr.*, **53**, 4879f (1959). Water–Formic acid–Ethylene chloride.

701A. V. V. Udovenko and L. P. Alexandrova, *Zhur. Fiz. Khim.*, **37**, 52 (1963); *Chem. Abstr.*, **58**, 10790g (1963). Water–Formic acid–Benzene.

702. V. V. Udovenko and L. G. Fatkulina, *Zhur. Fiz. Khim.*, **26**, 211 (1952); *Chem. Abstr.*, **47**, 4720c (1953). Water–Acetone–Phenol.

703. V. V. Udovenko and L. G. Fatkulina, *Zhur. Fiz. Khim.*, **26**, 892 (1952); *Chem. Abstr.*, **46**, 10794f (1952). Water–Ethyl alcohol–Ethylene chloride.

704. V. V. Udovenko and L. G. Fatkulina, *Zhur. Fiz. Khim.*, **26**, 1569 (1952). *Chem. Abstr.*, **49**, 6711f (1955). A parabolic curve requires horizontal tie lines.

705. A. Ulinska and L. Huppenthal, *Roczniki Chem.*, **35**, 1153 (1961); *Chem. Abstr.*, **56**, 8074i (1962). Water–Poly(methylacrylic acid)–n-Butyl alcohol–Heptane.

706. J. C. Upchurch and M. Van Winkle, *Ind. Eng. Chem.*, **44**, 618 (1952); Water–Acetic acid or Ethyl alcohol–n-Heptadecyl alcohol.

707. M. I. Usanovich and E. A. Bekturov, *Izvest. Vysshikh Ucheb. Zavedeniĭ, Khim. i Khim. Tekhnol.*, **3**, 837 (1960); *Chem. Abstr.*, **55**, 8013a (1961). Pyridine–Chloroacetic acid. Time factor in physical properties.

708. M. Usanovich and E. Kalabanovskaya, *Zhur. Obshcheĭ Khim.*, **17**, 1235 (1947); *Chem. Abstr.*, **42**, 6694a (1948). Stannic chloride–Formic acid; CST > 70 °C.

709. V. F. Ust-Kachkintsev, *Zhur. Obshcheĭ Khim.*, **7**, 2063, 2069 (1937); *Chem. Abstr.*, **32**, 32[7], 32[8] (1938). Water–Acetic, Oxalic (island curve), Phosphoric (island curve), Picric, Sulfuric, or Trichloroacetic acids–Phenol. Reactions between components.

710. V. F. Ust-Kachkintsev, *Zhur. Obshcheĭ Khim.*, **7**, 2620 (1937); *Chem. Abstr.*, **32**, 2416[6] (1938). Water, Ethyl alcohol–Phenol–Aniline.

710A. M. A. Ustraikh, B. I. Brounshtein, and V. I. Porkorskii, *Zhur. Prikl. Ohim.* **35**, 2454 (1962); *Current Chem. Papers*, **1963**, 285. Glycol–Benzene or Toluene–Heptane.

711. E. N. Vasenko, *Doklady L'vovsk. Politekhn. Inst.*, **2**, 118 (1958); *Chem. Abstr.*, **57**, 5360a (1962). Water–Diethylamine–Carbon tetrachloride.

712. E. N. Vasenko, *Nauch. Zapiski L'vovsk. Politekhn. Inst.*, No. **62**, 325 (1957); *Chem. Abstr.*, **55**, 24206g (1961). Water or Formamide–Diethylformamide–Benzene.

713. E. N. Vasenko and M. G. Blank, *Doklady L'vovsk. Politekhn. Inst.*, **2**, 115 (1958); *Chem. Abstr.*, **57**, 5359i (1962). Formamide–Acetone–Carbon tetrachloride.

714. E. N. Vasenko and M. G. Blank, *Ukrain. Khim. Zhur.*, **21**, 327 (1955); *Chem. Abstr.*, **50**, 3867e (1956). Formamide–Acetone–Benzene.

715. V. M. Vdovenko and N. A. Alekseeva, *Radiokhimiya*, **1**, 450 (1959); *Chem. Abstr.*, **54**, 12732e (1960). Water–Nitric acid–Diethylene glycol dibutyl ether.

716. V. M. Vdovenko et al., *Radiokhimiya*, **1**, 439 (1959); *Chem. Abstr.*, **54**, 8407h (1960). Water–Cobalt chloride–Tributyl phosphate.

717. V. M. Vdovenko et al., *Radiokhimiya*, **2**, 675 (1960); *Chem. Abstr.*, **55**, 17176h (1961). Water–Butyl acetate–Benzene.

718. V. M. Vdovenko et al., *Radiokhimiya*, **3**, 403, 555 (1961); *Chem. Abstr.*, **56**, 4156a, 4428h (1962). Water, Nitric acid–Uranyl nitrate–Trialkylamines.

719. V. M. Vdovenko and A. S. Krivokhatskiĭ, *Radiokhimiya*, **1**, 454 (1959); *Chem. Abstr.*, **54**, 11651h (1960). Water–Nitric acid–Butyl ether.

720. V. M. Vdovenko and A. S. Krivokhatskiĭ, *Zhur. Neorg. Khim.*, **5**, 494, 745 (1960); *Russ. J. Inorg. Chem.* (*English Transl.*), **5**, 236, 357 (1960); *Chem. Abstr.*, **55**, 3176h (1961); **56**, 4157f (1962). Synergistic solvent power of mixed solvents.

721. V. M. Vdovenko *et al.*, *Russ. J. Inorg. Chem.* (*English Transl.*), **5**, 449 (1960); *Chem. Abstr.*, **56**, 9499i (1962). Water–Hydrogen chloride–Uranyl chloride–Tributyl phosphate.

722. V. M. Vdovenko *et al.*, *Russ. J. Inorg. Chem.* (*English Transl.*), **5**, 1144 (1960); *Chem. Abstr.*, **56**, 13615a (1962). Water–Chlorides–Mixed solvents.

723. V. M. Vdovenko, D. N. Suglobov, and A. I. Skoblo, *Russ. J. Inorg. Chem.* (*English Transl.*), **4**, 1087 (1959); *Chem. Abstr.*, **54**, 14906d (1960). Water–Nitric acid–Butyl ether.

724. V. M. Vdovenko and I. G. Suglobova, *Zhur. Neorg. Khim.*, **3**, 1403 (1958); *Chem. Abstr.*, **53**, 17653d (1959). Water–Uranyl nitrate–Butyl ether.

725. G. Venkataraman and G. S. Laddha, *Ind. Eng. Chem.*, **47**, 1272 (1955). Furfural or Acetic acid–Oleic acid–Peanut oil.

726. G. Venkataraman and G. S. Laddha, *J. Madras Univ.*, **25B**, 219 (1955); *Chem. Abstr.*, **50**, 9763c (1956). Ethyl alcohol–Oleic acid–Groundnut oil.

727. G. Venkataraman and G. S. Laddha, *Trans. Indian Inst. Chem. Engrs.*, **8**, 42 (1955–56); *Chem. Abstr.*, **51**, 15151h (1957). Methanol (100%, 95%, 90%)–Oleic acid–Groundnut oil.

728. A. Venkataratnam, R. J. Rao, and C. V. Rao, *Chem. Eng. Sci.*, **7**, 102 (1957); *Chem. Abstr.*, **52**, 15219g (1958). Water–Acetone–Six esters.

729. A. Venkataratnam, R. J. Rao, and C. V. Rao, *J. Sci. Ind. Research* (*India*), **17B**, 108 (1958); *Chem. Abstr.*, **52**, 16852f (1958). Water–Acetone–Butyl or Hexyl alcohol.

730. D. J. Vink *et al.*, *Oil Gas J.*, **39**, No. 28, 34 (1940); *Chem. Abstr.*, **35**, 2305[8] (1941). Oil–Ethane, Propane, Hexane giving two liquid layers.

731. A. K. Vlček, *Chem. listy*, **28**, 262, 282 (1934); *Chem. Abstr.*, **29**, 7773[4] (1935). Water–Acetic acid–Chloroform.

732. A. K. Vlček, *Chem. obzor*, **8**, 198 (1933); **10**, 88 (1935); *Chem. Abstr.*, **28**, 3646[8] (1934); **31**, 3771[8] (1937). Water and seven Salts–Acetic acid–Acetone, Methanol, or Ethyl alcohol–Ether or Benzene.

733. A. K. Vlček, *Chem. obzor*, **10**, 206 (1935); *Chem. Abstr.*, **29**, 2828[9] (1935). Water–Acetone–Phenol. Small island ternary diagram.

734. H. Vogel, *Oel u. Kohle*, **36**, 547 (1940); *Chem. Abstr.*, **35**, 7762[9] (1941). Aniline–Methylcyclohexane–Heptane.

735. H. J. Vogt and G. J. Geankoplis, *Ind. Eng. Chem.*, **45**, 2119 (1953). Water–Formic acid–4-Methyl-2-pentanone.

736. A. A. Volkov, *Uchenye Zapiski Molotov Univ.*, **8**, No. 1, 125 (1953); *Chem. Abstr.*, **52**, 17931a (1958). Water–Acetone–Acetanilide, Salicylic acid, Succinic acid, or Dimethylglyoxime.

737. E. Voyatzakis, *Prakt. Akad. Athēnōn*, **26**, 111 (1951); **28**, 195 (1953); **29**, 426 (1954); *Chem. Abstr.*, **48**, 1786d (1954); **50**, 1339d (1956). Water–Acetic acid, Oleic acid–Five vegetable oils.

738. J. Vreeland and R. Dunlop, *J. Phys. Chem.*, **61**, 329 (1957). Nitroethane–Perfluorotributylamine–Iso-octane.

739. G. N. Vriens and E. C. Medcalf, *Ind. Eng. Chem.*, **45**, 1098 (1953). Water–Pyridine–Benzene, Toluene, or Xylene. Solutropes.

740. R. E. Wagner, *Dissertation Abstr.*, **16**, 1237 (1956); *Chem. Abstr.*, **50**, 14357e (1956). Water–Pyridine–Benzene.

741. C. A. Walker, *Ind. Eng. Chem.*, **42**, 1226 (1950). Water–*m*- and *p*-Cresols–Sodium hydroxide.

742. R. K. Warner, *Australian J. Appl. Sci.*, **3**, 156 (1952); **4**, 427, 581 (1953); *Chem. Abstr.*, **46**, 8937i (1952); **48**, 25f, 3763a (1954). Water–Nitrates of copper, thorium, uranium–Alcohols or Ketones.

743. H. I. Weck and H. Hunt, *Ind. Eng. Chem.*, **46**, 2521 (1954). Nitromethane–Benzene–Cyclohexane.

744. A. H. Wehe and J. J. McKetta, *J. Chem. Eng. Data*, **6**, 167 (1961). Water–1-Butene–*n*-Butane.

745. G. H. Weinreich, *Mem. poudres*, **38**, Annexe, 1 (1956); *Chem. Abstr.*, **52**, 4302b (1958). Water–Nitric acid–Nitrogen dioxide.

745A. H. G. Weiss and E. B. Klusman, *J. Am. Chem. Soc.*, **84**, 4993 (1962). Miscibility of reactive liquids by high speed photography.

745B. E. A. Werner, *J. Chem. Soc.*, **85**, 1381 (1904). Water–Chloral hydrate. CST 190 °C.

746. A. S. West, M. S. Thesis, Penn. State Univ., 1946. Aniline or Dimethyl sulfolane–Six pairs of Hydrocarbons.   *Cf.* references 148 and 226.

747. J. W. Westwater and L. F. Audrieth, *Ind. Eng. Chem.*, **46**, 1281 (1954); **47**, 451 (1955). Water–*tert*-Butyl alcohol–*tert*-Butyl hypochlorite.

748. F. E. W. Wetmore and D. J. LeRoy, *Principles of Phase Equilibria*, McGraw-Hill, New York, 1951, pp. 126, 127.

749. P. White, D. Moule, and G. C. Benson, *Trans. Faraday Soc.*, **54**, 1641 (1958). Water–Sodium chloride–Butyric acid.

750. K. E. Whitehead and C. J. Geankoplis, *Ind. Eng. Chem.*, **47**, 2114 (1955); *Chem. Abstr.*, **53**, 16673i (1959). Water–Formic and Sulfuric acids–4-Methyl-2-pentanone.

751. J. H. Wiegand, *Ind. Eng. Chem.*, *Anal. Ed.*, **15**, 380 (1943). Graphs for quaternary systems using rectangular tetrahedron.

752. R. H. Wiley and N. R. Smith, *J. Am. Chem. Soc.*, **73**, 1383 (1951). Water–Dimethylpyrone. Binary island curve.

753. A. L. Wilson, *Ind. Eng. Chem.*, **27**, 867 (1935). Water–Sodium hydroxide–Ethylenediamine.

754. H. Wolff and K. Bernstoff, *Z. Elektrochem.*, **62**, 1093 (1958); *Z. physik. Chem.* (*Frankfurt*), **14**, 208 (1958); *Chem. Abstr.*, **52**, 8661d (1958); **53**, 5797h (1959). Acetone–C$_2$ to C$_9$ paraffins. CST.

755. R. M. Woodman, *J. Soc. Chem. Ind.*, **52**, 185T (1933). Water–Sodium oleate–Phenol–Toluene.

756. A. Wroczynskii and P. A. Guye, *J. chim. phys.*, **8**, 189, 197 (1910); *Chem. Abstrs.*, **4**, 2759 (1910). Freezing curve of Methyl iodide and Pyridine.

757. S. J. Yosim et al., *J. Phys. Chem.*, **63**, 230 (1959). Bismuth–Bismuth chloride. CST.

758. C. Yüan and Y. C. Chang, *Jan Liao Hsüeh Pao*, **4,** No. 2, 164 (1959); *Chem. Abstr.*, **54,** 7271e (1960). Water–Acetic, Propionic, or Butyric acids–Ethyl acetate.

759. F. G. Zharovskiĭ and R. V. Chernov, *Ukrain. Khim. Zhur.*, **21,** 757 (1955); *Chem. Abstr.*, **50,** 8296d (1956). Water–8-Quinolinol or its iron compound–Organic compound.

760. A. K. Zhdanov and M. A. Sarkazov, *Zhur. Fiz. Khim.*, **29,** 602 (1955); *Chem. Abstr.*, **51,** 830h (1957). Water–Ethyl alcohol–Ammonium fluoride. Two liquid phases.

761. E. F. Zhuravlev, *Bull. inst. reserches biol. Perm*, **11,** 37 (1937); *Chem. Abstr.*, **32,** 2417i (1938). Water–Benzoic acid–Pyridine. Island curves at 115 to 124°C.

761A. E. F. Zhuravlev, *Izvest. Vysshikh Ucheb. Zavedeniĭ, Khim. i Khim. Tekhnol.*, **3,** 997 (1960); **4,** 199 (1961); *Chem. Abstr.*, **55,** 17186f, 21772c (1961). Two binary layers with differently directed critical points.

762. E. F. Zhuravlev, *Zhur. Obshcheĭ Khim.*, **8,** 1704 (1938); *Chem. Abstr.*, **33,** 4860^1 (1939). Water–Pyridine–Anthranilic acid. Island curves.

763. E. F. Zhuravlev, *Zhur. Obshcheĭ Khim.*, **10,** 1926 (1940): *Chem. Abstr.*, **35,** 3971^3 (1941). Sulfur–Allyl isothiocyanate–Methyl or Dimethylaniline or o-Toluidine.

764. E. F. Zhuravlev, *J. Gen. Chem. U. S. S. R. (English Transl.)*, **29,** 3144 (1959); *Chem. Abstr.*, **54,** 12760b (1960). Water–Chloral hydrate–Aminopyrine; Lower ternary critical point at 5°C.

765. E. F. Zhuravlev, *J. Gen. Chem. U. S. S. R. (English Transl.)*, **30,** 6, 11 (1960); *Chem. Abstr.*, **54,** 19135h (1960). Water–Aminopyrine–Triethylamine; Water–Diantipyrylmethylmethylamine–Aminopyrine. Latter has two separate binodal curves.

766. E. F. Zhuravlev, *J. Gen. Chem. U. S. S. R. (English Transl.)*, **30,** 1077 (1960); *Chem. Abstr.*, **54,** 23687h (1960). Two binary pairs with LCST, and a third homogeneous pair. (Theoretical.)

767. E. F. Zhuravlev, *J. Gen. Chem. U. S. S. R. (English Transl.)*, **30,** 3486 (1960); *Chem. Abstr.*, **55,** 20592g (1961). Aqueous systems of m-Nitrobenzoic acid–Phenylacetic acid; Phenylhydrazine–Succinonitrile; Isobutyric acid–Phenol; and Aniline–Hexane–Heptane. First two with cols.

768. E. F. Zhuravlev, *J. Gen. Chem. U. S. S. R. (English Transl.)*, **31,** 327 (1961); *Chem. Abstr.*, **55,** 23020h (1961). Water–Isobutyric acid, Phenylhydrazine, or Triethylamine; Hexane–Nitrobenzene or Phenol.

769. E. F. Zhuravlev, *J. Gen. Chem. U. S. S. R. (English Transl.)*, **31,** 1300 (1961). Krupatkin's explanation (ref. 367) is erroneous and unnecessary. Fig. 107.

770. E. F. Zhuravlev, *Zhur. Fiz. Khim.*, **12,** 639 (1938); *Chem. Abstr.*, **34,** 315^1 (1940). Acetic acid–Aniline–Gasoline. Island curve above 60°C.

771. E. F. Zhuravlev, *Zhur. Fiz. Khim.*, **13,** 679 (1939); *Chem. Abstr.*, **34,** 1544^6 (1940). Acetic acid–Methyl or Dimethylaniline–Gasoline. Upper ternary critical points at 48.2 and at 41.7°C, respectively.

772. E. F. Zhuravlev, *Uchenye Zapiski Molotov Univ. Gosudarst. im. A. M. Gor'kogo*, **8,** No. 3, *Mat. Fiz. i Khim.*, **3** (1954); *Chem. Abstr.*, **51,** 5525e (1957). Island curves. Aqueous systems of Antipyrine with Chloral hydrate, Catechol or Resorcinol, Pyridine with Chloral hydrate, or Resorcinol with m-Phenylene-diamine.

773. E. F. Zhuravlev, *Uchenye Zapiski Molotov Univ. Gosudarst. im. A. M. Gor'kogo*, **9**, No. 4, *Mat. Fiz. i Khim.*, 113 (1955); *Chem. Abstr.*, **53**, 9801b (1959). Water–Bromal or Butyl chloral. Three liquid phases with two components.

774. E. F. Zhuravlev *et al.*, *Uchenye Zapiski Permsk. Univ.*, **13**, No. 3, 51 (1959); *Chem. Abstr.*, **56**, 14990a (1962). Phenol–Aniline or Pyridine–Iso-octane.

775. E. F. Zhuravlev *et al.*, *Uchenye Zapiski Permsk. Univ.*, **13**, No. 3, 57 (1959); *Chem. Abstr.*, **57**, 2913g (1962). Phenol–Phenylhydrazine–Iso-octane.

776. E. F. Zhuravlev, A. D. Shevaleva, and S. V. Dudkina, *Izvest. Vysshikh Ucheb. Zavedeniĭ, Khim. i Khim. Tekhnol.*, **3**, 620 (1960); *Chem. Abstr.*, **55**, 1160f (1961). Water–Isobutyric acid–Aminopyrine.

777. E. F. Zhuravlev and A. A. Volkov, *Izvest. Vysshikh Ucheb. Zavedeniĭ, Khim. i Khim. Tekhnol.*, **3**, 427 (1960); *Chem. Abstr.*, **54**, 21977f (1960). Aniline–Acetic acid–Iso-octane. Twin island curves. Figure 94.

778. K. Zieborak and W. Brzostowski, *Bull. acad. polon. sci.*, *Class III*, **5**, 309 (1957); *Chem. Abstr.*, **51**, 14399b (1957). Acetic acid–2,6-Lutidine–Decane.

779. K. Zieborak and W. Brzostowski, *Roczniki Chem.*, **31**, 213 (1957); *Chem. Abstr.*, **51**, 14398g (1957). Acetic acid–Pyridine–Octane. Island curve.

780. E. N. Zil'berman, *J. Appl. Chem. U. S. S. R.* (*English Transl.*), **26**, 867 (1953); *Chem. Abstr.*, **48**, 6223h (1954). Water–Ammonia–Adiponitrile. Undercut curve.

781. E. N. Zil'berman, *Zhur. Fiz. Khim.*, **26**, 1458 (1952); *Chem. Abstr.*, **49**, 2848c (1955). Water–Hexamethyleneimine–Benzene.

782. E. N. Zil'berman and M. N. Bershtein, *J. Appl. Chem. U. S. S. R.* (*English Transl.*), **32**, 1587 (1959); *Chem. Abstr.*, **53**, 19548f (1959). Water–Sodium chloride or hydroxide–Hexamethyleneamine.

783. B. H. Zimm, *J. Chem. Phys.*, **20**, 538 (1952); *Chem. Abstr.*, **46**, 6886a (1952). Shape of binodal curve near CST.

784. B. H. Zimm, *J. Phys. & Colloid Chem.*, **54**, 1306 (1950). Opalescence near CST. Carbon tetrachloride–Perfluoromethylcyclohexane. CST 28.23°C.

784A. K. N. Zinov'eva and V. P. Peshkov, *Zhur. Eksperim. i Teor. Fiz.*, **37**, 33 (1959); *Chem. Abstr.*, **53**, 19545a (1959). Helium^4–Helium^3. CST 0.88 °K.

785. Z. Ziolkowski *et al.*, *Chem. Stosowana*, **3**, 475 (1959); *Chem. Abstr.*, **54**, 14806g (1960). Water–Phenol or Resorcinol–Butyl acetate or Benzene.

786. E. L. Zorina and V. K. Semenchenko, *Zhur. Fiz. Khim.*, **33**, 523 (1959); *Chem. Abstr.*, **53**, 21113h (1959). Water–Triethylamine–Isoamyl alcohol. Cf. reference 607.

787. E. L. Zorina and V. K. Semenchenko, *Zhur. Fiz. Khim.*, **33**, 961 (1959); *Chem. Abstr.*, **54**, 8254h (1960). Water–Sodium sulfate–Triethylamine.

788. O. E. Zvyagintsev and O. I. Zakharov-Nartsissov, *Russ. J. Inorg. Chem.* (*English Transl.*), **5**, 59 (1960); *Chem. Abstr.*, **55**, 19436h (1961). Water–Dicyanoauric acid–*n*-Amyl alcohol or five other alcohols or Cyclohexanone or five other ketones.

11 | GLOSSARY OF TECHNICAL TERMS

ANILINE POINT. Mixing temperature of equal volumes of pure aniline and another liquid, usually a hydrocarbon (close to the CST with aniline) (see Fig. 1).

APEX. Highest point on a binodal or phase boundary curve (not necessarily the plait point except in a binary system).

BINARY SYSTEM. A system with two components (Figs. 1 through 9).

BINODAL CURVE. Curve showing compositions of two liquid phases in equilibrium (most figures).

CLOSED CURVE. See ISLAND CURVE.

COL. Common plait point of two binodal curves meeting externally. In a triangular prism diagram it is the bottom of a ridge and the top of a pass; sometimes called a SADDLE POINT (see Figs. 58, 61, 67, 69, 72, 73, 75, 94).

COMPONENT. An independent chemical substance (significant in phase relations).

CONJUGATE LINE. Construction curve for graphical correlation of tie lines (Fig. 29).

CONSOLUTE COMPONENT. That one which in sufficient amount causes homogenation of two other partially miscible components (many figures).

CONSOLUTE POINT. Same as PLAIT POINT.

CREST. Continuous curve marking the highest temperature of a ridge (usually same as PLAIT LINE).

CRITICAL SOLUTION TEMPERATURE (CST). The minimum temperature for the mixing of two liquids in all proportions as liquid; or the maximum temperature of a system for two liquid phases in equilibrium (Figs. 1, 4, 5, 7, 8, 9, 13).

CRITICAL TEMPERATURE.   The maximum temperature for equilibrium of liquid and vapor phases of any substance (Fig. 6).

DEGREES OF FREEDOM.   The number of intensive properties that can be varied without changing the number of phases in a system.   The properties are temperature, pressure, and percentage of all but one component in any one phase.

EQUILIBRIUM (PHYSICAL).   The relation between two or more phases in contact in which the composition of each phase remains independent of time and agitation (most figures).

EUTECTIC.   Composition and minimum temperature of a liquid phase in equilibrium with two solid phases simultaneously (Figs. 7, 11).

EXTRACT.   Portion of charge removed by solvent extraction (Figs. 37, 38, 84, 85).

HOMOGENIZE.   To make homogeneous.   (In this book, not "to emulsify").

HYSTERESIS.   Phenomena exhibited by a system whose state depends on its history; or delay in reaching equilibrium (Figs. 97, 98, 99, 102, 103, 104).

ISLAND CURVE.   Binodal curve around an area of compositions separating into two liquid phases; the area is entirely surrounded by homogeneous compositions (Figs. 5, 57, 88 through 96, 107, 108).   Called also CLOSED CURVE or CLOSED LAYERING ISOTHERM (Russian).

ISOLOGOUS LINE.   Straight construction line from or directed toward one corner of a triangular diagram. It means "equal ratio" of two components and therefore the compositions on adding one component to a mixture of other components (Figs. 37, 38, 39, 54, 84, 92, 93, 94, 99, 107).

ISO-OPTIC.   A tie line connecting compositions having the same refractive index for one wave length (usually showing structural colors) (Figs. 9, 36, 41, 42, 104).

ISOPYCNIC.   A tie line connecting compositions having the same density (and so not settling into layers) (Figs. 8, 26, 27, 40, 41, 68, 69, 70, 82 (last graph), 91, 100, 104).

ISOTHERM.   Phase diagram at a single temperature (Figs. 56 through 58, and many others).

LOWER CRITICAL SOLUTION TEMPERATURE (LCST). A temperature below which complete mixing of two liquids occurs; immediately above the temperature some compositions seperate into layers (Figs. 4, 5, 12, 90).

METASTABLE EQUILIBRIUM. A state of equilibrium between two phases, usually liquid, which is unstable with respect to some other absent phase (crystals or gas) (see HYSTERESIS) (Figs. 7, 8, 9, 12, 97, 98, 102, 103).

MISCIBILITY GAP. Range of compositions separating into two phases (usually two liquids, and usually in a binary system) (most figures).

NUMBER OF COMPONENTS. The least number of independent chemical substances from which the system in all its variations can be produced.

PHASE BOUNDARY CURVE. Curve separating areas of homogeneous compositions from heterogeneous ones (often coincident with a binodal curve except in graphs similar to Figures 15, 16, 116, and117).

PLAIT LINE. Line in a three-dimension graph showing a series of plait points (Figs. 61, 122, 123).

PLAIT POINT. The point on a binodal curve at which the tie line becomes vanishingly short (same as CONSOLUTE POINT) (most figures).

POLYTHERM. (Used mainly by Russians.) A vertical plane in a triangular prism diagram, usually through the edge indicating one pure component (see ISOLOGOUS LINE).

QUATERNARY SYSTEM. System with four components (Figs. 122 through 125).

RAFFINATE. Residue of charge after solvent extraction (Figs. 37, 38, 84, 85).

RIDGE. Rounded phase boundary surface in a three-dimensional phase diagram (Figs. 56 through 76, 122 through 125).

SADDLE POINT. (See COL).

SOLUTROPE. A tie line parallel to the base line in a ternary system (Figs. 34, 35).

SUBCOL. Plait point of a binodal curve meeting another binodal curve not at its plait point (Figs. 66, 72 through 75. 81)

SYSTEM.   An assemblage of substances in equilibrium or tending toward equilibrium.

TERNARY SYSTEM.   System with three components.

TIE LINE.   A straight construction line connecting two compositions of different phases in equilibrium.

TWIN DENSITY LINE (or SURFACE).   Locus of compositions separating into two liquid phases of equal density. May be curved (in contrast to an ISOPYCNIC) when extra substances are present (Figs. 120 through 125).

TWIN INDEX LINE (or SURFACE).   Locus of compositions separating into two liquid phases of equal refractive index. May be curved (in contrast to an ISO-OPTIC) when extra substances are present (Fig. 121).

UNARY SYSTEM.   System with only one component.

UNDERCUT CURVE.   Phase boundary curve in which the miscibility gap increases with slight addition of the ultimately consolute component (Figs. 90, 91, 109).